CALL THE DOCTOR

CALL
THE DOCTOR

a social history of medical men

E. S. TURNER

London
MICHAEL JOSEPH

First published by
MICHAEL JOSEPH LTD
26 Bloomsbury Street
London, W.C.1
1958

Set and printed in Great Britain by Tonbridge Printers Ltd,
Peach Hall Works, Tonbridge, Kent, in Baskerville eleven
on twelve point, on paper made by Henry Bruce at Currie,
Midlothian, and bound by James Burn at Esher, Surrey

CONTENTS

ILLUSTRATIONS

THE DOCTOR'S OATH

I swear by Apollo the Physician, by Aesculapius, by Hygeia and Panacea and by all the Gods and Goddesses that, to the best of my power and judgment, I will faithfully observe this oath and obligation.

My teacher in the art I will esteem as my parents, and share my resources with him, if he is short of the necessities of life. His children I will regard as my own brothers; and if they desire to learn I will instruct them in the same art without any reward or obligation. The precepts, the explanations and whatever else belongs to the art, I will communicate to my own children, to the children of my master, to such other pupils as have subscribed the Physician's Oath, and to no others.

I will treat my patients to the best of my power and judgment, in the most salutary manner without any injury or violence; neither will I be prevailed upon by another to administer pernicious physic, nor be the author of such advice myself; nor will I recommend to women a pessary to procure abortion.

I will live and practise chastely and religiously.

I will not cut a person suffering from the stone, but will leave this to such as are skilled in the task.

Whatever house I enter, I will always make the patient's good my principal aim, avoiding all mischief and corruption, and any irregular relations with females or males, bond or free.

And whatever I see or hear in the course of a cure, or otherwise, relating to the affairs of life, no one shall ever know it, if it ought to remain a secret.

May I be prosperous in life and business, and for ever honoured and esteemed by all men if I observe, and not confound, this solemn oath; and may the reverse of all this be my portion, if I violate it.

—Adapted from Francis Clifton's translation from the works of Hippocrates, 1734.

INTRODUCTION

It may be presumptuous of a layman, who has never dissected a leg, certified a lunatic, remoulded a bust or been called out of bed at two in the morning to sniff the breath of an abusive alderman, to write a book about doctors. Anyone who does so risks being censured as an unqualified practitioner.

However, this is not a history of medicine. Those who want to know who invented the stethoscope or first tied the artery in aneurysm must look elsewhere. Obviously it is not possible to write a history of doctors without any reference to the march of medicine, but the purely medical background has been kept to a minimum and the emphasis has been laid on the doctor as a member of society and on the regard in which he has been held by the community.

Today there are thousands of doctors who are never seen at a patient's bedside. Doctor A travels to the Ministry with a brief-case. Doctor B spends his working life amid test-tubes, trying to put other doctors out of work. Doctor C is a detective who can tell whether a woman was hanged or strangled. Doctor D is retained to certify whether boxers are fit to continue bruising each other. Doctor E tests whether atom scientists have absorbed excessive radiation. Doctor F goes off on an expedition to the South Pole. And so on, through the alphabet several times over. In the main, the doctors who figure in this book are the bedside men, with special attention to the general practitioner who, rising from humble origins, came near to robbing his more learned superiors of their bread.

The general practitioner nowadays is apt to be on his dignity, quick to resent any suggestion that the *élite* of the profession are to be found exclusively among the ever-multiplying breeds of specialists. Why, he asks, should the doctor who studies the whole man be rated of less account than the doctor who learns more and more about less and less? As these lines were written the British Medical Association was busy rebuking a former president of the Royal College of Physicians for remarks which seemed to imply, but were not intended to imply, that the general practitioner was a failed specialist.

In his gloomier moments, the general practitioner sees himself, not as the guide, philosopher and friend of legend, but as the man who rough-sorts the patients and passes them on to others. The young he must send to paediatricians, the old to geriatricians. Specialists assure him that he is a key member of a team, that he can save lives by accurate early diagnosis as surely as a surgeon who cuts out a diseased organ; yet he has a feeling of being left stranded. Sometimes he is convinced that he is nothing but a filler-in of Government forms. At other times, faced with demands for tonics and tranquillisers from those in frenzied pursuit of inner calm, he will protest that he is expected to do the work of the parish priest.

Many years ago he was promised the use of a health centre which would take much of the strain from his domestic life, but health centres have been slow to materialise. Wistfully, perhaps, he thinks of a life in which he could say:

> So many hours must I tend my flock;
> So many hours must I take my rest;
> So many hours must I contemplate;
> So many hours must I sport myself . . .

Alas, when a medical Member of Parliament recited these lines during a debate on Mr Bevan's National Health Service, he was told that while this might be a fit aspiration for a homely swain or a fatigued monarch, it was an unworthy one for a doctor, who must expect to be always on duty.

The book is to a large extent a record of controversy: controversy not only between doctors themselves and between the democracy of medicine and the Royal Colleges, but controversy with the public on such themes as body-snatching, man-midwifery, woman doctors, vivisection, vaccination, anaesthetics, prostitution control, birth control, face-lifting, psycho-analysis and euthanasia. Today the profession seems much less shy about precipitating argument. Television viewers are accustomed to the sight of doctors interviewing homosexuals or the mothers of delinquents, or listening to doctors and priests debating the rights and wrongs of sterilisation and artificial insemination. Once, late-night viewers were conducted into a stately home which turned out to be full of slack-mouthed adult imbeciles playing furiously with primitive toys. The purpose of the visit, it was explained, was to awaken the public to the problems, human and financial, of mental treatment. Usually, the doctors in these programmes retain their anonymity, but there is a certain amount of agitation to end this rule. Why, it is argued, should not a doctor of eminence be able to join in such discussions, or even to perform with the Brains Trust, without being suspected of touting for patients?

Questions of ethics occupy a good deal of space in these pages. There are members of the public who vaguely believe that, at an early stage in his career, their family doctor went down on his knees to swear by various pagan gods the oath quoted at the beginning of this book. Some doctors may indeed have sworn a Christianised version of it at their medical schools. But not all the stipulations of the traditional oath are strictly applicable to life as it is lived today. The recommendation that a successful pupil should share his wealth with an impoverished teacher has probably not been acted upon for some time. As for the preservation of professional confidences, the courts have held, time and again, that the Hippocratic oath must take second place to the oath sworn in the witness-box.

In 1948, before the echoes of the 'doctors' trial' at Nuremberg had died away, there was talk of sub-editing and extending the Hippocratic oath to bring it into line with modern requirements. Delegates of the World Medical Association proposed to insert a clause in which a doctor would pledge himself not to take part in any crimes against humanity, no matter what pressure might be brought against him by the Himmlers of tomorrow. The *Manchester Guardian* thought, as many may have thought, that the delegates were being faintly ridiculous. 'Before we know where we are,' it said, 'these good doctors will be rewriting the Ten Commandments.'

The two big pitched battles over socialised medicine—the first in opposition to Mr Lloyd George's Bill, the second in opposition to Mr Aneurin Bevan's—receive a chapter each. It is probably impossible to describe these episodes with strict objectivity, but everyone should be able to find enough material to fortify his or her prejudices. That the doctors' case was poorly handled on both occasions happens to be the view of the writer, and it is not necessary to belong to a political party to hold this belief. It may be that doctors are better doctors when they are not Civil Servants, but the spokesmen of the profession talked a good deal of nonsense about the demoralising effects of a fixed salary. Judges do not seem to have lost their honour or independence, or atom scientists their enterprise, through accepting the State's dole.

It may be objected that this book starts at an arbitrary period in history. It could have begun equally well in the Stone Age, or in ancient Greece, or at the Norman Conquest. For no other reasons than those of space and homogeneity, it begins in the fourteenth century, when medicine was wakening from the sleep of a thousand years.

I

SAY THE CASE IS GRAVE

THE doctors of Chaucer's day inherited from the ancient world the rules of their profession as well as the bulk of their medical knowledge. They had, however, a more practical, workaday code in which the austere Greek ideals, as defined in the Hippocratic Oath, were relieved by a dash or two of cynicism and self-interest.

Some of these worldlier notions were gathered at Salerno, where medicine was privileged to flourish in the Dark Ages (Ages so Dark that even women were trained to become doctors). The early English writers on medicine sometimes passed off these maxims as their own, with pious or sardonic additions. It would be tedious to try to unscramble the sources, to trace such-and-such a piece of advice to Hippocrates or Galen, and such-and-such to Archimathaeus or Arnold of Villanova. The most convenient, if not the most scholarly, course is to summarise the code and to say that it represents, in part if not in whole, the views of men like John of Gaddesden, the first Englishman to hold the appointment of Court physician; John of Mirfield, who laboured in the priory of St Bartholomew, in London; and John of Arderne, the first outstanding English surgeon.

The rules are as follows:

Dress soberly like a clerk, not like a minstrel. Keep your finger nails well shaped and clean.

Do not walk hastily, which betokens levity, or too slowly, which is a sign of faint-heartedness.

When called to a patient, find out from his messenger as much about him as you can before you arrive. Then, if his pulse and urine tell you nothing, you can still surprise him with your knowledge of his condition.

15

On arrival, exchange greetings, accept refreshment in the spirit in which it is offered, remark on the beauty of the countryside and of the house, and praise the liberality of the family (but only if such compliments seem merited).

Whenever possible, ensure that the patient has confessed before you examine him. If you wait until after your examination before advising him to confess, he will suspect the worst.

When feeling the patient's pulse, allow for the fact that he may be disturbed by your arrival and by the thought of the fee you are going to charge him.

Do not be in a hurry to give an opinion on the patient. It will be more valued by the family if they have to wait for it.

Hide your instruments from the sight of the patient—and from other doctors.

Tell the patient that, with God's help, you hope to cure him, but inform the relatives that the case is grave. Then, if he dies, you will have safeguarded yourself. If he recovers, it will be a testimony to your skill and wisdom. When asked how long recovery will take, specify double the expected period. A quicker recovery will redound to your credit, whereas if a patient finds the cure taking longer than prophesied, he will lose faith in your skill. If he asks why the cure was so swift, tell him he was strong-hearted and had good healing flesh; he will then be proud and delighted.

Behave modestly and gravely at all times.

Do not sow dissension among the servants or offer them unsolicited advice, or brawl with anybody in the house.

Do not look lecherously on the patient's wife, daughters or maid-servants, or kiss them, or fondle their breasts (an affable old medieval custom) or whisper to them in corners. Such conduct distracts the physician's mind from his work and is likely to draw on the house the wrath of God, who is watching over the patient. It may also disturb the patient and fill him with suspicions and worries which will negative any good that may be wrought by the medicine.

If you are asked to dinner, do not be over-effusive in your gratitude, and do not quibble about accepting the place of honour at the table. Be neither indiscreet nor exacting. Do not criticise the food, even if it is millet bread which turns your stomach. Stay sober. During the meal, enquire frequently after

A physician and his servant, from a 13th century manuscript

the patient, lest he suspect that you have forgotten him in your enjoyment of his viands.

Do not talk boastfully, especially among great men, lest they trip you up in your own words.

Do not disparage your fellow physicians. If you do not know them personally, say you have heard nothing but good of them.

Avoid the company or friendship of laymen. They make a habit of mocking doctors, and besides, it is not always easy to extract a fee from an intimate.

Tell the patient funny stories as well as recommending him to serious contemplations and to the Scriptures.

If you do not wish to take on a case, pretend to be ill.

If you find the patient dead on your arrival, show no surprise. Say you knew from the account of his symptoms he would not recover and enquire the hour at which he died. This will enhance your professional reputation.

Missing from this list of instructions is the maxim which used to be quoted to medical students of a later day : 'The first thing to learn is not to kick the pot under the bed.' Also missing is the advice given by William of Salicet to the surgeon of the thirteenth century : 'A wise surgeon will refrain from stealing while he is in attendance on a patient.' This, surely, was written with tongue in cheek.

It is clear from the code that not all physicians were used to moving in polite society. It is also clear that they had their fees very much in mind. The sums they charged were far from nominal and it is not surprising that patients on recovery sought excuses to wriggle out of their obligations. A physician might find it expedient to give a rapidly recovering patient a drug which would cause him harmless physical discomfort, so that he should not think he had called the doctor unnecessarily. For a physican to be cheated out of his fee was a more serious matter then than now. He might have to travel many days to reach his patient and, once arrived, he would be expected to wait until the cure was effected.

Chaucer's Doctor of Physic, that 'verrey parfit practisour,' was not a man to wave aside his fee. A cautious spender, he 'kepte that he wan in pestilence' and was in fruitful league with the apothecaries who dispensed his medicines—'each of them made each other for to win.' Dignified in his red and blue robes, versed in all the authorities on medicine and astrology, he could talk confidently and plausibly about his art. He was a light eater and a light worshipper. Then, as now, the English liked a doctor whose 'studie was but litel on the Bibel.' George Eliot explains why in her *Middlemarch*.*

John of Gaddesden, who may have served as Chaucer's model, was a physician in holy orders with a fashionable practice in London. His gaudiest feat was to cure the son of Edward I of smallpox by robing him in scarlet and confining him to a room hung with drapes of the same colour. The scarlet held mysterious virtues similar, perhaps, to those which, in our own times, have been attributed to red flannel.

In his *History of Physick* (1727) Dr John Freind has this character sketch of John of Gaddesden :

* See page 168.

'He was . . . sagacious enough to see through the foibles of human nature; he could form a good judgment, how far mankind could be imposed upon; and never failed to make his advantage of their credulity. He is very artful in laying baits for the Delicate, for the Ladies, for the Rich; for the former he has such a tenderness that he condescends to instruct them even in perfumes and washes, especially some to dye their hair; and such a respect for the latter that he is always studying to invent some of the most select and *dearest* medicines for them. And if there is a very good thing indeed he orders twice the quantity for them as he does for the poor.'

This *rusé* practitioner even went so far as to publish a list of those illnesses which, financially, were beneath the physician's notice.*

On the theme of midwifery, says Freind, John of Gaddesden is 'very waggish,' and 'sometimes not only familiar but wanton, not to say luscious.' In another direction he incurs Freind's disapproval : 'he seems to have studied all the methods, and with great variety, to promote conception; and there is no doubt but he was much sought after for his secrets in this way.' Freind declines to quote any examples of this 'detestable practice of *provocatives.*' For a Prebendary of St Paul's, John of Gaddesden gave a generous all-round service.

John of Arderne, the surgeon, was a layman who lived for many years at Newark. He is supposed to have been present at Crecy and to have served the Black Prince. In the surgical craft he showed a talent rare in his day, and by his skill in treating anal fistula must have brought fundamental bliss to many a churchman and noble. His fee for the operation was high, having regard to the value of money. For 'a worthy man and a great' it was 100 marks or £40. Less worthy men paid smaller sums, but John of Arderne did not care to accept less than 100 shillings. From the highest clients he obtained a suit of clothes and an annuity of perhaps 100 shillings a year as long as the patient lived. It was, perhaps, of some encouragement to the patient to know that the surgeon had a financial interest in keeping him alive. Usually, half the fee was payable before the operation was started.

In the purely medicinal field John of Arderne's advice ranged from the macabre to the socially embarrassing. An epileptic, he thought, might benefit from having crumbs of roasted cuckoo blown up the nostrils. His recommended diet for a consumptive

* *Rosa Medicinae.*

was the milk of an attractive young brunette who had given birth to her first male child.*

Of the three Johns, John of Mirfield was perhaps the most serious-minded. He appreciated very clearly the benefit of indulging the patient's lesser whims. If a sick man was allowed a little of what he fancied he would be made more cheerful and comfortable and thereby strengthened to fight his illness. 'From Nature itself there proceeds a reaction which is more efficacious than that produced by the physician with his instruments and medicines,' he wrote. Such modesty was unusual and not always to be expressed in the presence of laymen. It was safer, he added, to leave a man in the hands of his Creator than to resort to doubtful treatment. Though in favour of charging a salutary fee, John of Mirfield nevertheless insisted that the physician should treat the poor, especially the Christian poor, with all diligence. He complained strongly about the dishonesty of some of his contemporaries who were not above spinning out an illness for their own gain, and who, while showing an outward honesty, lied with subtlety and killed with audacity.†

The art of medicine was well understood in Chaucer's day; only the science of medicine was lacking. The notion that a man must have confidence in his doctor was clearly established. So was the idea that any faith he might have in God should be harnessed towards his recovery, even if it meant drinking his medicine out of a church bell or wearing a scroll with a Gospel verse round his neck. Many doctors were churchmen and as such had a dual aura of holiness and learning. The learning had no practical value, but allied with the mien of one who held in his pale fingers the skeins of life and death, it helped to establish the doctor as a being from another world and enabled him to bend a weaker personality to his will.

When patients recovered, they did so, if not by powerful suggestion, then by the administering of such drugs as did not prevent Nature from performing her own cure, or by the ordering of rest, or exercise, and the simplification of diet. The physician suffered from limitations which had been recognised in Hippocrates' day : he was a poor navigator, whose mistakes were happily concealed in calm weather but which led to the wreck of the ship when the great gales rose.

* *De Arte Phisicali et de Cirurgia.*
† *Breviarium Bartholomei* and *Florarium Bartholomei.*

The major obstacle to medical progress was that physicians and surgeons alike were ignorant of all but the more elementary functions of the human body. Until the Renaissance was well under way, inquiring minds received little encouragement at the universities. Knowledge handed down from the ancient world, protected at such cost through centuries of lawlessness, was something to be revered, not refuted. There was no scientific research, save by alchemists dabbling in not always wholesome mysteries. The medical faculties were content to act as a guild, to maintain privileges and discourage those with unorthodox views. Their function was to befuddle knowledge with philosophy and theology, to speculate but not to experiment, to syllogise but not to observe. A good doctor was a good disputer. His gift for diagnosis mattered less than his gift for dialectics. This nimble-witted, grave-footed fellow left the university believing the heart to be a perpetual fountain of blood and the stomach an oven in which food was cooked with the aid of heat from the liver. He subscribed to the ancient theory of the four humours—the sanguine, phlegmatic, choleric and melancholic—which had to be maintained in a state of equilibrium in the human body. The choleric patient had too much blood (which came from the liver); the phlegmatic had too much phlegm (from brain, stomach and lungs); the choleric had too much yellow bile (from the gall bladder) and the melancholic too much black bile (from the spleen). The four humours, the names of which have passed into the language as descriptive of all-too-familiar types of human being, were supposed to be in affinity with the four natural elements of fire, air, water and earth. The physician, having divined whether the patient's symptoms betokened heat, dryness, wetness or cold, prescribed accordingly from a pharmacopeia as futile as it was fanciful. For 2,000 years stupendous quantities of rubbish, some of it lethal and much of it obscene, were shovelled into the human maw, and rivers of blood were drained away, in accordance with this ingenious theory, which still had its devotees in the eighteenth century.

Only by anatomising and dissecting the human frame could man obtain more accurate ideas of his bodily functions. The medieval Church had resolutely set its face against such practices, though a priest could always be found to officiate at that form of dissection which involved publicly disembowelling and quartering, or otherwise dismantling, a condemned criminal. Whether

Pope Boniface VIII meant to prohibit anatomy by his direction of 1300 has been disputed; all he was trying to do, it is said, was to stop Crusaders carving up their dead in order to ship home the bones. Whatever the intention, the decree was widely regarded as a ban on anatomy. (Incidentally the practice of carving up, or boiling down, distinguished commanders in the field does not seem to have been discouraged; the portly Duke of York was one of those parboiled in giant vats on the field of Agincourt.)

With the Renaissance the Church was forced to yield ground, and occasional dissections began to be authorised, notably in Italy. Inevitably the bodies were those of criminals. Anatomies were held publicly, with a good deal of pomp and circumstance. The fashionable vied with the morbid to get the best seats and the Church was there to hallow what it could no longer prevent. The lecturer had candles which enabled him, if not his audience, to peer inside the body. Nobody learned very much, except that the human frame was ingeniously packed with a number of colourful organs, but everybody felt able to do justice to a banquet afterwards. The use of criminals' bodies served to establish in the popular mind a peculiar detestation of the practice of anatomy. If dissection was part of the punishment of a murderer, why should an honest citizen allow the doctors to butcher him in death?

To learn anatomy, English physicians had to make the long journey to continental schools, the principal goals being Bologna and Padua. To the latter city went Andreas Vesalius, the Belgian, who had risked his neck snatching an almost perfect, bird-picked skeleton of a roasted man from a gibbet outside Louvain. In 1543—one of the great dates in history—he published his exposure of the hallowed errors of Galen's anatomy, thus bringing an ecclesiastic and academic storm about his head. In Britain there were some who thought that the subject of anatomy, if it must be studied, would be better learned at home, away from the aura of wickedness which overhung Italian cities; must doctors be trained in the use of aphrodisiacs and poisons? As early as 1505 the surgeons of Edinburgh arranged with the City Fathers to be supplied, once a year, with 'ane condampnit man' for anatomising. There were two not unreasonable stipulations : the criminal was not be handed over until 'efter he be deid,' and the surgeons were to do 'suffrage for the soule.'

II

TAKE SIX LIVE VIPERS

In the same decade that Vesalius published his iconoclastic work, a jovial though wayward cleric called Andrew Borde issued his *Breviarie of Health* in England. Borde is scarcely fit to be mentioned with the masters of medicine, but his book is notable because it was probably the first medical book published in English. Its title page bore the proud boast 'By Andrew Borde, Doctor of Physic, an Englishman.'

The writer seems to have taken a simple pleasure in using English expressions, as: 'The 25th chapter doth shewe of a mans ars or fundement . . . Anus is the Latin word. In Greke it is named Grans. In English it is a mans ars, let every man kepe that place cleane . . .' There was no false modesty about Borde, or indeed much modesty of any kind. He was eager to prescribe for those with such symptoms as 'belchinge,' 'bely ache,' 'stinking breath,' 'stertinge in the slepe' and 'grinding of one's teeth in one's slepe.' Repeatedly he warned his readers against 'too much venerious actes,' especially in summer, and on a full stomach. His high-light is a recipe for the cure of satyriasis—'to leape into a great vessel of cold water or put nettles in the codpiece.' Whether Borde was a sufferer from this affliction we do not know. We do know that he was charged by the Bishop of Winchester with keeping three loose women in his quarters in that city.

Borde's recipes were a mixture of common sense, piety, superstition and crude folly. Scurf could be cleared by anointing the head with the gall of a bull mixed in vinegar, but this was no cure for 'standing up of a man's hair,' for which the only remedy was trust in God. For King's evil (scrofula) he advised, 'Make friendes of the Kinges maiestie,' since monarchs, traditionally, had the healing touch. This was his treatment for madness: 'First, in the chamber where the patient is kept in, let there be no picters nor

23

painted clothes about the bed nor chamber . . . keep the patient
from musing and studying and use mirth and merry communica-
tion . . . if neede require, he must be punished and beaten . . .'

From Chaucer's day to Shakespeare's, it is possible to form a
reasonable picture of the physician from his code of behaviour
and his writings, but the image of the grave and subtle scholar
dissolves as soon as one looks at the nightmare medicines he
prescribed. Surely, one feels, only the most benighted of witch-
doctors, only men of diseased fancy, only coprophiles and necro-
philes and vampires could have dabbled in the medicines and
ointments which these wise and reverend men prescribed.

In the main, remedies were esteemed according to whether
they were rare, complex or unpleasant. A drug which combined
all three qualities was irresistible. Certain specifics were so rare
that they did not exist, and therefore had to be counterfeited.
Among these was unicorn's horn, for which the horn of a
rhinoceros or the tusk of a narwhal was often substituted. A
king of France jealously clung to what he fancied to be a real
unicorn's horn and valued it at more than 100,000 crowns.
Nearly as elusive as unicorn's horn was genuine Egyptian
mummy. Ambroise Paré explains that the rich Egyptians were
embalmed in myrrh, aloes, saffron, spices and other drugs with
or without therapeutic value; the poorer Egyptians were fobbed
off with asphalt. Paré was doubtful whether any good could be
derived from consuming powder even from a genuine mummy.
He was certain that no good was to be derived from the bogus
mummy in which many French apothecaries, 'men wondrous
audacious and covetous,' had set up a profane but profitable
trade. They had taken to seizing the bodies of the hanged,
embalming them in salt and drugs, drying them in an oven and
selling the results as genuine old Egyptian mummy. The only
effect on the patient, said Paré, was 'vomiting and stink of the
mouth.'*

Nor was Paré convinced of the virtues of bezoar, a stone
supposedly secreted in the stomach of an Asian goat. It formed
itself about a straw or similar substance, and the outer layers
could be peeled away in shining scales like those of an onion.
Since only the most dedicated healer, or dealer, would wish to
betake himself to the mountains of Asia to chase goats which
might or might not contain bezoars, a trade sprang up in bezoar

* *The Apologie and Treatise of Ambroise Paré.*

substitutes. Powder from the stone was supposedly an antidote against poisons, and when taken in rose water it promoted virility. To disabuse King Charles IX of the virtues of his favourite bezoar stone, Paré took part in a singularly hellish experiment whereby a condemned cook (convicted of stealing two silver dishes) was given a stiff draught of corrosive by an apothecary, bezoar being afterwards administered. The man was found crawling in his cell like a beast on all fours, with blood streaming from every orifice of his body. When an autopsy was held, his stomach was discovered to be black and dry as if cauterised. The King, satisfied that Paré had made his point, had the bezoar destroyed.

The vogue for revolting medicines sprang, perhaps, from the ancient notion that these would be likely to disgust the evil spirits tenanting the body, and force them to quit. Another theory is that they were prescribed according to the argument that since everything medicinal is vile, everything vile must be medicinal. Some, conceivably, were administered as shock medicines designed to accelerate childbirth. The category includes lice, the stale of a lizard, preparations of toad, the bowels of moles cut open alive and various exotic dungs. Rivalling these were recipes which rested on a traffic with evil, like babies' fat (as an unguent), the raspings of a hanged man's skull (for gout), moss from a hanged man's skull (to be used as snuff) and the halter of a hanged man (for headache).

Other cures called for a crude cruelty, not to mention much manual dexterity, in their preparation. Among them was oil of swallows, the recipe for which was still in vogue in the seventeenth century. One version ran : 'Take young swallows out of their nests, by number twelve, rosemary tips, bay leaves, lavender tops, strawberry leaves, of each a handful; cut off the long feathers of the swallows, wings and tails, put them into a stone mortar and lay the herbs upon them and beat them all to pieces, guts, feathers, bones and all . . .' The result was warranted, with God's blessing, to restore shrunken sinews. It is very hard to picture, say, John of Gaddesden teaching his apothecaries to mix oil of swallows in the long winter evenings.

A plague sore could be cured by applying half a live pigeon to it, in order to draw out the venom. A viper wine recipe began: 'Take six live vipers . . . and some spirit. Digest for six months without heat then strain off the wine.' The theory behind the use of vipers' flesh was that, since the viper is immune to its own venom, its flesh must be an antidote to poison, though this hardly explains why viper wine was used as an aphrodisiac, even in the late eighteenth century.

Vipers' flesh was also a constituent of theriac, which in its heyday contained more than 60 ingredients, among them frankincense and Falernian wine, but mostly herbs. All were largely futile, either separately or in combination. Theriac was a rich medicine for rich patients, who wished to preserve a social distinction even in illness, and who had grown tired of consuming grated gems or solutions of gold.

The poor need not have been envious. Their simple herbs, their homelier offals, did them less harm and sometimes even did good.

III

RIVAL INTERESTS

EVEN in the fifteenth century the vested interests of medicine were beginning to jostle each other, to form themselves into pressure groups, to discipline their members, to strive for State and parish privileges. The main groups were the physicians, the surgeons, the barbers and the apothecaries.

There were other interests which were unorganised, among them the quacks, who poached on the preserves of all the others; the midwives, who pursued a craft disdained by (and barred to) physicians and surgeons, save in emergencies; the herbalists, who treasured healing lore handed down from Saxon days; the alchemists, who flirted with the powers of light and darkness as they sought (so they said) the elixir of life; and the astrologers, who laid down the times at which physic should be taken or operations attempted.

The first four groups were mutually suspicious and tended to despise each other's pretensions, though for profit's sake, if not the patient's sake, they found ways of working together. Every now and again the prejudices and animosities boiled over. To fit and healthy citizens these quarrels were laughable enough. To the sick they did not seem so funny.

In 1518, ostensibly with the object of putting the quacks out of business, the more learned members of the profession formed themselves into the Royal College of Physicians. The moving spirit was Thomas Linacre, whose statue, heavily coated with guano, stands above the gloomy portal of the present College, just off Trafalgar Square. Linacre and his colleagues were granted power to license and control the practice of medicine and surgery within seven miles of the centre of London. A few years later the College's powers were extended to cover the whole of the country, but for reasons which have never been

27

adequately explained, it did not demand from provincial practitioners the degree of skill and learning required for Metropolitan practice. In a higher class than those physicians who were merely licensed to practise were the fellows of the College, chosen as much for their gentlemanly qualities as for their learning. As a sop to the Church, the Bishop of London and the Dean of St Paul's, sitting with medical referees, were still allowed to issue licences to practise in London, as they were already accustomed to do, but the Act did much to loosen the Church's grip on medicine.

In putting their case for the establishment of a college, Linacre and his colleagues complained that:

'. . . common artificers, as smiths, weavers, and women, boldly and accustomably take upon them great cures and things of great difficulty; in the which they partly practise sorcery and witchcraft, partly apply such medicines unto the disease as be very noxious and nothing meet therefor; to the high displeasure of God, great infamy of the Faculty and grievous hurt, damage and destruction of many of the King's liege people; most especially of them that cannot discern the uncunning from the cunning.'

To what extent the quacks had blackened the name of the London physicians is not clear. The Lord Mayors of London had waged spasmodic war on pretenders and occasionally the public had chased the more presumptuous of them from the gates. One at least, Roger Clerk, was hounded out in 1382 sitting bareback facing the tail of his horse with a circlet of urinals round his neck. In some quarters the physicians themselves enjoyed no great reputation. Margaret Paston, writing from Norfolk to her husband in 1464, added this anxious warning: 'Also, for God's sake, beware of medicines ye take of any physicians in London; I shall never trust to them because of your father and my uncle, whose souls God assoil!'*

The College had powers to fine and imprison unqualified practitioners and to search the shops of apothecaries for bad drugs and poisons. Its censors began to exercise these powers with a will. Tainted stocks were tossed contemptuously into the street or burned in the doorway of the shop. From time to time unlicensed practitioners were hauled up and questioned in Latin as to their qualifications. The conversation was apt to be one-sided. Though some dangerous rogues were put out of business

* *The Paston Letters.*

Medical research—late Elizabethan period

(or at least out of London), the bigger fry, invoking the influence
of eminent persons they had treated, were sometimes able to
defy the College for long periods. Of the prosecutions by the
College a critic has said that 'unauthorised practitioners were
deemed worthy of punishment or otherwise not as they killed or
cured His Majesty's subjects but as they were insolent or humble
to the College.'* It is difficult to dismiss this allegation on reading the record of prosecutions published in 1684 by Dr Charles
Goodall, a fellow of the College who was much concerned to
defend its reputation against detractors.† It is clear that uncouth,
unlettered and unrepentant offenders were jailed without ado;

* John Thomson: *Life of William Cullen.*
† *An Historical Account of the College's Proceedings Against Empiricks.*

more modest offenders, who could answer in Latin, had heard of Galen and seemed to have the instincts of gentlemen, were fined small sums and required to pass the College's examinations. If they did so, the deaths of their patients would be forgotten.

The College had much to endure from peers, bishops and lord high admirals who kept writing to ask for indulgence to be shown to their favourite quacks. Sir Francis Walsingham was a frequent offender. On behalf of Margaret Kennix, whom the College dismissed as 'an outlandish, ignorant, sorry woman,' he said that it was Queen Elizabeth's wish that she be allowed to administer her simples, as she was the sole support of her husband and family. Earnestly, he urged the president of the College to consider 'the readmitting of her into the quiet exercise of her small talent, lest by the renewing of her complaint to Her Majesty through your hard dealing of her you procure further inconvenience thereby to yourself than perhaps you would be willing should fall out.' The College countered this kind of threat as best it was able in letters of great skill and Oriental flattery, pleading always that it was oath-bound to protect the lives of the Queen's ignorant subjects. Goodall's record reveals very clearly the extent to which the great of the land were in the hands of impostors and empirics.

The College also disciplined a number of its own members for malpractice and unethical behaviour, or for speaking disrespectful of Galen. Roderigo Lopez, a Jew who became the first hospital physician at the old monastic foundation of St Bartholomew's, was ordered to return a fee paid him by a servant of Lord Burghley, whose swollen shin he had undertaken but failed to cure. Lopez was in trouble with the censors on other grounds, but he had the protection of Queen Elizabeth, whose chief physician he became. He seemed to be unassailable; but in 1594 he was convicted, probably on false evidence, of complicity in a plot to poison the Queen. The proud leaders of the Royal College of Physicians then had the dubious pleasure of seeing one of their fellows hanged, drawn and quartered.

Although the primary task of the College was to control and license, it did much in its early years to spread the new medical and anatomical knowledge (Lopez had been fined in 1569 for refusing to read an anatomy lecture). It took the College exactly a century, however, to issue its first Pharmacopeia, which contained specifics warranted to horrify the more liberal-minded quacks.

Physicians were almost exclusively the doctors of the well-to-do. They were to be found only in London and the bigger cities. The high fees they extracted from the prosperous were supposed to compensate for the services they gave free to the poor. How much time a physician devoted to the penniless was a matter between himself and his conscience. In general, the rural poor lived and died without benefit of physicians.

The surgeons formed only a small fraternity. By comparison with the physicians their social status was poor and their manners were rough. John of Arderne, who was mentioned in the previous chapter, was an exception, and was respected in the higher circles of his day. Rarely had the surgeon any academic background. If he had a university, it was the battlefield. The more daring would perform trepanning, extract stones, treat hernias, and even attempt to heal stomach wounds. Much of their skill was acquired in patching up broken nobles carried from the jousts. In 1559, when Henry II of France had his eye pierced by a splinter through his vizor, his surgeons beheaded four criminals and then thrust broken truncheons into their eyes at the same angle, in order to see precisely what injury the King had sustained. This was called the empirical approach to healing.

The surgeons knew that the physicians, while presuming to regulate their activities, looked down on them as men who worked with their hands, men who practised a craft instead of professing an art. This patronising attitude was not wholly the product of academic snobbery; it stemmed in part from the twelfth century papal bans on churchmen performing surgery, or touching those parts of the body which could not fitly be mentioned in polite speech.

In their turn the surgeons were able to look down on the barbers who, thanks to their skill with sharp instruments, as in the tonsuring of monks, had been encouraged by the Church to practise minor surgery, and in consequence looked on themselves as barber-surgeons. They were a numerous body and had possessed a charter since 1462. Although much of their surgery was confined to lancing boils, treating corns and pulling teeth, they frequently undertook to set broken limbs or perform amputations. Their less dignified activities (they had, at one time, a gift for brothel keeping), did not recommend them as associates of master surgeons. Nevertheless, in 1540, the surgeons, to strengthen their influence, contracted a marriage of expedience with the

barbers and Henry VIII personally presented a charter to th
new Barber-Surgeons Company. Like many a marriage of
expedience, it turned out an unhappy one. The surgeons were
now quite sure that they had married below them; the barbers
suspected that they had been espoused for the sake of their
property and civic privileges. Both parties were right, but they
were able to cohabit without excessive bickering for 200 years.
For most of that period it was the barbers who kept the household prosperous.

The Company had power to license all surgeons in the London
area. There was an agreement between the two parties which·
amounted to this : that the surgeons should not cut hair and the
barbers should not cut flesh. In practice, there was a high state
of confusion, since the Company now included three categories :
master surgeons, who would not have dreamed of cutting hair;
barber-surgeons, who performed minor surgery, let blood, pulled
teeth and cut hair if they felt like it; and barbers, whose main
function was to cut hair but who liked to dabble in blood-letting
and tooth-pulling too.

Not the least advantage of the union was that the Company
now received an annual dividend in the shape of four bodies of
executed felons, for anatomy. This, it was innocently hoped,
would eliminate the need to obtain bodies by surreptitious means.

At disciplinary sessions of the Barber-Surgeons' Court, surgeons
were rebuked for various forms of malpractice; for example,
accepting money in advance for cures they could not effect,
failing to present dangerously ill patients to the masters of the
Company and conducting dissections in their private houses.
Barbers were disciplined for rather more vulgar errors, like displaying bowls of blood in their windows (instead of pouring it
quietly in the Thames), using bad language, damaging each
other's premises, being improperly dressed at elections or funerals,
cutting hair on Sundays and maintaining more than one shop.

Both branches of the Company were at pains to train apprentices, who were probably no better or worse treated than any
other apprentices of the time. Sometimes the master was called
before the Court for beating, starving or neglecting his charge.
More often some obstreperous youth would be hauled up for
swearing, dicing, whoring, marrying, pilfering food or 'borrowing' instruments. There were some spirited lads among them. In
1572 Master Ralph Soda ran away from his master, Henry

An operation in the open air. From William Clowes' *A Proved Practice For All Young Chirurgians* (1591)

Lusshe, contracted himself to three women and 'dealt dishonestly' with Lusshe's maidservant.* Some of the offenders were chastised with rods.

The surgeons clashed repeatedly with the physicians, and not a few were fined and jailed by the Royal College for administering medicine on their own responsibility. Late in Elizabeth's reign the Lord Mayor of London sat with the Commissioners of the Queen to decide whether surgeons should be allowed to give internal medicines when treating such ailments as sciatica, the French pox, ulcers and wounds. John Caius, then president of the Royal College of Physicians, seems to have put up an irresistible case for the physicians, outshining the Bishop of London,

* Sidney Young: *Annals of the Barber-Surgeons* (1890).

B

who favoured the surgeons. Over and over again, the more responsible Elizabethan surgeons pointed to the folly of divorcing the two branches of medicine. On board ships of war and in camps, where no physicians were to be found, the surgeon was allowed to administer medicines, so why not elsewhere? The surgeons were convinced that the physicians' opposition was prompted by a desire to safeguard their own interests rather than to protect the patient; and they were probably right.

From an Elizabethan surgeon's book—*A Proved Practice for All Young Chirurgians*, by William Clowes, who served in the fleet against the Armada—can be gained curious glimpses of the types of patient who came the way of the more experienced Elizabethan sawbones. Among those on whom Clowes operated were : two gentlemen who had been drying gunpowder in a brass pan, stirring it briskly with their hands; a merchant shot accidentally at a march-past by a Dutch soldier who did not know he had 'one up the spout'; a Customs house waiter whose firearm exploded in his face while he was skirmishing; a merchant wounded by gunshot during a clash with Flushingers at sea; a man with a sinew damaged by an incompetent blood-letter; a spectator who broke his skull when the gallery of a bear garden crashed; and a man who was run through with a sword which came out of his back, but who was able 'with his own hands to pull out the sword.' The skill with which Clowes was able to patch up these unfortunates, notwithstanding his limited knowledge of the body's functions, commands high respect.

Less able surgeons were all too ready to deprive patients of diseased limbs and other valued adjuncts rather than try to effect a cure by treatment. To such as these John Woodall administered a solemn caution in *The Surgeon's Mate* : 'It is no small presumption to dismember the image of God'; which was very nearly what Lister said in his generation : 'To intrude an unskilled hand into such a piece of Divine mechanism as the human body is indeed a fearful responsibility.'

The apothecary has made only a brief appearance so far. He was an industrious, resourceful, lively fellow; sharp, perhaps, but intelligent and ambitious, and destined to go far. Like the surgeon, he was disdained by the physician, and he in turn found someone to disdain in the grocer, from whose ranks he sprang. On the grounds that the importation of many new drugs from the East justified splitting the two trades, the apothecaries agitated

for a separate charter, and in 1617 James I obligingly incor-
porated them as the Society of Apothecaries.

It was a matter for some satisfaction that they were now
empowered to search the premises of grocers, just as they themselves were liable to be searched by the physicians. The rule was
that grocers should not stock drugs. For generations to come
apothecaries and grocers were able to quarrel fruitlessly on the
theme, 'What is a drug?'

If Shakespeare is any guide, apothecaries were prone to
ornament their shops with stuffed tortoises, alligators and 'ill-
shaped fishes.' Alligators, in fact, seem to have been a standard
fitting. The cynical view, as expressed by Sir Thomas Overbury,
was that these and other hypnotic *bric-à-brac* were intended to
focus the gaze of the simple while the apothecary cheated them
at the scales. (Sir Thomas Overbury, in due course, was poisoned
at the hands of apothecaries.) A better asset than an alligator,
however, was a handsome wife behind the counter; young and
old would then bring their imaginary complaints to the shop. A
sensible apothecary would close his eyes to his wife's flirtations
with the physician, if the result was good for trade.

According to the physicians, it was no business of the apothecary to prescribe or administer medicines, but the apothecaries
claimed, on not very good grounds, to have been given this right
in 1542. Since there were not enough physicians to supply the
needs of the country at large, the apothecaries were able to go
their own way without much interference, except in London.
The ordinary mortal never thought of calling in a physician,
whose fee he could not afford. He had the choice of apothecary,
local wise woman, or quack.

In Scotland the vested interests fought each other no less keenly
than in England. The Guild of Barbers and Surgeons obtained a
Seal of Cause from Edinburgh Town Council in 1505, but opposition from Town, Gown, and Church prevented the physicians
from forming a Royal College until 1681. In Glasgow a charter
was awarded in 1599 to a joint Faculty of Physicians and
Surgeons, with power to license practitioners in the city and
neighbouring counties.

IV

JEERS AND CHAOS

THE physician rode into the seventeenth century on horseback, sitting side-saddle like a woman, and out of it in a carriage. One of the last to be horse-borne was William Harvey, who allowed his servant to follow him on foot, a fashion which John Aubrey thought 'very decent.'

On his passage through this disputatious age the physician had to dodge a good many brickbats. The public were ready to respect solemnity only so long as they thought there was something behind it. Now, in a more sceptical, more inquisitive day they began to suspect that, under the round velvet cap, flourished less wisdom than they had supposed. They were not satisfied to have an ailment identified by its Latin name; they wanted it cured. So the physician was mocked on all sides for his more vulnerable failings—his pretensions, his pedantries, his second-hand aphorisms, his quarrelsomeness and his covetousness. The Puritan pamphleteers went farther and painted him as the stallion of the boudoir, the repairer of lechers. Poets, wits and playwrights scoffed in his face. He was death's ally, the grave-digger's friend, the hangman's rival. Still, he was the only doctor there was, so when they felt out of sorts they sent him their urine and then jeered at the gravity with which he tried (in the words of an uncharitable bishop) to 'shake it into a disease.' In self-protection, the physician shed something of his Spanish gravity and tried to assume the protective veneer of a man of the world. If the public would not respect solemnity and learning, perhaps they would respect it when overlaid with sophistication and the trappings of prosperity.

John Aubrey has left pen-pictures of eminent and notorious physicians of the early Stuart period.* His sketch of William

* *Brief Lives.*

36

Harvey is intimate and possibly libellous. 'I remember,' he says, 'he kept a pretty young wench to wait on him, which I guess he made use of for warmth-sake as King David did, and took care of her in his will.' To treat his gout, Harvey would sit bare-legged in frost on the leads of his house, or put his feet in a pail of icy water until they were numbed, then move to his stove—'and so 'twas gone.' Although the profession conceded that he was a good anatomist, they thought little of his therapeutic methods, according to Aubrey, and if his treatment of gout was typical there is no occasion for surprise. After the publication of his great work on the circulation of the blood Harvey 'fell mightily in his practice,' the vulgar holding him to be crack-brained. He recovered prestige gradually. Nevertheless, says Aubrey, 'I knew several practisers in London that would not have given threepence for one of his bills; and that a man could hardly tell by one of his bills what he did aim at.' It is fair to say that there is other testimony suggesting that Harvey was a sound and respected doctor.

Each age has its medical eccentric. Aubrey nominates as 'the greatest physician of his time' William Butler, who died in 1618. Although he never took a degree he was allowed to practise in Cambridge. His fame, however, extended far beyond the banks of the Cam. One day he was 'at the Savoy in London,' on a balcony overlooking the Thames, when a patient called on him. After ordering a boat to lie in readiness below, Butler chatted to the patient at the window and then signalled to two or three 'lusty fellows' who came up and threw the sufferer in the Thames. 'This surprise absolutely cured him.' When a gentleman with 'a red, ugly, pumpled face' asked to be treated, Butler said, 'I must hang you,' and rigged up a rope to a beam in the room. When the patient was almost dead, the doctor lanced the veins that fed the 'pumples,' relieved him of black blood, and cured him. Another of his patients was a clergyman who, over-excited at the prospect of preaching before the King at Newmarket, consumed too much opium. Butler had a cow slaughtered and wrapped the parson in its warm belly, which revived him.

Dr Butler, like many a doctor after him, was reluctant to go on visits at inconvenient times. As he rode to call on a seriously ill patient his horse dropped him in a stream, and he decided to return home. The servant who was accompanying him persuaded him to change his mind with his sword point, with which he 'gave him ever and anon a little prick.'

Of Butler, a later biographer wrote: 'He seems to have . . . possessed a natural sagacity in the judging of diseases and what was more than all, his manners were extremely odd and capricious, which, with the vulgar, generally passes for a mark of extraordinary abilities.'*

Another Cambridge physician, the rich Dr Ravens, got himself talked about for less creditable reasons, according to an entry in the Diary of John Rous for December 1628. In a weak moment, he 'presumed to get into the chamber of a widow, an alderman's daughter, worth 20,000 li, and put his legge into the bedde; she asked who was there; he answered "Doctor Ravens"; she cryed out, and company came in.' For his indiscretion, the Doctor was fined £500 and imprisoned. On top of which, as the diarist noted, the widow's action against him was yet to come.†

The Universities of Oxford and Cambridge, whence the fellows of the Royal College of Physicians were chiefly drawn, were a long way from the van of medical progress. In 1605 the medical faculty of Oxford put on a special programme of 'academical exercises' for the benefit of James I when he visited the city. Sir William Paddy and Dr Matthew Gwinne discussed 'whether the morals of nurses are imbibed by infants with the milk' and 'whether the smoking of tobacco is favourable to health' (a topic of special interest to the monarch). If James had gone to Paris, no doubt the faculty there would have been ready to entertain him with witty disputations on topics like 'Is it healthy to get drunk once a month?' 'Is woman more lascivious than man?' and 'Are pretty women more fertile than others?' With such merry themes as these, all too many universities occupied themselves while humanity was scythed by fever and pestilence.

It was a pity that James, who held disillusioned views about doctors, was not able to hear the verdict of the surgeons who performed the autopsy on him. His skull, when opened, was found to be so full of brains that it was impossible to prevent them spilling. This, the explorers decided, was 'a great mark of his infinite judgment.'

It was a century of chaotic flux in medicine. Great discoveries were made, but their import was not always realised. Old follies were abandoned, but too many of them were retained. Six years after William Harvey published his treatise on the blood he was

* Benjamin Hutchinson: *Biographia Medica* (1799).
† Quoted in *A Peck of Troubles*, by Daniel George.

sent, with ten midwives, six surgeons and a lecturer in anatomy
to examine four Lancashire women accused of being witches, to
ascertain whether their bodies bore any unnatural teats. They
found none.

The originator of Boyle's Law, who as a seventh son and
fourteenth child would have had a flying start as a faith healer,
had not given up hope of turning base metals into gold. The
Philosopher's Stone remained the goal of many alchemists, who
hoped it might prove to be a universal healer. Nobody was quite
sure what it looked like, but every researcher was sure he would
recognise it if he saw it. Ben Jonson mocked the quest in his
play *The Alchemist*:

> '. . . 'tis a stone,
> And not a stone; a spirit, a soul and a body;
> Which if you do dissolve, it is dissolved;
> If you coagulate, it is coagulated;
> If you make it fly, it flieth . . .'

Sir Kenelm Digby contrived to hoodwink many, including
himself, with his powder of sympathy for the healing of wounds.
It was applied not to the wound but to the weapon which had
caused it, or to some detached part of the sufferer's clothing. An
elaborate theory was propounded to explain how forces radiating
from the blood and the balsam mingled together in a healing
cloud. It does not appear to have occurred to anybody that the
wound healed only because it was left alone. Bacteria were discovered in 1683 by Van Leeuwenhook who spied hordes of 'little
animals' through his new-fangled microscope. This was agreed
to be a very interesting discovery, though some thought it rather
disgusting, and it was then forgotten for a couple of centuries.
The first thermometer was devised, but the nineteenth century
had run half its course before the general practitioner carried his
clinical version. There were even dabblings in blood transfusion.
Samuel Pepys's Diary for 1665 has an account of a 'pretty
experiment' in this line at Gresham College. It involved 'the
blood of one dog let out, till he died, into the body of another on
one side, while all his own ran out on the other side. The first
died upon the place, and the other very well, and likely to do
well.' The experiment prompted various witticisms about what
would happen if the blood of a Quaker was let into the body of
an Archbishop, and so forth. Dr William Croome, who told

Pepys of the affair, obviously had ideas about using transfusion to restore the health of human beings. In 1666 Pepys noted that the Gresham College experimenters were trying transfusion on a human subject, 'a man that is a little frantic.' Presumably the subject was a little weak in the head, as he must have been to allow the experiment to be performed for a mere twenty shillings. However, he 'found himself much better.'

As for the long-suffering human stomach, it was still regarded as a basin with waste pipe attached; any blockage could be removed in an upward direction by a vomit or in a downward direction by a purge. One of Charles II's physicians devised an aid to gracious living in the shape of a stomach brush. The idea was that the patient should drink a draught of warm water or spirits of wine in order to loosen the foulness from the stomach walls. The brush, moistened in some convenient liquor, was then to be introduced into the oesophagus and slowly lowered into the stomach by twisting its wire handle. When it had reached its objective it was to be drawn up and down like a sucker in a syringe, the patient meanwhile drinking as much water as possible. A weekly use of the stomach brush was warranted to prolong life enormously.* A number of the King's subjects had the idea that they might digest their food more readily by swallowing a quantity of grit and small stones, as birds did. Sir Hans Sloane addressed the Royal Society on this practice, mentioning one of his friends who ordered a special round pebble by the peck from Kent—and then died suddenly. Sloane used to prescribe a more genial aid to digestion (to Sir Henry Morgan, the buccaneer, among others): a glass of water containing 50 live millipedes, twice daily.†

The proliferation of new medical theories resulted in much back-biting and jealousy. 'A doctor hates a doctor' ran the old saying. The *odium medicum,* or antipathy of one medical theorist for another, raged from generation to generation down to our own days, when the General Medical Council was able to bring about some state of discipline. France suffered from medical bickering too, perhaps more so than England. The warning which Molière put in the mouth of Filerin in *L'Amour Médecin* could have been addressed equally to the doctors of both nations:

'Do you not see how much harm this quarrelling does us in the

* William Wadd: *Mems, Maxims and Memoirs* (1827).
† E. St John Brooks: *Sir Hans Sloane.*

eyes of the world? . . . If we do not take care, we are going to ruin ourselves . . . Since Heaven has been good enough, for so many centuries, to make everyone infatuated with us, let us not disabuse mankind with our extravagant intrigues but benefit by their stupidity as gently as we can. We are not the only ones, as you know, who try to take advantage of human weakness. Do not, I say, foolishly destroy a system which gives bread to so many persons.'

The honoured name of Harvey was mocked by a quarrelsome namesake, Gideon Harvey, physician in ordinary to Charles II. In *The Conclave of Physicians* he expresses the view that 'anatomy is no further necessary to a surgeon than the knowledge of the nature of wood to a carpenter or of stone to a stone cutter.' The great anatomists of the day he dismisses as dog-slayers and calf's head dissectors. Students spend their prime in 'mangling of pigs, cats, dogs and plucks, or upon gazing and muzzling seven years upon a hedge, ditch or bankside to enquire for new faces of plants and herbs, which the petulancy of the earth doth thrust forth, to consume its excrementitious moisture and sulphurous sweats, which Nature never intended for the health of man but probably for garniture of the fields or to poison worms, flies and other insects . . .'

Gideon Harvey's contempt for anatomy and botany was to some extent shared by Thomas Sydenham, but there any resemblance ends. Sydenham, sometimes called the English Hippocrates, revived an interest in clinical observation. He took an irregular degree at Oxford (without having first taken an arts degree) and then, appalled by the sterility of his Oxford teachers, went on to Padua. Convinced that what the profession of medicine needed was a few facts, he began to observe, log, tabulate and classify diseases and their symptoms. Theories and syllogisms and speculations and systemisations he threw overboard. Nothing in the Pharmacopeia was of any use unless it helped Nature to perform the cure. His advice to Hans Sloane was: 'You must go to the bedside; it is there alone that you can learn disease.' Not the least of Sydenham's heresies was his belief that a patient with consumption ought to be surrounded with fresh air, instead of being confined in a closed room. Respect for Sydenham easily survives the discovery that he recommended the use of complaisant pups or kittens as hot water bottles, and even 'the warmth of young persons' to comfort the shivering.

One of the less-known Sydenham stories tells how he informed a wealthy patient that he could do no more for him and that the only man who could be of assistance was a Doctor Robertson of Inverness. Armed with a letter from Sydenham, the patient set off on the long journey north. At Inverness they told him there was no Doctor Robertson in the town and never had been; so, 'vowing eternal hostility to the peace of Sydenham,' he began the long journey home. Sydenham heard out his remonstrances and then said : 'Well, are you better in health?' The answer was : 'Yes, I am now quite well—no thanks to you.' To which Sydenham retorted : 'No, but you may thank Dr Robertson for curing you. I wished to send you on a journey with some object of interest in view; I knew it would be of service to you; in going you had Dr Robertson and his wonderful cures in contemplation; and in returning you were equally engaged in thinking of scolding me.'*

Sydenham, alas, had too few disciples. It was so much more attractive to fit a disease to a fancy, and then to rush out a book or pamphlet expounding the new theory. In such ways a doctor could be sure of catching the public eye. John Locke complained of the doctors who followed this 'romance way' of physic, who found it easier, as he said, to build castles in the air than to survey those on the ground.

For a picture of a sound type of English physician—that is, a practitioner who was neither famous, nor eccentric, nor quarrelsome, but who got on with a difficult job as best he could—it is hard to improve on Dr William Denton, who figures frequently in the *Verney Memoirs*. He was an Oxford graduate who, through the stresses of the Civil War, contrived to meet his responsibilities, not only to his patients but to four stepsons and five stepdaughters. Among his family patients were 'Mun' Verney's mentally unbalanced wife and young Mary Verney who became pregnant when unmarried. At this period girls like Mary were as big an embarrassment to their physicians as to their families, for a law passed by the Puritans in 1650 prescribed a penalty of three months' imprisonment for fornication. It was a law difficult to enforce, but the physician nevertheless ran considerable risk of denunciation and prosecution if he hushed up a pregnancy unhallowed by marriage. How Dr Denton solved this problem is not quite clear, but there was talk in the family of sending Mary to Ireland or the Barbadoes. Once, on his way to

* Dr J. A. Paris: *Pharmacologia*.

attend a confinement in Cheshire, Dr Denton lamed three out of four of his horses on the bad roads. On another occasion he was attacked and robbed by a highwayman, no rare event for a medical man. These risks must be borne in mind if physicians of the day are to be criticised for charging travelling expenses at the rate of a guinea a mile, or for prescribing by correspondence on receipt of an apothecary's letter setting out the sufferer's symptoms. Dr Denton, despite all his worries in the field of medicine and match-making, lived to be 86. He seems to have been on amiable relations with his apothecaries. A man of undoubted parts, he could make polite conversation, when occasion demanded, among the Court ladies, for he held appointments to both Charles I and Charles II. He is said to have kept abreast of medical developments, such as they were, but did not conduct any original research.

The seventeenth century was a peculiarly difficult one for the English Court physicians, who were reduced to unseemly shifts to disguise the inadequacies of their knowledge. It was, of course, no easier for the Sun King's physicians, who had to conceal the fact of their young sovereign's syphilis not only from the public, but from the patient himself, and who covered up an embarrassing attack of royal measles by issuing announcements of the expulsion of voracious, but fictitious, tapeworms from the royal body.

When James I's son Prince Henry lay dying the physicians could not agree on his treatment. Some, it appears, were reluctant to drain off too much royal blood. Others argued that 'in this case of extremity they must (if they meant to save his life) proceed in the cure as though he was some meane person.' Screwing up their courage, they bisected a cock and laid the reeking halves to the soles of the royal feet. Eventually James gave Sir Theodore Mayerne *carte blanche* to do what he liked; a risky step, since Mayerne was wont to prescribe nightmare items from gibbet and graveyard. For once, however, the physician declined to draw on his fund of novelties. He informed the King that he would never do anything unless on the advice of the other doctors, not wishing it to be said of him that he had slain the King's eldest son.*

* William Munk: *Roll of the Royal College of Physicians.*

Among sad stories of the deaths of kings, the account of Charles II's last days is a horror-comic. When the monarch fell ill on a Sunday evening of a kidney disease, accompanied by convulsions, Dr Edmund King was faced with the decision of whether to bleed him without consent of the chief ministers of the Crown, well aware that the penalty for such an act was death. Nevertheless, he acted. For his presence of mind as much as for his strength of purpose the Privy Council voted him £1,000, which he never received, the award being commuted to a knighthood. Not long was Dr King alone with his patient; the number of physicians built up to a dozen and more, dwindling to six at night. For five days, under Sir Charles Scarborough, they used the King with vastly more vigour than they would have applied to a mean person. Macaulay's view was that they tortured him like an Indian at the stake. To drain off his blood they put cupping glasses to his shoulders, scarified his flesh and tapped his veins. Then they cut off his hair and laid blisters on the scalp, and on the soles of his feet they applied plasters of pitch and pigeon dung. To remove the humours from his brain they blew hellebore up his nostrils and set him sneezing. To make him sick they poured antimony and sulphate of zinc down his throat. To clear his bowels they gave him strong purgatives and a brisk succession of clisters. To allay his convulsions they gave him spirit of human skull. To lower his temperature they administered Peruvian bark. At various times they gave him juleps for his spasms, a gargle for his sore throat, soothing draughts to temper his thirst, tonics for his heart and ale and light broth for his nourishment. Into the scarred and blistered hulk of a king they sent, now sedatives, now depth charges; cowslip, manna and mint, then Raleigh's antidote, with its animal, vegetable and mineral contents. Lest they be accused of neglect, they even administered bezoar. When the hulk slept, they woke it; when it spoke, they silenced it. In and out of the chamber passed physicians, priests, ministers, servants. On the Thursday night the King's mind was clear and undimmed. On the Friday morning they drew twelve more ounces of weak Stuart blood and then gave him heart tonics. He did not give in until noon, after apologising for being so long in dying. 'Three things only they denied him,' says Sir Arthur Bryant, 'light, rest and privacy; nothing else was left untried.'* Sir Arthur is wrong; they did not try that stomach brush.

* *King Charles II.*

It is tempting to speculate how this gallant band would have risen to the challenge which Louis XIV presented to his medical advisers in the following year. He was suffering severely from an anal fistula, the complaint which had carried off Richelieu. Among physicians and surgeons alike there was something like panic, for the operation to relieve this condition was but indifferently known. The only authority who could have tackled it confidently, John of Arderne, had been dead 300 years. As weeping crowds flocked to the churches, Charles François Felix experimented on hospital patients who were similarly afflicted and devised an instrument to make the operation less painful. Then, at seven o'clock one morning, Felix operated on the Sun King, who made no exclamation. At eight o'clock, though confined to bed, he held his morning reception as usual. Both monarch and surgeon could feel pride in the occasion. In Louis's eyes, surgery was now a liberal art, to be liberally rewarded. Felix, in whom the ordeal left a permanent tremble, received a sum of about £15,000, a country estate and a patent of nobility. He was now the only landed nobleman in France to treat for anal fistula.

William III seems to have suffered not only from the attentions of his physicians but from their impertinence. In 1697 Dr John Radcliffe, whom the King paid 600 guineas a year, told him : 'Your juices are all vitiated, your whole mass of blood corrupted and the nutriment for the most part turned to water. But if your Majesty will forbear making long visits to the Earl of Bradford (a convivial peer) I will engage to make you live three or four years longer; but beyond that no physic can protect your Majesty's existence.' (The King died five years later.) In 1699 the King showed his swollen ankles to Radcliffe and asked, 'Doctor, what think you of these?' The reply was, 'Why, truly, I would not have your Majesty's legs for your three kingdoms.' The jest seems to have been ill received.

Radcliffe was physician to Queen Anne until the day on which he told her that her indisposition was 'only vapours.' He declined to attend her in her last illness, on the ground that he had not been officially sent for and that he had just taken some of his own physic. To a friend he wrote : 'I know the nature of attending crowned heads, in their last moments, too well to be fond of waiting upon them without being sent for by a proper authority. You have heard of pardons being signed for physicians before a sovereign's demise, however, ill as I was, I would have went to the Queen in a horse litter had either Her Majesty or those in commission next to her commanded me so to do.'* Rightly or wrongly, the public blamed Radcliffe for the Queen's death and he went in some fear of the mob.

Radcliffe was the most famous English doctor at the close of the seventeenth century. The gossips do not seem sure whether he was witty and agreeable or ill-tempered and gruff. To his friend, Dr Richard Mead, he said : 'There are two ways, my boy, for a physician to treat his patients; either to bully or to cajole them. I have taken the first course and done very well, as you see. You may take the latter and perhaps do as well.'† In fact, Mead took the latter course and probably did better. Radcliffe was impatient at the fancies of his female patients, and is said to have demanded an Act of Parliament requiring women to be attended by nurses alone. Possibly he subscribed to the cynical notion that it pays to insult a tiresome woman patient, knowing that she will go off and complain angrily to her friends, who, while outwardly sympathising, will at once recognise the doctor's discernment in standing no nonsense from her.

Often at loggerheads with the Royal College of Physicians, who thought him an adventurer, Radcliffe had much practical skill as a physician and contrived to put into effect some of Sydenham's teaching. He had a sharp clash with the old Duchess of Beaufort who, when her grandson was ill with smallpox, demanded that the windows should be sealed tight according to custom. Radcliffe threw them open and said he would go back to Chelsea if they were shut again. A practitioner more susceptible to the browbeatings of venerable duchesses would have given in, at the risk of losing the patient. In Radcliffe's view all the mystery of physic could be written on half a sheet of notepaper. His library consisted of little more than a textbook or two, a herbal, a few phials and a skeleton. That he should be remembered by the famous library in Oxford is (in the phrase of Sir Samuel Garth) 'as if an eunuch should found a seraglio.'

Anecdotes, many of them improbable, have been fathered on Radcliffe as freely as witticisms on Wilde. One of the less probable tells how he arranged a slapstick pudding-throwing act in order to cause a fit of laughter in a patient suffering from quinsy— with the result that 'the quinsy burst and discharged its contents.'

---

* Benjamin Hutchinson: *Biographia Medica*.
† Annual Register, 1792: *Essay on Physic and Physicians*.

Hard, too, to swallow, is the story that a Grenadier visited the Doctor at a tavern to request him to call on his colonel, and on meeting with a refusal, picked him up and bore him off by force —not to treat the colonel but to tend a sick comrade.

VI

RULE-MAKERS AND RULE-BREAKERS

IN the midst of its other preoccupations, the Royal College of Physicians tried, through the seventeenth century, to maintain some semblance of discipline in the profession and to consolidate a code of ethics. It was let down, consistently, by the Court, which sheltered quacks, but it also let itself down on a notorious occasion in 1665.

The College's embarrassments were not lessened, in the days of Archbishop Laud, by those doctors who persisted in dabbling in matters spiritual and, in consequence, were reduced to walking about without their ears.

Dr Alexander Leighton, a puritanical Scot of dubious medical qualifications, had been censured by the College for unlawful practice before he became the subject of ecclesiastical vivisection. For his animadversions on the bishops and the Queen he was sentenced in 1630 to have his ears cut off, both sides of his nose slit and the letters 'SS' (sower of sedition) engraved on his face. The sentence was to be carried out in two phases, but phase two was remitted.

Three years later Dr John Bastwick, who practised in Colchester, fell foul of the High Common Court on similar grounds. He was sentenced to be fined £1,000, excommunicated, debarred from practising physic, to see his books burned, to pay the costs of the prosecution and to stay in prison until he recanted. The Royal College of Physicians dutifully revoked his licence to practise. In 1637 he published another inflammatory work which he had written in the Gatehouse and was hauled before the Star Chamber, where he exclaimed: 'Will you cut off a scholar's ears, will you cut off a doctor of physic's ears, able to cure lords, peers, kings and emperors? Will you cut off a Christian's ears, will you make curs of Christians, my lords?'*

* William Munk: *Roll of the Royal College of Physicians.*

48

The answer was in the affirmative. Bastwick shared the pillory with William Prynne, a lawyer, and Henry Burton, a divine; all three learned professions were thus represented. The doctor was said to have been 'very merry' in the pillory. His wife took custody of his ears and carried them away in a clean handkerchief. Bastwick was also fined £5,000 and sent to prison for life. The Long Parliament rescinded the sentence and awarded £5,000 compensation to be drawn from the funds of the Archbishop and the dignitaries of the Star Chamber. Then the College of Physicians restored his licence to practise and all he lacked was his ears, which no doubt his wife still had.

To the College, episodes like these were a melancholy distraction from the harrying of quacks. In this salutary activity they had little support in high places. The censors took action against a presumptuous alchemist called Arthur Dee, who hung up at his door a list of cures he professed to perform. Charitably, James I gave Dee a letter of recommendation to the Czar, whose physician he then became. Later the Czar gave him an introduction to Charles I, and Dee came back as physician in ordinary, doubtless with a friendly sneer for the College.

In James's reign, also, the College observed that a Dr Saul had been appointed one of the Queen's physicians. The president wrote to Lord Sidney to point out that, in 1591, this same Dr Saul had been brought up before them, had been unable to answer questions in Latin, and, while professing a knowledge of the works of Galen, had been unable to name any of them. A little sarcasm seemed to be called for : 'We do not a little marvel how he cometh by this credit in physick unless either by infusion learning hath been powered into him or else by some extraordinary means he hath of late obtained a special gift of healing.' The president added that, of course, he was not actuated by malice but by 'loyal fidelity' to the Queen. What action was taken, if any, does not emerge.

About this time, also, the College questioned Simon Forman, an astrologer. 'Being examined in the principles of astrology he answered so absurdly and ridiculously that it caused great mirth and sport amongst the auditors,' says Goodall. Forman took refuge from his merry inquisitors in Lambeth, supposing that the Archbishop would give him sanctuary. Thereupon the College wrote a letter of complaint to the Archbishop, who said, 'My officers shall give you assistance or else they shall be no officers of mine.' Thus did the Church help the devotees of a bogus science to hound one who had not studied his humbug at advanced level.

More successful than Forman in defying the College was Francis Anthony, who persistently prescribed, publicised and defended his sovereign remedy, drinkable gold. A disinterested contemporary described Anthony as 'a man of unaffected piety, untainted probity, of easy address, great modesty and boundless charity.' The College's objections were twofold : firstly, that gold was not soluble in water, and secondly, that if it was, it would not constitute a universal healer. Once, it generously provided Anthony with an ounce of gold and a quantity of water, and invited him to dissolve it for them. Anthony had powerful patrons, however, and long resisted persecution. His physician sons are said to have lived handsomely on the family recipe.

In Charles I's reign the censors scotched the activities of James Leverett, purporting to be the seventh son of a seventh son, who claimed to have a healing touch. By popular superstition, a seventh son often had supra-normal gifts; it followed that vastly greater gifts must be possessed by the seventh son of a seventh son. In fact, Leverett was the fourth son of a family of six. To prosecute him was a delicate task, for it was important to say nothing which would undermine faith in the ability of English monarchs to cure by the 'Royal touch' (a talent in which many physicians believed). The College indictment against Leverett reveals that he did not believe in overworking his mysterious powers. 'He saith,' runs the document, 'that upon touching 30 or 40 in a day he finds himself weakened by the virtue which goes out of him, more than when he was a gardener by digging up eight roods of ground; so that he is brought to that weakness by touching that he is forced to go to his bed to recover his strength, which in his daily labour he was not wont to do . . . he said he is not always disposed to touch especially if his hands be cold . . . he saith he hath cured 300 at the least, he takes money for his cures, but not by contract . . .' Once, it appears, Leverett was assaulted by jealous surgeons who strained his thumb; he touched it with his other hand and cured it. More than once, the College gave him opportunities to demonstrate his powers but he seems to have been unlucky in the patients offered him. The indictment accuses him of 'scornfully slighting His Majesty's gift' by saying he could touch more successfully than any monarch. One Edward Pate said that when he took his child to be touched, Leverett

Valentine Greatorex (or Greatrakes) 'Most Remarkable for Curing
Many Disorders by the Stroke or Touch of his Hand Only'

exclaimed to onlookers: 'Do you see this fellow? He left me and
went to the king for the cure of his child but I will now make
him wait my leisure before I touch him.' It was two or three days
before Leverett condescended to treat the child. After all, there
were lords and ladies waiting for his services and for a chance to
buy the sheets in which he had slept.*

There were bemused doctors ready to explain how men like
Leverett performed their cures. Valentine Greatorex, whose
speciality was stroking rather than touching, could cite this
tribute from Henry Stubbe, a physician of Stratford: 'God had
bestowed on Mr Greatorex a peculiar temperament, or composed
his body of some particular ferments, the effluvia whereof being
introduced, sometimes by a light, sometimes by a violent friction,

* Charles Goodall: *An Historical Account of the College's Proceedings Against Empiricks.*

should restore the temperament of the debilitate parts, reinvigor-
ate the blood and dissipate all heterogenous ferments out of the
bodies of the diseased by the eyes, nose, mouth, hands and feet.'*

Quacks multiplied during the Civil War and were strengthened
in their pretensions after the Restoration. Charles II sheltered
many, including John Archer who advertised secret remedies for
disreputable sins, and even promised protection against future
debauches, the only form of preventive medicine practised under
the Merry Monarch.

The Royal College does not appear to have picked up the
scent of an unlicensed adventurer calling himself Alexander
Bendo, who in 1676 began to peddle 'wonderful secrets and infallible remedies' from an address in Tower Street. Bendo was,
in fact, the wayward Earl of Rochester, who had grown tired of
masquerading as a City merchant and was eager to try out a new
disguise, until such time as he should be in favour again at Court.
Like all good quacks, Rochester issued a high-flown address in
which he enumerated the cures he professed to perform. He
offered to relieve his fair clients of excessive fat, and 'to add flesh
to those who want it, without the least detriment to their con-
stitutions.' He was prepared to cure 'the worst of breaths, provided the lungs be not totally perished,' and, by rejuvenating the
lips, to make 'soft as you could wish your lawful kisses.' All who
had travelled in Italy, according to Dr Bendo, would agree that in
that country art performed miracles in the preservation of beauty.
'Women of 40 bear the same countenances with those of 15; ages
are in no way distinguishable by faces; whereas here in England,
look a horse in the mouth and a woman in the face you presently
know both their ages to a year.' Dr Bendo was willing to practise
his restorative arts on Englishwomen and also to cure them of
barrenness. 'My usual contract is, to receive half of what is
agreed upon, when the party shall be quick with child, the other
half when she is brought to bed.'

With his tongue firmly in his cheek, Rochester delivered the
customary blast at the orthodox profession, whom he styled 'a
bastard race of quacks and cheats.' He also claimed credit for
reticence : 'I would put no word in my bill that bears any un-
clean sound; it is enough that I make myself understood; I have
seen physicians' bills as bawdy as Aretine's dialogues; which no
man that walks warily before God can approve of.'

* Benjamin Hutchinson: *Biographia Medica.*

Before the joke palled, Rochester had worked up a small but pleasantly indiscreet practice among the maids of the maids-of-honour. His apparently intimate knowledge of the frailties of the Court ladies startled his patients, whose gossip in turn startled their mistresses.

It was in Charles's reign that the Royal College of Physicians was induced, without much difficulty, to limit its fellowship almost wholly to graduates of Oxford and Cambridge, that is, to such as were prepared to swear to the 39 Articles. In the past, occasional outsiders had been admitted. The new ruling was in accordance with the general policy of eliminating 'security risks' in influential places. Henceforth Nonconformists and Roman Catholics who wished to take up medicine had no option but to go to Continental schools and universities. When they had qualified, the College was prepared to licence them to practise but would not admit them to its inner councils. In enforcing this policy, the College stored up much trouble for itself and shut its doors against an imposing array of talent.

An old, old problem of medical ethics cropped up, in acute form, in 1665, when the plague descended on London with unprecedented virulence. In earlier visitations the physicians, with very rare exceptions, had fled from the city along with the wealthy among whom their practice lay. This time the Royal College saw no reason to vary its policy and most of its fellows and licentiates pulled out of the stricken city, along with the higher clergy and the Court. Before the College closed down the Lord Mayor requested that it should publish directions for a remedy against infection, in order to discourage the public from flying to rapacious quacks and astrologers. The College obliged wtih two recipes—one for the rich, incorporating pearl, onyx and unicorn's horn, and one for the poor. At the King's request Dr Thomas Wharton, physician to St Thomas's Hospital, stayed behind 'to look after the soldiers.' He was promised the first vacant appointment of physician in ordinary to the King, if he survived; but when the opportunity to reward him occurred he was given an armorial distinction instead. Dr Nathaniel Hodges, an Oxford graduate, was one of 19 physicians who stayed behind throughout the visitation. He examined patients for three hours before breakfast and then visited others in their homes. After a hearty dinner he received more patients and went on more visits.

His personal precautions included the sucking of lozenges, the burning of disinfectant on hot coals, and the consumption of large quantities of food and sack, in order to ensure himself a sound sleep. Defoe says that of the doctors who stayed behind few 'cared to stir abroad to sick houses'; one fortified himself throughout with drink and in consequence became a sot. Big risks were taken by the 'able and discreet surgeons' appointed by the Lord Mayor to accompany the searchers. They were to have twelve pence in respect of every person examined, this sum to be paid by the examinee or by the parish. As danger money goes, it was a modest enough fee.

When the fugitive physicians returned they found that the treasure-chest of the Royal College had been rifled by the mob. More disagreeable than this, however, was the temper of the public. Old patients who had survived the plague boycotted them; their doors were adorned with mocking bills reading 'Here is a Doctor to be Let.' It was little consolation that the clergy were being similarly derided. 'Several of those physicians,' says Defoe, 'were fain for a while to sit still and look about them, or at least remove their dwellings and set up in new places and among new acquaintance.'*

Apologists of the Royal College have been at pains to justify the physicians' exodus, if only on the grounds that they could have done no good if they had stayed. It is possible that the more realistic among them saw their predicament in the same light as foot soldiers who are garrisoned in a city during a long-range bombardment : when there are no effective weapons with which to fight the enemy, the best place is in the shelter. In his biography of Sydenham, J. F. Payne says : 'Had the West-end physicians remained, they would have found themselves almost in solitude, among empty houses.' At this remove it would appear that if the physicians had stayed behind and taken the trouble to seek out patients they would have done themselves immense credit in humble eyes, and would have robbed the apothecaries of a taunt which was to be flung at them for a generation afterwards.

What one apothecary thought about the runaway physicians is to be found in the *Loimographia* of William Boghurst, of St Giles-in-the-Fields, who remained behind, treating up to 60 patients a day. 'The great doctors and such as undertake to write about the disease,' he says, 'are the first to run away from it; and

* *A Journal of the Plague Year.*

so it follows . . . all the learning about it can be but opinionative
and conjectural.' Boghurst's view was that magistrates, ministers,
physicians, apothecaries, surgeons and midwives should all stay
at their posts, 'but those apothecaries who have their work and
dependence from the physicians are not, I think, obliged to stay
behind when their masters lead the way; for who shall direct
them? They say it is not our business to direct or undertake to
give physic out of our own heads . . . but those apothecaries
which stand upon their own legs and live by their own practice
are bound by their undertakings to stay and help as in other
diseases. Every man that undertakes to be a member of a profession or takes upon him any office must take all parts of it, the
good and the evil, the pleasure and the pain, the profit and the
inconvenience altogether and not pick and choose . . .'

It is hard to quarrel with Boghurst's point of view, or to accuse
him of vainglory in his description of how he physicked, bled and
purged his fated patients, holding them in his arms, suffering
their breath in his face, sitting up with them until they died,
closing their eyes, helping to coffin them and then accompanying
them to the grave. It was service far exceeding that demanded
by the ordinary call of duty.

That was but one field of ethics. The notion that remedies
should be made freely available for suffering humanity, and not
kept as a source of revenue for individuals, was becoming fairly
well established, but there were some exceptions to be noted.
Not a few leading physicians derived an income from widely
marketed elixirs. The widow of Nicholas Culpepper (who had
infuriated the Royal College by translating its Pharmacopeia
from Latin into English) lived on her late husband's recipe for
drinkable gold, which she claimed would not only cure fevers and
gout but prevent miscarriages. In a treatise on the subject published
in 1656 she explains why she does not reveal the recipe: '. . . it
had been in vain to leave me this medicine as a legacy and to
make it common to everybody.' That she should live comfortably
while babes were aborted does not seem to have worried her.
Gideon Harvey wrote two pamphlets in which he outlined treatment for the French pox, but hinted that he had a superior secret
remedy if anybody cared to apply to him. A major outrage to
medical ethics was that perpetrated by the Chamberlen family,
with their secret instrument, the obstetrical forceps. Three generations of the family succeeded in preserving the secret of this device

for delivering unwilling babes. Peter Chamberlen, who was for a period a fellow of the Royal College of Physicians, justified secrecy on the strictly commercial grounds that 'the draper is not bound to find clothing for all the naked because he has enough in his shop, nor yet to afford it at the buyer's price.'* The view of a French obstetrician was that anybody seeking to make private profit from such a device deserved to have his vitals gnawed by a worm through eternity. Eventually Hugh Chamberlen divulged the secret, or some part of it, at a price to the Dutch, after failing to sell it to the French. How many babes might have been saved if the Chamberlens had been actuated by more humane feelings will never be known (certainly more than would have entered the world if Mrs Culpepper had not hogged her drinkable gold); on the other hand, when the secret did leak out, many babes were unnecessarily mangled by the device. In modern eyes, the great mystery is that nobody else was able to produce a comparable instrument. Its 'secret' lay chiefly in the fact that the two blades were locked together after the baby's head had been gripped.

One who held, strongly, that all medical knowledge should be free was Sir Hans Sloane, who bought up and publicised a cure for a mad dog bite which had been held a secret by the Dampier family of Devon. He prided himself on always being free and open in his practice, unlike 'some physicians of good morals and great reputation,' whom he could have named, but did not.

* *Dictionary of National Biography.*

VI

POETS JOIN THE FIGHT

In 1696 a brisk fire sprang up from the embers of old quarrels between the physicians and the apothecaries. The flames were eagerly fanned by poets and pamphleteers, and the citizens of London found much innocent pleasure in the spectacle.

All through the century the pushing apothecaries had been strengthening their status. The middle classes were finding it consistent with their dignity to call in a tradesman to attend them for lesser ailments. It was lighter on the purse and the man seemed to have more practical knowledge of illness than some of those young physicians who, at their universities, had learned every science except that of healing.

To a struggling graduate from Oxford or Cambridge there was no more galling sight than that of a prosperous apothecary riding about London in his carriage, trying to look as if he had never swept out a shop in his life. If the fellow had any duty at a bed-side, it was to do the drudgery a gentleman could not be expected to perform but which could not be left to a nurse. Yet here he was, revelling in the flesh-pots, and growing daily richer by the sale of knowledge filched from wiser men.

The apothecary made it clear that he was not prepared to accept NCO status in the ranks of medicine. During long apprenticeship he had drilled and trained for his job. Why should he stand aside for those who obtained their commissions by virtue of being gentlemen?

All the old reproaches began to be hurled about again, along with a few new ones. The apothecary mocked the physician for disdaining contact with his patients, neglecting the poor and making himself scarce in times of plague. The physician grumbled that the apothecary, like the quack, passed on only those patients whom he had already botched, and alleged that, as a shopkeeper, his only concern was to sell off his drugs before they went stale.

The charge of neglecting the poor was one which the physicians could not wholly rebut. It was true that some of them gave free advice and prescriptions to the sick poor and that others offered their services in hospitals, as William Harvey had done at St Bartholomew's and Sir Hans Sloane now did at Christ's Hospital. Yet many a poor man lived and died without seeing a physician, other than as a proud figure riding by in a carriage.

In 1689 the Royal College went out of its way to urge all its members to give free advice and prescriptions to the sick poor of their neighbourhood. When the poor took these prescriptions to the apothecaries they found they could not afford to pay the shopmen's bills. This, to the physicians, was clear proof of the rapacity of the apothecaries. At the suggestion of the City Council, the College considered a proposal that it should provide drugs at a reasonable sum from its own premises. It seemed a happy opportunity of thwarting the parasitic apothecaries while at the same time befriending the poor, but by no means all the fellows of the College favoured the scheme. Those who were already on good terms with their apothecaries, and who valued the trade which they introduced, had no wish to antagonise them. Others argued that it would lower the dignity of the profession to make the Royal College a depot for the sale of pills and boluses, like Apothecaries' Hall. Eventually, the critics were overborne, and in 1696 the Royal College opened the first of three dispensaries. Now, more than ever, the golden ball on the roof of the College symbolised a golden pill. The disputing factions aligned themselves as was to be expected. The pro-dispensary physicians found themselves boycotted not only by the apothecaries but by many of their professional colleagues.

In 1699 Sir Samuel Garth, a physician and member of the Kit Kat Club, wrote a long heroic poem attacking the insolence of the apothecaries and the obtuseness of his colleagues in the opposite camp. According to a Victorian chronicler, Garth's The Dispensary is the only literary product of the controversy that 'can now be read by a gentleman without a sense of annoyance and disgust.' At this day, it cannot be read without a sense of ennui, though its early passages are of interest for their references to the type of research allegedly carried on by the College. It seems there had been investigations into the mystery of how nerves

> '. . . are fashion'd to sustain
> The greatest pleasure and the greatest pain,'

and also

> 'How body acts upon impassive mind,
> How fumes of wine the thinking part can fire,
> Past hopes revive and present joys inspire . . .'

Garth mocks the apothecary, as Shakespeare did, for the mumbo-jumbo of his shop—the crocodile, the tortoise, the shark's head, the flying fish, the mummies 'most reverently stale,' and the floor strewn with musty drugs, dried bladders and drawn teeth. He also offers a glimpse of the apothecary's inner sanctum, where

> 'Globes stand by globes, volumes on volumes lie,
> And planetary schemes amuse the eye.
> The Sage, in velvet chair, here lolls at ease,
> To promise future health for present fees.'

The apothecary, according to Garth, made a speciality of curing the ills of Venus and of 'kindling in cold veins the sparks of love.'

In due course, more eminent poets ranged themselves on Garth's side. The word apothecary was ill-designed to fit in their iambic pentameters, but they did their best. In his *Essay on Criticism,* Pope says:

> 'So modern 'pothecaries, taught the art
> By doctors' bills to play the doctor's part,
> Bold in the practice of mistaken rules,
> Prescribe, apply and call their masters fools.'

Dryden cheerfully accuses them of indiscriminate homicide:

> 'Th' Apothecary-Train is wholly blind.
> From files, a random recipe they take,
> And many deaths of one prescription make.
> Garth, gen'rous as his muse, prescribes and gives;
> The shop-man sells; and by destruction lives;
> Ungrateful tribe! who like the viper's brood
> From Med'cine issue, suck their mother's blood!'*

Generous Garth may not have been amused by this later couplet:

* *To My Honoured Kinsman, John Dryden.*

'Let them, but under their superiors, kill,
When Doctors first have signed the bloody bill.'

Born in bitterness, the dispensaries were not a great success
and were closed down after a few years; but similar institutions
multiplied under other auspices later in the eighteenth century.

To Dr Richard Mead has been given credit for trying to
narrow the breach between physicians and apothecaries after the
dispensary battle. Along with Dr Radcliffe (whose apothecary
Dandridge is said to have left £60,000) he popularised the
practice of consulting apothecaries at his coffee-house. After
listening to a recital of patients' symptoms, he would write out a
prescription and charge half the usual guinea fee. Mead would
have been shocked to hear the harsh things that were said about
this second-hand diagnosis by physicians of a later day. It was
richesse oblige on his part; after all, he was a busy man. No
doubt patients were gratified to be able to obtain his advice, even
at second-hand. But the coffee-house consultation became something of a farce when practised by physicians of lesser attainments
than Mead and Radcliffe; that is, by idle fellows from the
universities, ignorant of the *materia medica,* whose vanity was
gratified by keeping a servile apothecary waiting while they
conversed with poets and wits.

The apothecaries won two notable successes against the
physicians in the courts. Although they had long claimed the
right to prescribe and treat without reference to a physician,
their members had been frequently prosecuted by the Royal
College for doing so. In 1703 William Rose, an apothecary, was
convicted of this offence. He appealed to the Lords, who reversed
the decision of the lower court, making it clear that they did so
in the public interest. In its wider sense, the case of the Royal
College was untenable, for if the apothecaries had not taken it
upon themselves to prescribe and treat, the sick poor in the
country at large would have lacked almost all medical attention.
Nevertheless, the Royal College had some sharp comments to
make on the case of William Rose. This martyred apothecary, it
pointed out, had treated a butcher called John Seal for 12
months, charging him nearly £50, and had done him no good,
whereas when he attended the dispensary of the Royal College
he had been cured in six weeks for less than 40s.*

---

* *Observations Upon the Case of William Rose, an Apothecary* (1704).

The other victory by the apothecaries over the College was secured when one of their number won damages against a group of eminent physicians for illegal seizure of his wares. After this the censors of the College displayed a great deal more caution in exercising their ancient privilege of inspection.

One of the apothecary's undoubted faults was a tendency towards high-pressure salesmanship. His delight was to find a wealthy patient willing and eager to try out new medicines. The patient would then be progressively debauched until his apothecary's bill exceeded that of his tailor and his grocer. At his worst, an apothecary could be as rapacious as the most unregenerate of moneylenders. In Bernard Mandeville's *Treatise of the Hypochondria* (1711) is a passage describing how an apothecary, on an idle afternoon, called at the house of a person of quality:

'There happened to be nobody at home but children and servants who from the highest to the lowest were all in perfect health; if here he came for business (you'll say) he was disappointed; but you are mistaken; the courteous gentleman with an engaging familiarity accosts every servant in the house and puts off a purge to the cook, a vomit to the butcher, a box of pills to one of the footmen and a pot of lucatellus balm to old Nurse. The children absolutely refused to take any physic . . . at last he coaxes the little master into the use of a charming dentifrice and a sweet scented collyrium to rinse his mouth with after it . . . to pretty miss he'll send a lotion for her hair and a paste for her hands . . . with a beauty wash for their maid that assisted in the pursuit of them . . . The children are pleased, the servants commend him, my lady is obliged to him . . . and probably drives to thank him for the care he took of her family in her absence.'

Dr Thomas Dover, that proponent of quicksilver, says in his *Ancient Physician's Legacy* (1732):

'I never affronted an apothecary, unless ordering too little physic, and curing a patient too soon, is in their way of thinking, an unpardonable crime. I must confess I could never bring an apothecary's bill to three pounds, in a fever; whereas I have known some of their bills, in this disease, amount to forty, fifty and sixty pounds. If I can't cure with less charges, I can't forbear saying that I have the same opinion of their integrity as I have of their understanding.'

Yet, with all his faults, the apothecary could not be held back. He had prised open the back door of medicine and the law had given him permission to enter and make himself at home. The Society of Apothecaries pursued its advantage by securing the

passing of Acts of Parliament which enabled it not only to discipline its members but to improve their education. Already the
middle classes and the higher tradesmen were beginning to
apprentice their sons to apothecaries and to pay good money for
the privilege.

Because there was obviously a good living to be gained as an
apothecary, numbers of needy persons set themselves up as such
without going to the fatigue of obtaining a diploma from the
Society of Apothecaries. They served for brief periods as assistants or apprentices to licensed apothecaries and surgeons and
then felt themselves qualified to embark on all-round practice on
their own. Though they were, strictly speaking, quacks, many of
them became highly respected members of the community. They
were, in fact, the forerunners of the general practitioner of the
nineteenth century.

Professionally, the apothecary—whether he flourished a diploma or called himself surgeon-apothecary—still ranked below
the physician and the surgeon. Socially, he still ranked below the
parson and the lawyer. But he was the man who sat up with the
seriously ill patient while physician, lawyer and parson slept—
and the public did not forget.

VII

GOLD-HEADED CANE

THE symbol of the doctor in the eighteenth century was his gold-headed cane. It was a wand of office which helped to impress the patient. At the same time it sometimes had a utilitarian function, for it contained in its head aromatic material designed to offset the foul vapours of sick rooms and hospital wards.

In their candid moments, the priesthood of the gold-headed cane were ready to admit that even after 2,000 years of medicine there was still not one certain cure for any disease. The doctor's role was very nearly as defined by a character in Fielding's *Tom Jones*: 'Nature should be left to do her own work, while the physician stands by, as it were, to clap her on the back and encourage her when she doth well.'

Lady Mary Wortley Montagu, whose views on physicians were waspish, complained that money once given to monks for the health of the soul was now thrown to doctors for the health of the body, 'and generally with as little prospect of success.' Voltaire's considered opinion was that the physician was a person who poured medicine of which he knew nothing into a body of which he knew less.

Yet, through the eighteenth century, the way was slowly prepared for the tremendous advances of the nineteenth. In hospitals and elsewhere, the work of Sydenham in observing and classifying diseases was continued. Isolation and quarantine began to be accepted as essential in the treatment of fever. Sir John Pringle showed that there was no valid reason why British battalions should be wiped out regularly by fever and pestilence, and the Admiralty came to recognise that the entire ship's complement need not necessarily be sacrificed to scurvy on a long voyage. The notion that every other babe must die was challenged. So was the tradition that childbirth was below a doctor's notice.

Inoculation against smallpox, thanks in no small measure to
Lady Mary Wortley Montagu, made headway, to be succeeded,
in the closing stages of the century, by vaccination. Even the
horrors of mad-houses, both public and private, began to be
cleared up, but handcuffs, leg-irons and strait-waistcoats remained in general use until Queen Victoria's reign. George III
described the strait-waistcoat as the best friend he ever had.

What the medical profession chiefly needed was a proper
system of education and training. The Royal College of
Physicians, sulking at its defeat by the apothecaries, did not
regard this as its responsibility; its charter merely said that it
should hold examinations. Would-be physicians who had private
means idled through the academic futilities of Oxford and
Cambridge or set off to medical schools on the Continent.
Aspirants of modest means were left to apprentice themselves to
such practitioners as would accept them, picking up the virtues,
prejudices and faults of busy men for whom they performed
much ill-requited drudgery. They might in due course walk the
wards of a hospital, and take the examinations of the Apothecaries and the Surgeons, or even go on to a university; but many
went into practice as soon as this apprenticeship was over.

It was left to the Scots to found the first medical school in
Britain. Dr Alexander Monro modelled his establishment in
Edinburgh on the lines of the Boerhaave School at Leyden, and
was soon attracting students who would otherwise have gone to
that city. Scots doctors began to drift south, ready to snatch at
any medical post from naval surgeon's mate upwards. They were
viewed with disapproval by the Royal College and not without
hauteur at Surgeons' Hall. Those who had studied under Dr
Monro might know their science, but there were others flourishing diplomas which they had obtained by irregular means, or
after inadequate study, and even *in absentia*. The universities of
Aberdeen and St Andrews, in particular, were prone to give
diplomas to those who had undergone no examination, but who
had been able to persuade a couple of not very eminent physicians
to certify them fit for practice. These universities took no particular pride in the game, but funds were low and professors had
to live. Scots degrees could even be obtained from brokers in
London.

The prestige of the physicians was saved, to some extent, by
the founding, in the early half of the century, of the big voluntary

hospitals. In the metropolis these included the Westminster, Guy's, St George's, the London and the Middlesex. Most were built by wealthy philanthropists (Thomas Guy's fortune was made during the South Sea Bubble); others were founded by physicians themselves. These great institutions could not be left for apothecaries to seize, and the elect of the Royal College were quick to compete, and intrigue, for posts on their staffs. The physicians now had what they had so long lacked, save at the venerable institutions of St Bartholomew's and St Thomas's : an unending pageant of fevers and assorted diseases, other than gout, paraded daily for their personal study. In the long ill-smelling wards the more conscientious physicians risked their lives along with their reputations, receiving little if any financial reward. Others, to whom a hospital appointment was primarily a source of social prestige, sniffed disdainfully at the pageant of sores and left the wards as soon as they decently could.

The patients were made suitably aware of the privilege conferred on them by the attendance of great physicians. Those who were not gravely ill would be expected to wait on the visitor in his consulting room. The hospital background lent dignity to a man who was already an impressive figure in his wig, scarlet satin, buckled shoes and muff (to keep the hands sensitive, as well as warm), and whose least Hippocratic appendage was a sword. Such a figure could not be expected to tour the hospital without a supporting cast of minor characters and a welcoming committee in each ward. When he stopped at the bedside of an awed patient he could afford to be gravely affable and solicitous. A few physicians abused their position, however, one of them being the poet Mark Akenside, whose stanzas were more felicitous than his manners (he is said to have changed his name from Akinside on the ground that, for a doctor, it lent itself too readily to jests). Evidently this one-time butcher's son had adopted Dr Radcliffe's advice to 'treat mankind ill,' and he shared Radcliffe's testy impatience with women patients, singling them out for especially harsh treatment. The supercilious Akenside, with his 'pale strumous countenance' framed in a full-bottomed wig, and with a long sword clanking, would order the hospital servants to precede him with brooms to clear the way and to prevent the patients approaching too closely; an edifying spectacle in an institution bearing the name of Christ's Hospital. At St Thomas's the sick poor cowered at his approach. If they did not give a

C

clear, direct answer to his questions they were liable to be summarily discharged. 'He could not bear to see anyone smile in the presence of an invalid,' said a contemporary.

Dr J. C. Lettsom, in his younger days, was 'inexpressibly shocked' when a patient who was unable to swallow his medicine was ordered by Akenside to be removed forthwith—'He shall not die in my hospital.' The patient, as it happened, was impertinent enough to die as he was being wheeled away. Once a Governor of St Thomas's said to the physician who spoke of 'my hospital': 'Know that thou are a servant of this Charity.'* Akenside died, unrepentant, in the bed in which Milton died.

In St Bartholomew's Hospital it had been the custom in the previous century to allow students to walk the wards, and this facility was extended to the new voluntary hospitals. As will be seen, it was a privilege which was sometimes badly abused. The average patient looked no more kindly on a flock of inquisitive students than does the patient of today. The poet Martial had summed up the sufferer's reaction centuries before:

> 'I send for Symmachus to ease my pain.
> A hundred pupils follow in his train,
> And feel me with their frigid hands. I vow
> I had no fever but I have one now.'

Working up a successful practice called for much enterprise and impudence. Not every physician was as fortunate as Dr William Battie, who had hardly set up at Uxbridge before Dr Godolphin, Provost of Eton, sent his coach-and-four for him. The Provost explained: 'You need not trouble to prescribe. I have sent for you to give you some credit in the neighbourhood.'†

Advertising had to be done by oblique methods. Thus, gentlemen's chariots would be stopped in the street by anxious-seeming servants enquiring whether Dr So-and-So was aboard; the occupants would be well aware that this was merely Dr So-and-So's way of spreading his name. In coffee-houses the question, 'Is Dr Such-and-Such here?' was liable to be received with derision.

Tobias Smollett, who was unsuccessful in his attempts to set himself up as a physician in London and Bath, drenches the pro-

* *Memoirs of J. C. Lettsom* (ed. T. J. Pettigrew, 1817).
† William Wadd: *Nugae Chirurgicae.*

ET PLURIMA MORTIS IMAGO

'A Consultation of Physicians' by William Hogarth (1736(. Top centre is Mrs Sally Mapp, the bonesetter. On her right, Chevalier John Taylor, the oculist. On her left, Joshua Ward, the pillman

fession with the juice of sour grapes in *The Adventures of Count Fathom*. In his view, a carriage was the first essential of an aspiring doctor, for 'a walking physician was considered as an obscure pedlar, trudging from street to street with his pack of knowledge on his shoulders and selling his remnants of advice by retail.' There were patients who were ready to judge a walking doctor as summarily as did that gouty old gentleman mentioned in *The Spectator* : 'Go, send the knave about his business. Was his business as infallible as he pretends he would long before now have been in his coach-and-six.' Yet there were physicians who could put up a brave show even on foot. Dr John Huxham, a butcher's son with a Leyden degree, who was not above suspicion of having himself called from dissenting conventicles on fictitious errands, used to walk in a scarlet coat with his gold-headed cane, followed by a footman a pace or two in rear carrying his gloves.

A fruitful cause of traffic accidents in London, says Smollett, was to be found in the coaches of physicians, surgeons and apothecaries all driving in spirited fashion nowhere in particular. So barefaced was the aimless parading of the medical profession that even the apprentices at the shop doors used to ridicule it. Count Fathom, not wishing to incur this mockery, took the trouble to study a map of London. Then he 'used to alight at the end of long narrow thoroughfares and paved courts, when the chariot was ordered to wait till his return; and walking with great gravity through the diverse turnings of these alleys, regain his carriage by another passage and resume his seat with an air of vast importance.' Sometimes he beguiled his peregrination by stopping to read a quack's advertisement, to swallow a dram or to use a urinal. Continues Smollett :

'The other means used to force a trade, such as ordering himself to be called in church, alarming the neighbourhood with knocking at his door in the night, receiving sudden messages in places of resort and inserting his cures by way of news in the daily papers had been . . . injudiciously hackneyed by every desperate skuller in physic . . .'

The Count, however, hoped 'to erect a hospital, lock or infirmary, by the voluntary subscription of his friends, which had succeeded to a miracle with many of the profession, who had raised themselves into notice upon the carcasses of the poor. Yet even this branch was already over-stocked, in so much that almost every street was furnished with one of these charitable receptacles, which, instead of diminishing the taxes for the maintenance of the poor, encouraged the vulgar to be idle and dissolute, by opening an asylum to them and their families . . .'

The main thing, says Smollett, was to become the talk of the town, even if the talk was about one's own malpractice. Some members of the Faculty had been heard to complain that 'they had never had the good fortune to be publicly accused of homicide.'

It is noteworthy that the practices which Count Fathom dismissed as too hackneyed were freely employed by Dickens' Bob Sawyer.

If Smollett is any guide, the medical profession, like the theatrical profession today, put much value in word-of-mouth recommendation. A lady felt ill. Her maid recommended a nurse. The nurse in turn recommended an apothecary. The apothecary recommended a physician. The physician, deciding that the patient needed bleeding, brought along a surgeon. 'They always appear in a string, like a flock of wild geese, and each confederacy maintains a correspondence with one particular undertaker.'

Another literary man who failed to establish himself as a physician was Dr Oliver Goldsmith. He began his medical career, such as it was, as an apothecary's assistant. Later, friends helped to set him up as a physician in a humble way at Bankside, Southwark. One of his contemporaries described him as 'conventionally attired' in tarnished green and gold, but with 'a shirt and neck-cloth which appeared to have been worn for at least a fortnight.' His velvet coat had an ill-sewn patch on the left breast and he used to hold his hat over it when visiting a sick-bed. This mannerism soon became known and caused mirth among his clientele.

On his second attempt to work up a practice, Goldsmith spared no expense. He had a 'scarlet roquelare buttoned to the chin,' wig, cane, sword and manservant. His practice seems to have ended after a brawl with an apothecary at the bedside of a Mrs Sidebotham. Eventually the two practitioners decided to ask the patient whose advice she would prefer and she chose that of the apothecary. Probably she was wise.*

A notable example of a 'walking physician' was Robert Levet, doctor and companion to Dr Samuel Johnson. His professional qualifications are not clear. According to Boswell, Levet's walk was from Houndsditch to Marylebone, all his clients being poor

* Austin Dobson: *Life of Oliver Goldsmith.*

people. 'Such was Johnson's predilection for him, and fanciful
estimation of his moderate abilities, that I have heard him say he
should not be satisfied, though attended by all the College of
Physicians, unless he had Mr Levet with him.' It was customary
for Levet, who had a room in the Doctor's house, to wait upon
Johnson every morning, 'through the whole course of his late and
tedious breakfast.' Unkindly, the Bishop of Dromore used to say
that Levet breakfasted on a roll which Johnson, after tearing out
the best part, tossed to him.

Some of Levet's patients were in the habit of paying their
indebtedness with a glass of spirit. According to Johnson, 'he
would swallow what he did not like, nay what he knew would
injure him, rather than go home with an idea that his skill had
been exerted without recompense.'

If Dr Johnson tossed his medical attendant a half-eaten roll
for breakfast, he made amends with a dignified epitaph. The
verses on Levet include :

> 'Well try'd through many a varying year
>   See Levet to the grave descend;
> Officious, innocent, sincere,
>   Of every friendless name the friend.
>
> Yet still he fills affection's eye,
>   Obscurely wise, and coarsely kind;
> Nor, letter'd arrogance, deny
>   Thy praise to merit unrefined.
>
> When fainting Nature called for aid,
>   And hovering Death prepared the blow,
> His vigorous remedy display'd
>   The power of art without the show.
>
> No summons mock'd by chill delay,
>   No petty gains disdained by pride,
> The modest wants of every day
>   The toil of every day supply'd.
>
> His virtues walk'd their narrow round,
>   Nor made a pause, nor left a void;
> And sure the Eternal Master found
>   His single talent well employed.

Dr Johnson, says Boswell, had 'in general a peculiar pleasure
in the company of physicians.' He once commented, however,

that the travelling fellowships established by Dr Radcliffe appeared to have done the profession little good. 'It is in vain to send our travelling physicians to France and Italy and Germany, for all that is known there is known here; I'd send them out of Christendom; I'd send them among barbarous nations.'

In this, Dr Johnson was echoing the view of the cantankerous Dr Thomas Dover, who wrote in *The Ancient Physician's Legacy* that more benefit would be derived from Radcliffe's grants if candidates first studied physic for ten years, by which time their observations would be of some use to them. Then, instead of travelling in polite lands, they should go to 'the most intemperate climates, where all acute diseases are the most violent.' Dr Dover added : 'If travel be necessary to make an accomplished physician I am very sure that I have travelled more than all the physicians in Great Britain put together.' It was he who discovered Alexander Selkirk ('Robinson Crusoe') on Juan Fernández island.

Though they did not talk so much learned nonsense as their forbears, physicians still gave themselves weighty airs. Any deviation from the pattern was sufficiently unusual to call for remark. The biographer of Bishop Newton says of Sir John Eliot that 'he had nothing of the formality and stiffness of other physicians, he made no mystery of his art, and communicated his prescriptions and explained what they were, for what purpose he gave them and what effects he designed should follow them; and was a lively friend and companion as well as an excellent good physician.'*

This may have been the Sir John Eliot who sailed as a surgeon in a privateer and won enough prize money to enable him to study for his doctor's degree.

A *malaise* peculiar to the Age of Reason was hypochondria. It was not a disease to which a modern name can be given, for it covered everything from constipation to manic depression, from dyspepsia to religious doubt. Mostly, it attacked the sedentary and those who had too much time to think; the busy and the abstemious did not usually suffer from it. Dr Mead has a story of a don whom inactive life had brought to such a state of morbid gloom that, convinced he was dying, he ordered the

* Dr L. Twells: *Life of Dr Thomas Newton.*

passing bell to be tolled from a near-by church. The bells were
rung so atrociously that, in disgust, the sufferer climbed out of
bed, rushed over to the church and showed the sexton how the
job should be done. Through this unaccustomed exercise he
'wrought himself into a muck sweat,' then returned home to
expire content. His strenuous outing, as it turned out, was the
means of restoring him to life and health.*

James Boswell, a great hypochondria fancier, beguiled his
Grand Tour by exchanging symptoms with fellow sufferers and
collecting anecdotes of irrational, suicidal and apathetic behaviour to which victims of the malady were subject (a Bruns-
wicker said he would not stir two feet to get £2,000). Like
venereal disease, hypochondria became known on the Continent
as the English malady. It is probable that a good many hypochondriacs were anxious only to be in the fashion, to have their
status as intellectuals made manifest. The smart thing to take for
the complaint was opium, which doctors seem to have prescribed
all too freely. Today the disease has been broken down into its
many constituent ailments, and a hypochondriac is merely a
gloomy fellow excessively concerned with the state of his health.

No one has given a better description of the hypochondriac
state than the advertiser in *The Spectator* whose 'Famous Drops'
were capable of 'comforting the brain and nerves, composing the
hurried thoughts, and introducing bright lively ideas and pleasant
briskness, instead of dismal apprehension and dark incumbrance
of the soul, setting the intellectuals at liberty to act with courage,
serenity and steady cheerfulness, and causing a visible diffusive
joy to reign in the room of uneasy doubts, fears, etc.' Undoubtedly there were forms of hypochondria which could be
cured by powerful drops at 3s. 6d. a bottle, but equally there
were sufferers who, like Lady Macbeth, stood more in need of
the divine than of the physician.

Bernard Mandeville's *Treatise on Hypochondria* (1711) takes
the form of a dialogue in which a physician propounds what are
presumably the author's own views. The principal causes of
hypochondria, it appears, are 'the immoderate exercise of the
brain and excess of venery' (which includes marital venery). It
can also be induced by 'immoderate grief, cares, troubles and
disappointments.'

Much hypochondria can be dispersed by fresh air and exercise,

* *The Medical Works of Richard Mead* (1762).

in Mandeville's view. His physician prescribes a rugged regimen for a young unmarried woman :

'Every morning as soon as she rises (which I would have her do by six) let her be swung for half-an-hour, then eat her breakfast and get on horseback for at least two hours, either galloping or trotting, as much as her strength will permit her. Immediately after this let her be undrest, and by some nurse or other chafed or dry-rubbed for a considerable time till her skin looks red and her flesh glows all over; let her begin to repeat the same exercise about three in the afternoon and after supper keep upon her legs two hours before she goes to bed.'

Elaborating on the methods of swinging, the physician says that 'a flying horse makes a very agreeable motion; but if she be apt to be giddy she may be swung in a chair,' or even in a rope tied to a beam. He defends horse riding on the grounds that there is nothing like the 'repeated succussations of a horse' to dispel the 'morbific remainders in the intestines.' The physician is then asked : 'But might not marriage be as effectual as all this exercise?' He replies : 'Yes, but I never prescribe an uncertain remedy.'

How many young women were subjected to the Mandeville treatment we do not know. Swinging was a fashionable pastime, but it was regarded more as a form of amorous dalliance than a system of therapy.

One of the best doctors for hypochondria was Dr George Cheyne, a man weighing 32 stone who scarcely looked like an apostle of the simple life, which in fact he was. Cheyne had lived a riotous tavern life in the early days of his London practice until his health broke down and he, too, suffered from dark incumbrance of the soul. He recovered, thanks to a judicious course of Bath water and plenty of milk and vegetables. Cheyne had many eminent patients whom he steered from the paths of surfeit by the same diet, though without inflating their figures to the same degree as his own.

The wealthier classes, surveying each other's bellies, could hardly fail to be aware that they ate and drank too much. But why (they reasoned) should they limit their pleasures when it was the physician's function to keep them in condition? Why should a gentleman go to the fatigue of exercise, or travel at huge inconvenience to a primitive Highland spa for a diet of goats' whey, when the physician could achieve the same results by a system of

bleeding and purging, followed by cordials, volatiles, bracers
and strengtheners? After all, what was the doctor for? Dryden
summed it up :

> 'The first physicians by debauch were made;
> Excess began and sloth sustains the trade.'*

Joseph Addison assured readers of *The Spectator* that blistering, cupping and bleeding were of use only to the idle and the
intemperate, that the apothecary was 'perpetually employed in
counter-mining the cook and the vintner.' Most physicians recognised these truths. A few, like Cheyne, were bold or honest
enough to practise their beliefs and to recommend a simple life
when it would have been more lucrative to send a medicine with
50 ingredients to punish a sauce with 100. But there remained
all too many doctors who were content to order what the patient
expected them to order, rather than insult him, and lose him, by
advising him to do some active work.

When the ordinary routine of bleeding and purging failed, the
patient was packed off, grumbling, to a spa, either at home or
abroad. Steadily, the number of health resorts was multiplying.
The prosperity of Bath, Epsom, Tunbridge and Moffat was an
incitement to ambitious doctors to discover and exploit new healing springs. Others tried to synthesise the waters of such resorts
as Carlsbad, thus rendering long pilgrimages unnecessary. More
audacious doctors even began to discover virtues in sea-bathing.
The transformation of Brighton from a fishing village to a
fashionable resort began in the 1750s when a Dr Russell of
Lewes proclaimed the benefits he had derived from bathing
there (his patients were urged to swallow as much sea water as
they could). Almost every seaside resort can point to a doctor
who has helped to put it on the map; Filey, if it wishes, can boast
of being publicised by Dr Edward Pritchard, the poisoner.

Some of the excesses of that hydropathy which became all the
rage in Victorian England were already to be noted in the reign
of George III. Horace Walpole wrote to the Rev. William Cole
in 1775 :

'Dr Heberden (as every physician, to make himself talked of, will
set up some new hypothesis) pretends that a damp house, and even
damp sheets, which have ever been reckoned fatal, are wholesome;
to prove his faith he went into his own new house totally unaired and

* Epis. XIV.

survived it. At Malvern they certainly put patients into sheets just
dipped in the spring . . .'

Philip Thicknesse, an ex-apothecary's apprentice-cum-cooper-
cum-soldier, had a more attractive idea. In *The Valetudinarian's
Bath Guide* (1780) he recommends that the best way to live long
is 'by partaking of the breath of young virgins, or what is perhaps
the same thing, by partaking of the breath of youthful persons.'
He elaborates thus :

'Everybody has experienced the sweetness of the breath of cows
and for that reason it is esteemed wholesome, and as the fragrancy
of young people's breath, who are brought up under proper regimen,
falls little short of that of cows, it is natural to suppose that it is
productive of some virtue. The brisk and lively motion in the blood
of young people is the cause of their health, vigour and growth; and
I see no reason to doubt but that the re-respiring their breath may
rouse the sluggish circulation of men advanced in years.'

Schoolmasters, says Thicknesse, have a natural advantage in
this respect. A Frenchman 'never gives up the society of young
women nor young company till he is unable to keep any.'

Thicknesse had his lucid moments, however. He scoffed with
some justification at the ways of overfed patients who went to
Bath, drank three pints of the water and followed up by a large
meal of Sally Lunns or hot spongy rolls.

One of the more unusual health establishments, at the century's
end, was the Pneumatic Institute for Relieving Diseases by
Medical Airs, founded at Clifton, near Bristol, by Dr Thomas
Beddoes, for whom mere fresh air was not fresh enough. It contained an expensive apparatus, built by James Watt, for the
production of 'factitious airs,' the inhalation of which, it was
hoped, would cure a variety of diseases. It was here, in 1799,
that young Humphry Davy, who had been engaged as superintendent, began his experiments with nitrous oxide. Cautiously
inhaling it, he 'experienced the most vivid sensation of pleasure
accompanied by a rapid succession of highly excited ideas.'
Robert Southey was privileged to take a sniff and wrote to a
friend : 'Oh, Tom, such a gas has Davy discovered, the gaseous
oxide! Oh Tom! I have had some; it made me laugh and tingle
in every toe and fingertip. Davy has actually invented a new
pleasure for which language has no name. Oh Tom, I am going
for more this evening; it makes one strong and so happy! so

gloriously happy!'* It was not long before Samuel Taylor Coleridge also came along for a sniff.

Dr Beddoes himself hardly needed to inhale nitrous oxide in order to induce 'a rapid succession of highly excited ideas.' He had suffered from them all his life. The new laughing gas seemed to him well worth adding to the range of vapours and gases already on tap at the establishment. Unfortunately it was administered too freely to a highly hysterical female patient, whom the doctor had to hustle into his own home to treat. Inhalation of gases had been claimed as a remedy for scrofula, melancholia, some forms of dropsy, asthma and consumption; but the number of patients treated by Watt's least successful engine gradually decreased and all interest in pneumatic medicine died with its only begetter. Nitrous oxide, however, had a modest future as an anaesthetic—and as a cheap intoxicant for medical students of the next generation.

In one of his many proposals for lightening the lot of the human race Dr Beddoes was well ahead of his time. His commonplace book contains a note on what he regarded as the ill-effects of washday on women. He asks: 'Can no good genius invent a machine by which opulent neighbours, attentive to their hard-fated fellow creatures, may be able to relieve some of them from this destructive drudgery?'

Wealthy patients were heard to grumble much at the fashion whereby one physician called in another, and the second a third. The cantankerous Duchess of Marlborough was firmly of the view that one reliable doctor was of more value than a multitude. If 20 were called in, they would all defer to the doctor who was most fashionable, either for the sake of peace or for fear of not being called in by his patients. It was popularly supposed that the junior doctor, who, traditionally, gave his opinion first, was bound to defer to his seniors if their opinions clashed; but according to the Royal College of Physicians the rule was 'if there are only two physicians either the junior must submit to the senior or they must call in a third to determine the matter.'†

Leading physicians were never so highly paid as during this century. In 1739 that stormy petrel, William Pulteney, later Earl

* *Correspondence* of Robert Southey.
† Sir William Browne: *A Vindication of the Royal College of Physicians* (1753).

of Bath, lay prostrated by a fever at Lord Chetwynd's house at Ingestre, Staffordshire. The illness cost him 750 guineas. According to one chronicler: 'Dr Hope, Dr Swynsen and other physicians from Stafford, Lichfield and Derby were called in and had about 250 guineas of his money. Dr Freind came down post from London with Mrs Pulteney and received 300 guineas for his journey. Dr Broxholme came from Oxford and received 200 guineas.' These physicians, who were Pulteney's particular friends, quickly decided that their journey had been unnecessary. Like the doctors in Hilaire Belloc's poem:

> 'They answered, as they took their fees,
> "There is no cure for this disease." '

The patient had not abandoned hope, however. He kept asking for small beer, which eventually they gave him by way of humouring him. He perspired violently, slept and recovered.*

Of the fashionable Sir Richard Jebb a sympathetic biographer has written that he was 'obliged by private practice to resign his hospital appointment.' In the three years 1779–81 his fees were said to have reached 20,000 guineas, and he might well have improved on this if he had bothered to humour some of his more tiresome patients. Although his manners left something to be desired, he could employ tact of a sort. When a nobleman paid him only three guineas instead of the expected five, Sir Richard dropped the coins, as if accidentally, on the floor. A servant picked them up and Sir Richard said, 'There must be two still on the floor for I have only three.' The deficiency was then remedied. A rather less subtle technique was that employed, at a later date, by John Bell, the surgeon, when a rich Lanarkshire laird paid him a too-modest fee of £10. As he was being shown out, Bell said to the butler, 'You have had considerable trouble opening the door to me. Here is a trifle for you,' and handed over the fee. In due course he received a draft for £150.

In 1768 Dr Thomas Dimsdale, of Hertford, earned a fee that was gratifying even by the standards of Louis XIV. He was a busy inoculator and author of a popular book on the subject which seems to have attracted the attention of the Empress Catherine of Russia. At her invitation he travelled to Russia to inoculate her and her son, the Grand Duke Paul, against small-pox. The Empress, well aware of how the populace would react

* Dr L. Twells: *Life of Dr Thomas Newton.*

if the operation miscarried, secretly arranged for relays of horses
to be waiting along the routes from St Petersburg to the borders,
in order that Dr Dimsdale might make a safe escape.* Happily,
these precautions were unnecessary. The doctor from Hertford
received a £10,000 fee, £2,000 for expenses, a life annuity of
£500 a year and was made a baron of the Russian empire.

In accordance with a custom of long standing, many physicians
declined to accept fees from unbeneficed clergymen, though
sometimes this indulgence was not accorded to clergymen of
unorthodox beliefs. Dr Mead was sorely tried by a clerical
patient, Robert Leake, who kept comparing his treatment with
that which he had been receiving from Dr Cheyne. Mead
administered this stately rebuke :

'Sir, I have never yet in the whole course of my practice taken or
demanded the least fee from any clergyman, but since you have
been pleased, contrary to what I have met with in any other gentleman of your profession, to prescribe to me, rather than to follow
my prescription, when you had committed the care of your recovery
to my skill and trust, you must not take it amiss, or will I hope think
it unfair, if I demand ten guineas of you.'†

The patient paid up with some reluctance. Later, Mead
returned six of the ten guineas.

Clergy in high offices, or with private incomes, did not expect
or receive free treatment. Dr John Fothergill, the Quaker,
excusing himself for failing to charge a churchman who could
well have paid, said : 'I had rather return the fee of a gentleman
with whose rank I am not perfectly acquainted than run the
risk of taking it from a man who ought perhaps to be the object
of my bounty.'‡ In his *Medical Ethics* (1800) Thomas Percival
said that not only clergymen but fellow doctors, apothecaries and
their families should be treated free, though travelling fees might
be charged if long distances had to be covered. Military and
naval officers in poor circumstances were also 'proper objects of
professional liberality.' When a shabby, sickly Nelson expressed
surprise at the modest fee of a physician at Bath, the physician
said : 'Pray, Captain Nelson, allow me to follow what I consider
my professional duty. Your illness, sir, was brought on by serving

* *Dictionary of National Biography.*
† Benjamin Hutchinson: *Biographia Medica.*
‡ John Timbs: *Doctor and Patient.*

your King and Country, and believe me, I love both too well to
be able to receive any more.'* Percival ruled that a physician
degraded himself and his profession by accepting a small fee
from a wealthy man. It was equally wrong for a wealthy
physician to give advice gratis to the affluent, as this injured his
fellow brethren. 'The office of physician,' he wrote, 'can never
be supported but as a lucrative one.'

Whether or not a physician charged his personal friends the
standard fee was left to his discretion. The attitude of Sir
Theodore Mayerne in the previous century had been unsenti-
mental. One of his friends who called for a consultation afterwards placed two broad gold pieces on the table, confident that
they would be refused and that he could therefore afford to seem
generous. Sir Theodore, however, pocketed the coins, explaining
to his startled friend, 'Sir, I made my will this morning, and if it
should appear that I refused a fee I might be deemed *non
compos.*'† Perhaps it is not surprising that Sir Theodore left the
prodigious sum, for his days, of £140,000.

* Carola Oman: *Nelson.*   † John Timbs: *Doctors and Patients* (1873).

VIII

NOT ENOUGH ACCIDENTS

ONE surgeon, William Cheselden, did more than any other man to bring much-needed prestige to his craft in the early eighteenth century. His reputation was built on the skill with which he operated for the stone, and that operation was based on one popularised by a French quack.

Thanks largely to the gross eating habits of the time, dread of the stone constantly harassed the wealthier classes. The operation for this affliction (to be performed, according to the Hippocratic Oath, only by specialists) was one of exquisite pain and indignity, and the patient had little more than an even chance of survival. In Europe it had been the custom to celebrate the more heroic extractions in poems and paintings. Dutch artists liked nothing better than to depict a proud lithotomist holding up his trophy, beaming as might an alchemist who had found the Philosopher's Stone. Samuel Pepys was relieved of an obstruction the size of a tennis ball, which he kept in a glass case specially made for the purpose. This boulder was an object of veneration at the annual feast in honour of its extraction and served to encourage other sufferers to undergo the grim operation.

It was left to the notorious Frère Jacques, in 1697, to demonstrate a new method of extraction. His performance was a sensational one to watch and resembled not so much an operation as an assassination. The friar had a dagger-pointed knife which he boldly drove into the hip of the sufferer, thrust home into the bladder, then enlarged his incision upwards and downwards until, after a few moments, he was able to extract the stone.

The friar claimed that he had received heavenly guidance in his art, but heaven had endowed him with an indifferent knowledge of anatomy. He asked no reward for performing the operation, other than a few pence for food, or the repair of his shoes, and a certificate testifying to his skill.

Frère Jacques' awesome operation, in the words of John Bell, 'roused the learned lithotomists and physicians of Paris from their vigorous slumbers.'* Here was a mere charlatan slashing his knife through an organ which, according to the learned, should only be dilated. From all parts of Europe came physicians and surgeons to watch the operation. The friar performed in hospitals and even on public stages, with sentries holding back the fascinated mobs. For all his signed certificates, however, Frère Jacques could not conceal the fact that very often the patients who had signed them subsequently died. When their deaths occurred in hospital wards, he was not above blaming the nurses for deliberately mangling the wounds. Probably his post-operational deaths were no more numerous than those of orthodox surgeons, but the friar had to face bitter persecution. If heaven lent him his skill, why did heaven let his patients die?

William Cheselden began performing his improved version of Frère Jacques' operation in 1727 and soon worked himself up to such professional and social eminence as no surgeon had hitherto attained in England. The rich paid him a fee of 500 guineas for a feat of skill and audacity which, on occasion, he could complete in fewer than 60 seconds; a feat which, nevertheless, caused him to blanch beforehand at the knowledge of the pain he was to inflict. In the three hospitals to which he was lithotomist, he performed the same operation free on the poor. Sometimes the public prints recorded the size of the stones he conjured from his more distinguished patients and the number of minutes and seconds he took to do so. No one looked on this as an invasion of privacy. After all, gentlemen were deeply interested in these matters.

Cheselden's fame, however, did not rest wholly on this speciality. He stimulated that passion for anatomy which gripped all surgeons as the century advanced. Early in his career his enthusiasm involved him in a clash with the Barber-Surgeons Company, who accused him of attracting away from them not only the bodies of felons, but large numbers of students. Cheselden was able to talk his way out of this trouble. He was less successful in talking his way out of an uproar which arose when it was learned that he was preparing to perforate the ear-drum of a condemned criminal, in an attempt to discover the cause and cure of deafness. There was a recent precedent of sorts for experiments of this kind in the trial of smallpox inoculations, in 1721,

* *The Principles of Surgery* (1826).

on six condemned criminals—and then on six charity children. However, the ear-drilling proposal had to be abandoned and the criminal lost his chance of pardon.

One of Cheselden's pupils was the Scotsman, Alexander Monro, founder of the Edinburgh medical school. Under Cheselden, he is said to have dissected more bodies than, with the utmost application, he could properly use. In Edinburgh it was another story. Bodies were scarce and the populace were jealous of their dead. Monro's pupils tried to make do with the odd 'condampnit man,' suicide or foundling babe, the bodies sometimes being divided into ten or a dozen parts. In 1725 Monro, after a clash with the public over the violation of graves, moved his school within the shelter of the university. Apprentices were called upon to sign a promise that they would not rob graves, but they signed with reservations. Under Dr Monro's son the scarcity of bodies was chronic and crippling. Writes John Bell : 'On the remains of a subject fished up from a tub of spirits are demonstrated those delicate nerves which are to be avoided or divided in our operations; and these are demonstrated once at the distance of 100 feet! Nerves and arteries which the surgeon has to dissect at the peril of his patient's life!'*

The rank and file of surgery figured frequently as the butts of literature. In Sir John Vanbrugh's *The Relapse* (1696) the crafty surgeon Syringe happens to be passing when Lord Foppington is pinked by an angry husband. 'Oons, what a gash is here!' exclaims the surgeon to the victim, 'why, a man might drive a coach and six horses into your body!' Then, in an aside, he says, 'A little prick between the skin and the ribs, that's all.' The dialogue continues :

Loveless : Let me see his wound.
Syringe : Then you may dress it, sir; for if anybody looks upon it, I won't.
Loveless : Why, thou art the veriest coxcomb I ever saw.
Syringe : Sir, I am not master of my trade for nothing.

Only after extracting a promise of a £500 fee does the surgeon concede that there may be a chance of saving Foppington's life,

* *The Principles of Surgery.*

provided that the victim is removed to Syringe's own house, 'the properest place to bubble him out of his money.'

A very similar sort of surgeon turns up in Henry Fielding's *Tom Jones*. He is venal, he luxuriates in his own jargon, and he is at pains to correct what he supposes to be the misapprehensions of the laity. Thus, when fears are expressed that Tom's skull may be fractured, the surgeon says :

'Fractures are not always the most dangerous symptoms. Contusions and lacerations are often attended with worse phenomena, and with more fatal consequences than fractures. People who know nothing of the matter conclude, if the skull is not fractured, all is well, whereas I had rather see a man's skull broke all to pieces than some contusions I have met with.'

Finding that Tom Jones is not the gentleman he had supposed him to be, the surgeon quickly and angrily submits a bill for 'two journeys at five shillings each, two dressings at five shillings more and half-a-crown for phlebotomy.'

Surgeons were believed to spend their time lamenting the decay of such practices as nose-slitting (a form of mayhem widespread in the previous century) and duelling, though as yet there were few signs that the latter practice was declining. For a surgeon with a conscience (and such did exist) duelling presented certain ethical difficulties. It was legitimate to tend the wounds of a victim, but was it legitimate to accompany a principal to his rendezvous at dawn? In this way a man became an aider and abetter of a practice banned by Church and State; yet was it not desirable to be instantly ready to save the life of an honourable man who had been called out by a rake? It was a subject on which Thomas Percival, writing at the end of the century, sought to give advice in his *Medical Ethics*. He did not find it easy.

Aside from duelling, what grist was there for the surgeon? The casualties of industry were as yet few. By twentieth century standards, traffic accidents were inconsiderable. That left dog bites, kicks from horses and fishbones in the throat. A surgeon therefore had to look to bleeding for his bread-and-butter. Unfortunately it was such a simple-seeming operation that barbers, apothecaries and quacks all felt themselves competent to perform it, and the surgeons as a body lacked legal powers to restrain them. Fortunately the population did not have to be badgered to give up their blood. Young and old, hearty and anaemic, they rolled up in spring and autumn (and sometimes oftener) to be lanced, then after a spell of giddiness and gasping, staggered bandaged home. In Yorkshire were two farrier brothers who would bleed a hundred countryfolk at a time on Sunday mornings, one opening the veins, the other tying the arms. The patients sat on benches in a room, like so many tapped casks of claret, their blood draining away in troughs on the floor. Periodically surgeons called at the big houses to bleed the master, his family and all his servants. Those who raised their voices against this abuse of Nature were looked upon as cranks. Dr Samuel Johnson's objection to blood-letting was based on the argument that this was an evacuation which Nature could not make of herself; thus if a person who was habituated to being bled missed this regular relief, he might be suddenly suffocated.

To the gormandising, port-swilling rich bleeding undoubtedly gave temporary surcease. In certain illnesses and fevers it quietened the pulse and alleviated pain, and was less harmful than violent vomits and purges. Often the amount of blood drawn off depended less on the constitution of the sufferer than on the whim of the surgeon. Country folk who had nothing wrong with them would expect to lose between 10 and 20 ounces; an apoplectic cleric would be drained of perhaps 50 ounces. Many patients were bled because the surgeon could think of no other treatment. Men thrown from horses, half-drowned bathers, sickly boys, pregnant women, the suddenly bereaved, even infants—all these would be called on to yield a blood sacrifice.

If he cared to compete with quacks, the surgeon could also treat venereal disease. Gentlemen of spirit were not over keen to resort to a reputable surgeon because his treatment usually required them to be confined to quarters for the period of the cure. James Boswell, when he found that 'too, too plain was Signor Gonorrhea,' took himself to his friend Andrew Douglas, surgeon, of Pall Mall. Already he had shared Douglas's hospitality on a happier occasion. Now he complained that Douglas, surgeon, was another man from Douglas, friend, and was 'as ready to keep me long under his hands and as desirous to lay hold of my money as any man.'*

It was ironic that, while surgeons were lamenting lack of opportunity, every town could furnish its crop of overdue surgical

* *London Journal.*

An operation at the Royal College of Physicians. From Tom Brown's
Works (1719)

cases (as they would now seem) in the shape of men and women with monstrous wens and tumours, of a size and repulsiveness rarely seen today. The owners of these appendages had too little faith in the surgeon to invite him to cut them away, and for his own part the surgeon was not anxious to risk his reputation in making the attempt. Few surgeons, again, were willing to face such gambles as trying to preserve from amputation a limb with a compound fracture. The problem was brought home forcibly to Percival Pott, the outstanding surgeon of mid-century, when he was thrown from his horse one winter's day in Southwark and sustained a multiple fracture of the leg. In the ordinary way such a sufferer would have been bled by the first surgeon who happened along and then manhandled clumsily into bed. Pott, on the frozen pavement, refused to let anyone move him. He sent to Westminster for two chairmen, and while waiting for them bought a door from a house. When the chairmen arrived with their poles, he gave explicit orders as to how he was to be lifted on to the door and carried to his home, which was near St Paul's. A consultation of surgeons decided that, notwithstanding all the precautions taken, the leg ought to be taken off and Pott, realising that no man can be a sound judge of his own case, concurred. By chance a senior colleague from St Bartholomew's arrived and gave it as his opinion that the leg might be saved. It was.

A surgeon without a hospital has been likened to a gardener without a garden. Hence the opening of the big voluntary hospitals was of perhaps greater benefit to the surgeons than it was to the physicians. In the wards a keen man could observe, compare, classify, specialise. If his treatment proved unsuccessful he could open the body—surreptitiously, if need be—to ascertain whether death was due to his handiwork or to other causes.

In 1745 the fretful marriage between the surgeons and the barbers was dissolved. Men like William Cheselden and Percival Pott had no more in common with barbers than they had with bonnet-makers or pepperers. The barbers, however, were by no means in favour of divorce. They had been good enough for the surgeons in the struggling days of their union, yet now they were to be cast aside by their more ambitious partner. Nevertheless, the breach was made, and the new Company of Surgeons soon found that pride was not enough to live on. It accepted shelter for a while from the Stationers, pending the building of its own Surgeons' Hall, at the Old Bailey. In this headquarters it assiduously mismanaged its affairs until the end of the century, when, as a result of defalcations, neglect and incompetence, the Company had to go into dissolution.

The first master of the new body was John Ranby, a rough-mannered, choleric fellow who was nicknamed 'the blockhead' by Queen Caroline. Had it been set a more gentlemanly example, the Company might have had a happier history. One of its more churlish acts, in the light of history, was to impose sharp fines on William Hunter when he decided to leave the Company and become a physician. The medical school which Hunter established in Great Windmill Street, London, in 1768 (after failing to persuade the Government to give a piece of land for a similar purpose) was of infinite benefit to many succeeding generations of surgeons.

One result of the divorce was that all surgeons were now at liberty to dissect human bodies, if they could obtain them, on their own premises, always supposing that they could persuade wives, landladies and neighbours that such exercises were necessary for the advancement of science. Most surgeons preferred to conduct their anatomical studies at the new Surgeons' Hall, with its notorious ground-level door through which were admitted, after many an unseemly scuffle with the mob, the bodies of those executed at Tyburn for pocket-picking, theft of washing and, occasionally, murder. Often the Company's beadles were beaten up and the windows of the Hall stoned. At each year's end the executioners, on whose goodwill the surgeons were dependent, called at the Hall for their Christmas box.*

Another result of the divorce was that dentistry was left an orphaned art. Those who wished to specialise in this branch (that is, all who had ideas beyond mere tooth-pulling) had to learn their skill as best they could. Dentures held in position by wires and springs were on the market, but many fashionable folk preferred to have the newly extracted teeth of young persons transplanted into their gums. Rowlandson has a cartoon in which this ruthless traffic is portrayed. It is an impressive thought that a pretty girl from the country could sell her hair to the wig-maker and her teeth to the dentist before being faced with the need to

* Sidney Young: *Annals of the Barber-Surgeons.*

sell her virtue to a baronet. (In her youth Lord Nelson's Emma was on her way to dispose of her teeth when she was lured into a fate worse than extraction.)

Since there was no censorious Dental Board a practitioner could adopt any whimsical method of extraction that appealed to him. A Dr Monsey, who was friendly with Garrick, would attach one end of a piece of catgut to the offending tooth and the other end to a bullet which he then fired, using a full measure of powder. Not many patients could be persuaded to try this method. One who agreed to do so lost his nerve at the last minute and cried 'Stop!' Calling him a fool and a coward, Dr Monsey discharged the firearm and the patient was delighted with the result.*

It was William Hunter's younger brother John, that indefatigable dissector and collector, who put not only the surgeons, but the physicians, the apothecaries and the midwives in his debt. Thanks to the zeal of anatomists the structure of the body was reasonably well known, but the functions of its various parts were not. No living organism in the human or animal kingdom went unexplored by Hunter if it seemed likely to contribute to the knowledge of the basic processes of life, or yield a clue as to how the diseases which threatened it could be fought. The records show that Hunter dissected more than 500 different species of creature, and 'some thousands'† of his fellow humans. If he could not obtain the rare beasts he required from circuses and zoos, he wrote begging letters to correspondents in Africa and Asia. To the long-suffering Edward Jenner he sent requests for salmon spawn, cuckoos' gizzards and porpoises' nipples. He would turn from the problem of distinguishing between male and female eels to the dissection of a whale, marvelling at the vigour of a heart, too big to put in a wide tub, which could pump 10 or 15 gallons of blood in one stroke at high velocity through a foot-wide pipe. In the grounds of his house at Earl's Court roamed zebra, buffalo, jackal and leopard, along with more domesticated beasts,

* J. C. Jeaffreson: *A Book About Doctors* (1861).

† When John Hunter gave evidence in the trial of Captain John Donellan, for poisoning Sir Theodosius Boughton, in 1781, this exchange occurred:

'You have been long in the habit of dissecting human subjects. I presume you have dissected more than any man in Europe?'—'I have dissected some thousands during these thirty-three years.'

like bulls, with which he playfully and perilously wrestled. Old medical theories and systems impressed him no more than they had impressed Sydenham. 'Why think, my dear Jenner, why not try?' was his much-quoted advice. Hunter experimented on living creatures, too, causing a human tooth to grow from a cock's comb, and a cock's testicle to flourish in the belly of a hen. His least happy experiment was on himself, when he infected his system inadvertently with syphilis. In the intervals between dissecting he contrived to lecture, tour the wards of St George's Hospital and interview or visit patients.

This is not the place to assess John Hunter's wide-ranging contribution to all the branches of medical knowledge. It is sufficient to emphasise that he, more than any other man in the eighteenth century, raised the status of surgery from that of a rough-and-ready craft to something approaching a science. Henceforth a surgeon who meant to reach the top must be not only an anatomist but physiologist and pathologist. It was a career to attract keen, questing and cultivated minds. Sir James Paget says: 'In the lessons of Hunter, surgery gratefully repaid medicine for the teachings of a century.' And he adds: 'Hunter did more than anyone to make us gentlemen.'*

Whether Hunter himself was a gentleman, even in the days when he maintained his great and fashionable establishment in Leicester Square, was a subject on which not all his colleagues were agreed. At least his attitude to charging fees showed gentlemanly instincts. When asked 'How much?' his answer would be, 'Why, that you must determine yourself; you are the best judge of your own circumstances and it is far from my wish to deprive you of the comforts of life.' If he thought a patient had paid a bigger fee than he could afford, he would return a portion of it. His 'free list' included not only unbeneficed clergymen but authors and artists.

Knighthoods and baronetcies are a poor measure of medical reputations, but it is worth note that in 1778 surgery could point to its first baronet, Sir Caesar Hawkins, whose services had been much valued at Court. He was said to derive £1,000 a year from the letting of blood, and probably did equally well out of inoculating the middle classes.

---

* *Memoirs and Letters.*

Among the most versatile of surgeons were those who, despairing of sharpening their skill at home, went off to follow the wars. (John Hunter sought to recover his health, threatened by too much dissection, by treating the wounded at Belleisle.) Though nominally surgeons, they acted also as physicians, apothecaries and even midwives. It was small wonder that they grew to look with scorn on the squabbling factions of their profession when they returned from battlefields blue with flies and isles manured with the victims of Yellow Jack.

Outstanding among naval surgeons was the Scot James Lind, who in 1754 published his treatise showing how scurvy could be prevented. After a seemly interval of 40 years the Admiralty decided to issue lemon juice to ships. No one can believe, says a modern sailor,* that if Lind had been in command of Anson's tragic round-the-world voyage he would have allowed nine men out of ten to die of scurvy before his return. Lind was by no means the first to realise the need for fresh fruit and vegetables at sea, but the surgeons who begged for such supplies were up against apathy, callousness, cheeseparing and 'the exigencies of the service.' A few gave up the struggle and devoted themselves to rum, leaving their mates to practise as they willed on the crew.

If ever a man was left to stand on his two feet it was the naval surgeon. The shore authorities were pleased to suppose that he abused his independence by trafficking in medicines and passing off substitutes on his patients. They therefore took care that he should be supplied with the minimum of medicaments, in order to lessen his temptations. John Atkins, author of *The Navy Surgeon* (1734), complained that the Society of Apothecaries and their supervising physician 'put up not what the surgeon wants but what they say he wants.'

To a city surgeon cases came singly and sparsely; he could afford to lavish full and even unnecessary attention on each one. To a naval surgeon, sooner or later, came the day when he was called on to do the work of twelve, when his cockpit began to fill with halves of men and the decks ran, all too literally, with blood and rats. In this smoking, dust-filled shambles, with tourniquets, hot irons and bubbling pitch, the surgeon would salvage such portions of the King's servants as seemed worth saving, while the deck tilted, plunged and shuddered beneath his feet. The rest

* Surgeon-Admiral Sir Sheldon Dudley: *Our National Ill-Health Service.*

of the ship's company had daring, blood-tingling tasks to do, but the surgeon's pulse did not race like those of other men. He stayed calm and used his judgment amid scenes of agony and exultation. Many of his patients died, as they would have died if he had not sawn them, but in every seaport, and on many a quarter-deck, the presence of sailors with hooks for hands and pegs for legs was a testimony to his rough skill. And this was the man who, on being captured, was liable to become the subject of a humiliating dispute about status: was he a surgeon or was he a barber?

Even in times of peace the naval surgeon's life was apt to be an uncommonly exacting one. Many an operation came his way that a city surgeon might have preferred to dodge. John Atkins gives some haunting details which help one to picture a trepanning operation at sea. The feat was to be performed 'in a close place by candlelight,' the justification being that air was 'an enemy to the brain and bone.' The patient's ears were plugged with wool 'for preventing an ungrateful sensation' as the well-oiled instrument bit into his skull. His most grateful sensation, perhaps, was when they swept away the bone dust from time to time with a feather brush. Afterwards, Atkins warned, the patient's hands might have to be tied to stop him tearing off his bandages.

Another grisly glimpse of naval surgeons at work comes from Thomas Dover. In the South Seas, before the storming of Guayaquil, the crews of his privateering expedition caught a form of plague contracted, according to Dover, from the stacks of unburied dead in the Spanish churches. One hundred and eighty men were violently ill. 'I ordered the surgeons to bleed them in both arms,' writes Dover, 'and to go round them all with command to leave them bleeding till all were blooded, and then come and tie them up in their turns. Thus they lay bleeding and fainting, so long, that I could not conceive they could lose less than an hundred ounces per man.'* This mighty blood-letting, says Dover, saved the lives of the crew.

John Knyveton left a colourful record of his activities as surgeon's mate in the Seven Years' War.† His labours on board *Ramillies* began before she sailed from Portsmouth; some 62 out of 200 sailors had to be rejected because they suffered from the

* *The Ancient Physician's Legacy.*   † *Surgeon's Mate* (ed. Ernest Gray).

pox. After that there were bruises from the press gang to be healed. When the voyage began he was kept busy attending men who had fallen from the rigging, or who had been too heartily belaboured in the name of discipline. He also treated men bitten by the captain's dogs, and for good measure treated the dogs too. One captain depicted by Knyveton was like a caricature from Smollett. Taking upon himself to diagnose the sick, he ordered a string to be tied round each man's waist. If the pain was above the string, the man received an emetic; if below the string, a purge. According to Knyveton, two men treated in accordance with this diagnosis died violently.

The least pleasant task of a ship's surgeon was one he shared with the army surgeon : to superintend the flogging of a male-factor and judge to a second and a sinew when the man had had enough. The mere fact that backbone and ribs were laid bare did not necessarily mean that it was time to call off the punishment. Sometimes the surgeon's judgment was at fault and the man died; sometimes, in the captain's view, he intervened earlier than he need have done, thus frustrating justice and weakening dis-cipline. It was one of those occasions on which the surgeon's duty to humanity—to allay or avert pain, not to prolong it—clashed with his duty to society.

The army surgeon, no less than his naval colleague, had to be able to turn his hand to all tasks. From that satirical work *Advice to Officers of the British Army* (1782), attributed to Francis Grose, it is clear that his more routine duties are concerned with bleeding, purging, poulticing and treating sufferers from venereal disease ('tenderness towards patients of that kind is only an encouragement of vice'). Evidently there were perquisites other than those to be derived from passing off substitute drugs. 'Inoculation affords a pretty comfortable douceur to gentlemen of your profession,' runs the advice, 'a guinea per head being allowed by the Government for that operation. But as it is only to be performed with the soldier's consent, you should recollect, that the common people are commonly blind to their own interest, and therefore persuade as many as you can to agree to what is so much to their advantage.' Another instruction is : 'Keep two lancets; a blunt one for the soldiers, and a sharp one for the officers; this will be making a proper distinction between them.' That this is no idle jest is clear from Knyveton's diary.

The surgeon under whom he served on *Ramillies* kept a special set of instruments to use on officers.

In times of peace, the surplus surgeons of the Services became general practitioners and were as skilled and reliable as any in the country. 'What a pity,' wrote Dr Thomas Beddoes, 'that such men are not more solidly grounded, and more highly finished by those who undertake to form their minds.'

IX

THE WICKED MAN-MIDWIFE

TOWARDS the middle of the eighteenth century a new kind of name plate was to be seen in the towns of England. It bore the legend 'Surgeon, Apothecary and Man-Midwife.'

The man-midwife edged on to the scene nervously. He knew that he was a figure of suspicion, fun and contempt. He was fighting the prejudice of many thousands of years.

The objections to his trade were these: midwifery was by ancient tradition a woman's task; it was unseemly and immoral for a man to be called to attend a woman in labour, unless her life was in danger; the practice would put an end to female modesty; even if midwifery were a fit task for a man, it was no task for a gentleman; it was a mere money-catching innovation by doctors who had built up a superfluous science and were trading on the fears of ignorant women; and it was a gross waste of a doctor's time and training to expect him to officiate at such a routine commonplace as childbirth.

Under the laws of the medieval Church man-midwifery had been a capital offence. In 1522 the impious Dr Wertt, of Hamburg, dressed himself as a woman in order to study the problems of a woman in labour, and for his enterprise was burned at the stake. Ambroise Paré, it may be supposed, came up against clerical opposition during that same century, when he reintroduced the art of podalic version, that is, turning the child in the womb in order to ensure an easier delivery. If this was not trying to improve on the work of Providence, what was it? Long after Paré, the man-midwife continued to be the victim of a prudery which sometimes forced him to operate blindly beneath a sheet, one end of which might be tied to his neck, the other end to that of his patient. If the child was lost, at least modesty was saved. This system did not render any easier the task of witnesses

Mary Tofts gives birth to rabbits: 1726

charged with guarding against substitutions at royal births. On the other hand, it doubtless aided the Chamberlen family to preserve the secret of their forceps. Prudery, of course, did not go with pregnancy alone; an excessively sensitive woman troubled with bodily pains anywhere between neck and knee might indicate their whereabouts to her physician by reference to a doll specially manufactured for that purpose.

The fashion of the man-midwife came to Britain from France, whence those equivocal fellows, the man-hairdresser and the man-staymaker had already been imported. Louis XIV called for *accoucheurs* to attend his mistresses, and what was good enough for royal mistresses was good enough for the *grandes dames* of the French court. Soon the trade of *accoucheur* was booming. High-born ladies in England were not to be left behind and gradually the vogue spread to the middle classes.

The first man-midwife of distinction in England was Sir Richard Manningham, who established a ward for parturient women in Britain, at the parish infirmary of St James, Westminster. It was he who, in 1726, exposed the famous imposition at Godalming by Mary Tofts, the 'rabbit breeder.' Her story was that she had been so frightened by a rabbit that her reproductive system had undergone a change and she was able to give birth only to rabbits, of which she had borne 15 that year. The local apothecary, John Howard, endorsed her story and said that he had felt the rabbits leaping in her womb. Nathanael St André, surgeon to Westminster Hospital, was called in and was tricked to such good purpose that he wrote a pamphlet testifying that in his presence Tofts had given birth to two rabbits or portions thereof. By this time the country was agog and not a few citizens lost their taste for rabbit pie. The rents of warrens fell. At Court pregnant ladies began to fear they were in the same predicament as Mary Tofts. Conscious of public alarm, George I sent his German physician, Cyriacus Ahlers, to investigate. This gentleman was left holding a portion of another rabbit but was not quite satisfied with the way in which it had come into his possession. The King, after hearing Ahlers' sceptical report, sent down Sir Richard Manningham, who speedily disposed of the miracle. The rabbits and portions of rabbits, he said, were concealed about the lady's person. The only mystery was whether the affair was a vulgar hoax or whether Tofts suffered from an obscure form of mania. The case prompts the reflection that eminent physicians had still a good deal to learn about the potentialities and limitations of the human reproductive system. If the illustrations are any guide Mary Tofts was protected throughout by her prude's bedsheet, without which the nonsense could never have been perpetrated.

One who did much to break down the superstition and prejudice surrounding childbirth was Dr William Smellie, of Lanark. In 1741 he taught midwifery at his own house in London with the aid of a lay figure composed of human bones encased in leather, and 'little stuffed babies.' He is said to have instructed some 1,000 pupils, who paid the expenses of more than that number of poor women whom they attended. Mrs Elizabeth Nihell, a leading West End midwife of the day, resented this male competition and mocked Smellie as 'a great horse-god-mother of a he-midwife.' She said that in his loose gown, behind which he concealed his instruments, he not only played the part of a man-woman but looked like one. Smellie was a friend of William Hunter, who in mid-century switched his interest from surgery to midwifery.

Smellie's writings on midwifery fell into the hands of the ineffable Philip Thicknesse, who wrote a pamphlet *Man-Midwifery Analysed, and the Tendency of the Practice Detected and Exposed* (1764). Addressed to 'all men in general and to all married women in particular,' it was designed 'to put a stop to impure acts, immodest actions and the indelicate, unchaste and unnecessary transactions of men-midwives, such as they avowedly and publicly profess, and such that every man of sense, decency, sentiment and spirit must and will disapprove or be totally indifferent as to his wife's conduct or his own honour.'

Dr Smellie's handbook contained references to clinical touching, and that was enough to sustain Thicknesse in a long diatribe against the 'Touching Gentry.' He declares: 'I never meet any of these charioted mongrel physicians, that I do not look on them as I should on the Emperor of Morocco or the Bashaw of Tangier, going to his seraglio.' There is only one state in which 'a fine woman' can present herself without stirring base passions, says Thicknesse, and that is in the act of dying.

Of Thicknesse it was said, as of a more eminent writer, that he scattered his dung with an air of majesty. If he had been a lone critic, his protests would not have been worthy of examination, but he was bold enough to voice the fears of many appre-

D

hensive husbands. He made one point that was worth making : that man-midwives tended to make unnecessary use of the new mechanical aids to delivery. No one who has read *Tristram Shandy* will forget Dr Slop, who knocked out three of his own teeth while manipulating his forceps. Nor was that his only dangerous device—'Good God,' cried my Uncle Toby, 'are children brought into the world with a squirt ?'

Although eminent physicians were assisting at the births of princes and princesses, the Royal College of Physicians still looked on man-widwives as outside the professional pale. Nor were the Surgeons any more eager to countenance the practice. This negative attitude gave ammunition to the critics who, year in, year out, accused the two corporations of being hopelessly out of touch with their commonalty.

X

COUNTRY DOCTOR

Dr Foster
Went to Gloster
In a shower of rain.
He fell in a puddle
Right up to his middle,
And never went there again.
—Nursery rhyme

WHEREAS the London physician demanded a guinea a mile for his forays by coach into the country, the rural practitioner was content to ride his horse perhaps 4,000 miles a year over moor and bog to earn £200.

It was an employment for the physically strong and the mentally independent, and as such made a special appeal to former Army and Navy surgeons, hardened by campaigning in barbarous places. As a rule the country practitioner was an apothecary with some training as a surgeon. He was ready to administer physic, perform amputations on kitchen tables, or deliver babies. He might have a small shop in the high street, or what passed for the high street, where seekers after novelty could buy soap and toothbrushes and the local Calvinists could snort at the sight of perfumery and scented soap. There might be a jar of leeches kept for the squire or laird, but the chances were that the leeches would go hungry. Like his colleagues in the bigger towns the country doctor might display a human skull or a monkey's skeleton in his window to attest his knowledge of anatomy. It was a humble enough business, but at least the owner of it did not have to suffer the ignominy of seeing his more *passé* drugs tossed into the street by liberally educated gentlemen.

Sir Walter Scott in *The Surgeon's Daughter* gives an excellent picture of the conditions which faced the rural practitioner in Scotland in the late eighteenth century:

'He has none of the ample resources proper to the brothers of the profession in an English town. The burgesses of a Scottish borough are rendered, by their limited means of luxury, inaccessible to gout, surfeits and all the comfortable chronic diseases, which are attendant on wealth and indolence. Four years, or so, of abstemiousness enable them to stand an election dinner; and there is no hope of broken heads among a score or two of quiet electors, who settle the business over a table. There the mothers of the state never make a point of pouring, in the course of every revolving year, a certain quantity of doctor's stuff through the bowels of their beloved children. Every old woman, from the Townhead to the Townfit, can prescribe a dose of salts, or spread a plaster . . .'

In this type of community the doctor was sent for only in emergencies. There were some parts of Scotland, notably in the Outer Isles, where a doctor was regarded, not only as a luxury, but as a superfluity. The isles folk were fatalists, and justified their refusal to call a doctor on the grounds that 'the hour has come.' This attitude survived even into the twentieth century.

The Scots explorer Mungo Park practised physic in and out of Peebles when not exploring the basin of the Niger. According to Scott, he preferred the rigours of African travel to those of his native hills. 'He mentioned having once upon a time rode 40 miles, sat up all night, and successfully assisted a woman under influence of the primitive curse, for which his sole remuneration was a roasted potato and a draught of butter-milk. But his was not the heart which grudged the labour that relieved human misery. In short, there is no creature in Scotland that works harder and is more poorly requited than the country doctor, unless perhaps it may be his horse.'

The horse was, indeed, a heroic partner. There were times when the doctor slept in the saddle, and the beast was left to pick its own way by bog and ravine. The doctor's patients would see the sleeping figure riding up the glens and perhaps give thanks that he was asleep, for it was hard to look him in the eye when they owed him so much; but they could show their sympathy by seeing that the horse took the right turn at the crossroads. Occasionally the doctor would be intercepted by a labourer with toothache. Then he would dismount and perform the necessary extraction at the roadside, watched perhaps by a group of delighted children whom he had brought without fee into the world.

In snowstorms even the faithful horse would lose its way. Doctor and beast might wander for hours on their native moors, hopelessly lost, or fall into deep pits which the snow concealed. Flooded rivers would compel the doctor to make long detours— or, if the call was urgent, he would wade through and arrive at the bedside drenched. On stormy, moonless nights he might be guided over the moors by a peasant carrying a burning peat. If not, he would have to trust to instinct—and his horse.

It was one of the ironies of the country doctor's lot that, having returned from a spot twenty miles away, he might have to turn round and visit another patient who lived perhaps only a mile or two from the first. This hardship was accepted more stoically than it would be in an age of telephones.

Not all country doctors lived obscure lives. One who helped to change the course of history was Edward Jenner, discoverer of vaccination, who practised at Berkeley in Gloucestershire. It will be remembered that he kept up a correspondence with his old master, John Hunter, whom he supplied with unusual specimens for dissection. If he could not listen to learned orations in London, at least he could exchange knowledge with his colleagues in near-by towns; he attended a gathering at Alveston which he styled convivio-medical and one at Rodborough which he called medico-convival. Though Gloucestershire was less rugged than Scotland, it could provide unusual rigours. There was a January day in 1786 when Jenner, riding to Kingscote in intense cold, arrived ice-caked and almost senseless, unable to dismount. 'I had just recollection and power enough to prevent the servants from bringing me to a fire,' he said afterwards. They carried him to the stables, where he partially thawed, then at length into the house. On that bitter journey the horse lost part of the cuticle and hair on the upper neck and ears. Not very far away a man died of the cold.* Such was country practice.

International fame did not lure Jenner for long from his beloved countryside. For once, the services of a man honoured by almost every medical body in the world (except the Royal College of Physicians) were available to cottagers and thatchers. His wider interests failed to impress at least one of his patients, a beldam who told him : 'So your book is out at last. Well, I can tell you there beant a copy sold in this town nor shan't be if I can help it.'

* John Baron: *Life of Edward Fenner* (1838).

There was another country doctor who achieved a measure of limelight at this time, the Rev. Francis Willis, of Gretford, who trained originally for the Church. In a hospital at Lincoln, and in his own house at Gretford, he was unusually successful in treating the mentally deranged. In 1788, when George III suffered his breakdown, Willis was called to Court, despite the misgivings of the Queen who realised that his visit would confirm to the world the nature of the King's malady. Already the mobs were stopping the Court physicians in their carriages, accusing them of incompetence and threatening to murder them. Willis was all but ostracised by some of the Court physicians but bore the snubs bravely, bringing a breath of fresh air to a Court that badly needed it. Madame d'Arblay in her Diary called him 'a man of ten thousand, open, honest, dauntless, light-hearted, innocent and high-minded.' Some of Willis's pronouncements suggest that he was not quite such a repository of the virtues as this might suggest; the Opposition belaboured him as a tool and a fool. Willis tried to cure the King by kindness and trust, horrifying his colleagues by giving him a razor with which to shave. Once the King asked Willis whether, as a clergyman, he was not ashamed of himself for practising as a physician. 'Our Saviour, sir, went about healing the sick,' replied Willis; to which the King retorted, 'Ah, yes, but he didn't get £700 a year for it— hey?'

So far, medical treatment of the poor has not figured very largely in these pages, though it will call for much attention later. Since Queen Elizabeth's day the parishes had been responsible for looking after their own poor, and this duty they discharged with varying degrees of conscientiousness. In *The Village* George Crabbe has left an unforgettable picture of the worst type of parish apothecary, going his perfunctory rounds in the poorhouse:

> 'Anon a figure enters, quaintly neat,
> All pride and business, bustle and conceit;
> With looks unalter'd by these scenes of woe,
> With speed that, entering, speaks his haste to go,
> He bids the gazing throng around him fly,
> And carries fate and physic in his eye:

A potent quack, long versed in human ills,
Who first insults the victims whom he kills;
Whose murd'rous hand a drowsy Bench protect,
And whose most tender mercy is neglect.
Paid by the parish for attendance here,
He wears contempt upon his sapient sneer;
In haste he seeks the bed where Misery lies,
Impatience mark'd in his averted eyes;
And, some habitual queries hurried o'er,
Without reply, he rushes to the door;
His drooping patient, long inured to pain,
And long unheeded, knows remonstrance vain;
He ceases now the feeble help to crave
Of man; and silent sinks into the grave.'

But not all the poor suffered at the hands of insolence. Men like the Quaker Dr J. C. Lettsom did their best for the humble. Once, he sent to the overseers of a parish a note reading: 'A shilling *per diem* for Mrs Maxton : Money, not physic, will cure her. Lettsom.' Whether Mrs Maxton received her shilling *per diem* is not told; it seems unlikely.

Dr Lettsom was reputed to disburse at the houses of the poor more money than he took. His fellow Quaker, Dr Fothergill, often made the act of feeling the pulse a cover for slipping money into the patient's hand. Nor were these two unique. Many parish doctors paid for meat and porter for the poor out of their own pockets.

It was Lettsom who, in 1770, founded the General Dispensary, the first of many such institutions to be opened in the latter quarter of the century. Within their walls, doctors extended their knowledge of the poor and saw something of the cleaning-up problems, physical and moral, which faced the industrial age.

XI

HUMBUGS

If the aristocrats of medicine were to be believed, the ranks of quacks were composed of sow-gelders, shady apothecaries, unfrocked priests, French shampooers, corn-cutters, bath-house keepers, urinarians, mystics, executioners, presumptuous midwives, itinerant abortionists, sleight-of-hand men, 'mechanick fellows,' shiftless craftsmen and runaway husbands turned satyr.

Not usually listed were the kings and queens of England who for centuries, abetted by their physicians, had set an example of bare-faced quackery by 'touching' the afflicted; a custom which died only with Queen Anne.

Most of the characters enumerated in the opening paragraph did, indeed, adorn the gallery of quacks in the eighteenth century, but there were others who, while lacking university degrees and the ability to abuse each other in Latin, could perform cures, often by manipulation, which orthodox practitioners either could not or would not attempt.

There were infinite categories of quacks, among them the following:

Those who honestly believed they had a skill or a medicine of benefit to humanity;

Those who believed their medicines were no worse than those of the orthodox;

Those who manufactured medicines from the Pharmacopeia under a different name, advertised them widely and sold them cheaply;

Those who knew their medicines or treatments were worthless but who were able to cure, or alleviate, certain conditions by instilling confidence in recovery;

Those who had no skill and no morals and were intent only on extracting the maximum income from the credulous (as by pretending to remove a stone from an insane patient's head or by using hot wires to burn out 'worms' from aching teeth).

The borders of quackery were as ill-determined as they are today. A Scots doctor would be regarded as a quack because he had studied only three years instead of five. Yet a physician with an Oxford degree might espouse a new-fangled theory of treatment which would bring cries of 'Quack' from his more conservative colleagues—and even from Scots doctors.

George Crabbe, writing on quacks, found it mortifying—

'That creatures, Nature meant should clean our streets,
Have purchased lands and mansions, country seats.'*

No doubt many doctors shared these sentiments, and deplored the way in which quacks were draining away custom from the profession. A more powerful, and more disinterested, objection was that quacks had no responsibility to their patients. If an illness took a turn for the worse they could vanish, leaving a physician, summoned too late, to explain away the patient's death. Few quacks had any diagnostic ability or knew how to regulate the administration of drugs according to the needs of the individual; but objections on these grounds did not come very well from physicians who diagnosed at second-hand in coffeehouses. The story of quackery is not without its triumphs, but it is also a story of roguery, criminal neglect and culpable homicide, and it was this aspect which, chiefly, roused the orthodox profession to anger.

The Court throughout the eighteenth century was nearly as hospitable to quacks as in Elizabeth's reign. It was not impossible for an unlicensed operator to pick up a knighthood, as Sir William Read, Queen Anne's favourite oculist, succeeded in doing. From this eminence, a man could thumb his nose at the Royal College of Physicians, or write impudent pamphlets dedicated to them. Joshua ('Spot') Ward, the most famous quack of his day, was called in by George II to examine that monarch's painful thumb. The view of the *élite* of the Royal College was that the condition of the thumb was caused by gout, but Ward knew a dislocation when he saw one. Without making any comment, he seized the thumb and gave it a violent jerk. When the monarch had finished cursing him and kicking him on the shins, he found that he could wag his thumb again. As part

* *The Borough.*

of his reward, Ward was given the right to drive through St James's Park, and for good measure a coach with six horses in which to do so. Without the knowledge of her physicians, Princess Caroline was persuaded by Lord Hervey—the King and Queen concurring—to take a Ward's pill for her rheumatism. The Queen was assured that the pill had driven nobody mad except Dr Mead. Perhaps Ward's greatest triumph was to be excused, by special direction of Parliament, from compliance with the Apothecaries Act of 1748, which was designed to stop unqualified persons compounding pills.

Although many quacks found it convenient to change their addresses frequently, others could boast a fixed abode. One might keep a shop and display in his window a row of bottles, each containing a worm conjured from a satisfied patient. Another might set himself up near a hospital, in order to catch the overflow of out-patients. Others, according to their handbills, were ready to consult patients at coffee-houses.

Quacks who sought custom outside London did so with little fear of interference by orthodox physicians. The worst that could befall them was to be thrown into the village pond by dissatisfied customers. Those who peddled the more perilous cures would be careful not to return to the same district too often, thus giving the blinded a chance to die off and the widowed time to remarry.

According to his state of prosperity, a quack might travel by foot, horse or carriage. He might stage a popular entertainment in the market place or on the village green, with clowns and tumblers, wire-walkers and trumpeters, and award bottles of elixir as prizes in lotteries. He would know all Joe Miller's jokes by heart. Any patient dissatisfied with the medicine would reflect that at least he had enjoyed a free entertainment.

A more conservative type of quack would take rooms at the local inn and post up notices inviting sufferers to call at stated times, 'bringing their waters with them.' If prosperous enough, he might employ an advance publicity man to precede him with stories of his miraculous cures. Once established in residence, he would ornament his headquarters with his diplomas and letters patent, and deck his person with the medals bestowed on him by foreign courts.

In *The Tatler*, Addison relates that quacks were fully conscious of the need to support themselves by 'collateral assistances' or 'supernumerary accomplishments.' In modern slang, every quack

The Water Doctor, or Urinarian. From a pamphlet by Dr J. C. Lettsom (1776)

had a 'gimmick.' At one time, Addison says, it was impossible to walk the streets without having thrust into one's hand an advertisement of a doctor 'who was arrived at the knowledge of the green and red dragon, and had discovered the female fern seed.' He comments : 'Nobody ever knew what this meant; but the green and red dragon so amused the people that the doctor lived very comfortably upon them.' Another prosperous fellow plastered the street corners with the magic word TETRACHY-MAGOGON; much impressed, the sick 'would have nobody but this learned man for their physician.' Addison also mentions receiving the advertisement of 'one who had studied 30 years by candlelight for the good of his countrymen,' and comments : 'He might have studied twice as long by daylight and never been taken notice of.'

Dr Tom Saffold, heelmaker turned pox-doctor, was one of many who sought to fascinate potential patients by skill at doggerel, but a more successful poetaster was Saffold's successor, Dr Case, who rubbed out his predecessor's verses and substituted:

'Within this place
Lives Doctor Case.'

Testifies Addison : 'He is said to have got more by this distich than Mr Dryden did by all his works.'

Scorning doggerel, 'Chevalier' John Taylor, an eye doctor of Norwich, who toured the courts of Europe for 30 years, preferred to make speeches in what he called 'the true Ciceronian, pro-digiously difficult and never attempted in our language before.' It consisted of starting every sentence with the genitive and end-ing it with a verb, and was probably as good a way of impressing the uneducated as any. Dr Samuel Johnson described Taylor as 'an instance of how far impudence will carry ignorance.' Taylor's autobiography, which fortunately is not written in the true Ciceronian, is a disappointing effort for one who claimed acquaintance with 'every Court, kingdom, province, state, city and town of the least consideration in all Europe without excep-tion.' It is full of unauthenticated, second-hand stories with titles like 'An account of a young lady who lost her reason from dancing with a married man at an assembly, whom she supposed to be single,' and 'Making love to nuns shewed to be a species of cruelty.' In his travels, says Taylor, he met many quacks who faced sentences of death if they returned to their native lands.

He claims to have learned many secrets of medicine, but says
that only harm can befall if he publishes his knowledge to the
ignorant; the information will be passed on to his 'respectable
successors.' In passing, the Chevalier complains about critics who
cast up at him his occasional unsuccessful operations, 'though
transacted in the beginning of my life.'

A Barnum-style quack was Martin Van Butchell, whose most
famous advertising asset was provided for him by William
Hunter. At the quack's request Hunter embalmed the body of
the first Mrs Van Butchell, giving it the lifelike treatment afforded
by the American mortician in our own times. The mummy was
then displayed in Van Butchell's dwelling, where no doubt it
instilled a sober and reflective state of mind in his patients. His
second wife, jealous of the pretty relict, persuaded her husband
to send it to John Hunter's museum.

Quick wits were indispensable weapons in the quack's armoury.
Sir Edward Halse, physician to George III, was driving through
the Strand when the progress of his carriage was impeded by a
crowd listening to a harangue by one Dr Rock. The latter,
recognising the equipage, ordered a quantity of boxes and phials
to be handed to the footman, saying, 'Give my compliments to
Sir Edward and tell him these are all I have with me but I am
sending for ten dozen more tomorrow.' The crowd were quick to
appreciate that even the King's physician took his medicines from
Rock. Later Halse is said to have tackled Rock, who had once
been a fellow student: 'My old friend, how can a man of your
understanding condescend to harangue the populace with such
nonsense as you talked today? Why, none but fools listen to you.'
The reply was: 'Ah, my good friend . . . do you give me the fools
for my patients and you shall have my free leave to keep the
people of sense for your own.' (A similar exchange is said to
have occurred between Dr Radcliffe and Dr Case.)

It was left to a woman quack to pull off a much-admired coup,
of which the only victims were the taxpayers. She was Mrs Joanna
Stephens, whose solvent for the stone enjoyed a vogue in higher
circles. Why, she argued, should not the nation pay her for her
valuable secret? As an experiment, a sufferer from the stone was
treated with Mrs Stephens' compound and the obstacle dis-
appeared. By dint of much intriguing, with encouragement from
nobles and churchmen, and not least with the aid of two pamphlets from David Hartley, philosopher and Fellow of Jesus College,

Cambridge, Parliament was induced to vote £5,000 to Mrs Stephens for her secret. It turned out that the solvent was compounded of snail shells, egg shells and soap. It also turned out that the patient on whom the experiment was tried still had his stone; at his autopsy it was found in a pouch at the back of the bladder. Since then, writes William Wadd, 'there have been as many human calculi formed by His Majesty's liege subjects as would macadamise one side of Lincoln's Inn Fields.'*

Had Parliament contained fewer who suffered from the stone and more who needed the bonesetter, it is possible that Mrs Sally Mapp might also have been honoured by a grant. Crazy Sal, a roaring, uncouth creature, whose sister married a Duke of Bolton, settled in Epsom, where she treated many of the fashionable world. So many did she attract that the town authorities are said to have offered her 100 guineas to continue in residence there. Percival Pott, the surgeon, described her in the contemptuous terms reserved by the profession for unlicensed bonesetters as 'an ignorant, illiberal, drunken, female savage.' In her prime she rode in a coach-and-six and looked opulent and ugly enough to be mistaken by the crowd for one of George II's mistresses.

One of the most derided, yet indestructible, quacks was the water-doctor, variously known as the urine-caster, the urinarian and the piss-prophet. He professed to be able to discern, from holding a phial to the light or merely weighing it in his hands, the sex, age, ailment and prospects of his client. Like the physician of Chaucer's day, the water-doctor would be at pains to gather advance information about his patients. In the ante-room, where the patients sat nursing their phials, would be a creature of the doctor in the guise of a patient. It was this individual's function (never a very difficult one) to start up a conversation in which the patients would babble away about their symptoms, or about the symptoms of those whose contributions they bore. Behind a thin wall containing a spyhole would lurk the doctor, busily taking notes and descriptions. When satisfied that he had amassed sufficient information, he would put on his street clothes, leave the house by the back and come bustling in at the front door as if he had just returned from his rounds. The patients would then be called in one by one, and the doctor in his gravest manner, glancing at the phial and asking no questions, would tell them what they already knew, namely that their husbands

* *Mems, Maxims and Memoirs.*

had back pains or that their mistresses were pregnant. Such
would be the visitor's astonishment and respect that the doctor
would have no difficulty in selling his expensive drugs. The
patient would perhaps have heard already the story (which each
water-doctor took care to circulate about himself) about the joker
who brought a specimen of horse urine and was told by the
undeluded water-caster, 'Feed the patient with hay and oats and
let him work less.' So many light-minded individuals tried to
score off the water-doctor by bringing him bogus specimens that
he made a point of subjecting each new patient to a solemn
scrutiny, under which the impostor was liable to break down.

In the 1770s a Dr Myersbach came to England from Germany
and amassed a respectable fortune by water-divining. The public
had a high regard for any 'doctor' with a German accent.
Asserting that this uncouth fellow knew less about urine than a
chambermaid, Dr J. C. Lettsom set out to expose him in a
pamphlet.* This related how a male patient who had offered a
phial of gelding's urine had been told that his wife suffered from
a disorder of the womb, and that a phial of cow's urine had been
identified as the produce of a young gallant who had been too
free with the ladies of the town. Myersbach's main source of
intelligence was his porter Schroeder, an adept at encouraging
confidences from the patients, and there were other servants who
lurked about the house listening in to unguarded conversations.
When a person of rank came to consult the doctor and the porter
was unable to obtain information about his disease, the caller
would be told that the Doctor was not at home but would be
willing to see him next day. In the interval it would be the
servants' duty to make contact with some member of the patient's
household and find out his habits and ailments.

The simple but indestructible faith of the public in the
efficacy of this form of diagnosis exasperated more orthodox
physicians. Dr Radcliffe, when visited by a shoemaker's wife with
a vial of her husband's urine, is said to have refilled it with some
of his own and said : 'Go tell your husband to make me a pair of
shoes by this water; for he will know by it how to fit my foot as
well as I can by his water know what disease he has.' Shakespeare's Falstaff entertained the same simple faith as the shoemaker's wife, to judge by the following :

'Boy ! what said the doctor to my water?'

* Observations Appropriate to the Use of Dr Myersbach's Medicines (1776).

'He said, sir, the water itself was a good healthy water; but for the party that owned it he might have more diseases than he knew for.'

It was inevitable that the more disreputable diseases should attract the quacks. Dr Case undertook to cure what he modestly called 'the Grand P——' and one of his handbills carried this invitation :

> All ye that are of *Venus* Race
> Apply yourselves to Dr Case;
> Who, with a box or two of PILLS,
> Will soon remove your painful ILLS.

Since not all afflicted citizens were willing to be seen striding up to, and into, the P—— Doctor's premises, many quacks stressed the secrecy, not only of their remedy, but of their premises. The man who had 'sought over-rashly for pleasure' was urged to call 'at such a place, the Golden Head or Ball, a Light at the Door at Even, and a good shelter to bolt in, or some back door in such an alley, left open for the purpose.'* There he would find, as the author of the foregoing explained, that there were medicines at all prices as well as mistresses. Treatment would start with 'a three half-crowns bolus,' a half-crown box of pills or a five shillings pot of electuary; but the patient would pay out fifty half-crowns before finding his way to hospital. Some quacks treating the Grand Pox would drum up trade by employing servants to dog gentlemen home from brothels. Then the quack would call on the errant prospect and say that, on the day before, he 'durst have sworn he see him go into such a house; but no matter for he was always tender of a gentleman's reputation.' The gentleman would then buy his peace as best he could, recognising blackmail when he saw it. Many quacks in this field undertook to cure the patient without confining him to quarters or requiring him to undergo any form of self-discipline. No effective legislation was passed against self-appointed pox-doctors until 1917.

There were few aids to health which could not be furnished by quacks— balsams and boluses, drenches and drops, electuaries and elixirs, ointments and opiates, salves and sugar-plums. All were described by such adjectives as angelical, royal, sovereign, incomparable, odoriferous, admirable, infallible, unfailing, glori-

* Anon: *The Modern Quack, or Medicinal Impostor* (1724).

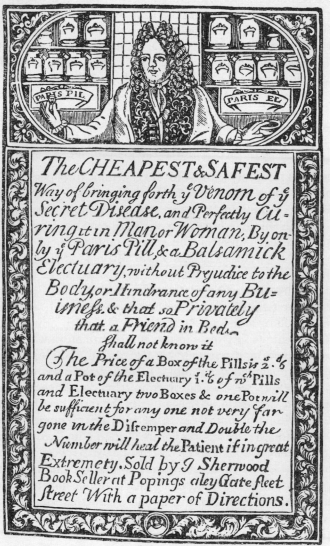

The 'Paris Pill'—a quack's bill

ous and imperial. One of the best-known of all specifics was the Famous Anodyne Necklace, the beads of which, by giving off a 'salutiferous emanation,' speeded up teething in children. Supposedly the beads were made of the bones of St Hugh, whose skeleton was smuggled home from the Orient by a priest and converted into beads in a turner's garret. St Hugh in his lifetime had had a way with children. When he dipped his finger in holy water and rubbed it nine times over the gums of an infant, out popped the tooth. The Anodyne Necklace was marketed by a member of the Chamberlen family and must have brought in considerably more wealth than even the secret forceps.

The Necklace, at least, did no harm. Nor, perhaps, did Jerusalem waters drawn from the Thames. But at their worst the specifics of the quacks, incorporating as they often did antimony and arsenic, were lethal stuff. One charlatan bought and marketed a great parcel of 'the coarsest and foulest horse aloes' which had been refused by numerous farriers for fear of killing their beasts. The results of taking such mixtures were unpredictable : 'it is like ten or twenty people's falling down a precipice where one or two only have the luck to escape and that not by their own skill or foresight.'*

Towards the end of the century the electrical quack, fired by the nerve-twitching experiments of Galvani and Volta, seized his opportunity to exploit the gullible. To most people the qualities of the 'electric fluid' were as dimly comprehended as they were by the Duke of Cumberland when, in 1746, he took an experimental shock with the tip of his Culloden sword. Dr James Graham made a fortune out of his notorious Celestial Bed, in which the magnetico-electrical influences, combined with sweet harmonies and perfume, spurred jaded couples to blissful and productive union (fee per night £100 and upwards). Even more successful, in his way, was Elisha Perkins, a Yale graduate, who marketed on both sides of the Atlantic his electrical tractors. These were small rods made up of various kinds of metal, said to be able to remove pain when rolled back and forth over the affected area. A poet hymned them :

> 'See, *pointed metals,* blest with power t'appease
> The ruthless rage of merciless disease!'

* *The Modern Quack.*

A Perkinean Institution was opened in London and British sufferers contributed £10,000 to the inventor's fortune. The tractors cost up to five guineas a pair, and as Oliver Wendell Holmes has pointed out, buyers of such expensive devices were determined to be cured by them—and consequently were.* Perkins received copious testimonials from persons in all ranks. He was discredited largely through the efforts of Dr John Haygarth, a Yorkshireman, who achieved similar results using rollers made of wood, and even bones and slate pencils. The tractors were a triumph, not of electro-therapy, but of psycho-therapy.

Quacks abused each other in pamphlets, just like qualified doctors. They also abused the profession at large. 'Can it be expected,' wrote Francis Spilsbury, only begetter of Spilsbury's Anti-Scorbutic Drops, 'that those so opulent practitioners, already drowned in profusion of voluptuousness, pleasure and luxury, will exert their thickened and congealed imaginations in the improvement of an Art the very defects and imperfections of which alone constitute that unfathomable golden mine whence they draw all their wealth?'

'The man who turns all his thoughts on the study of one sole disease, its cause, source, principle and antidote and attends to no other whatever is infinitely more likely to discover a true and efficacious remedy against it than those who, forced to practise on a larger scale, cannot bestow a sufficient time upon any in particular...'

Spilsbury subscribed heartily to the fallacy of a later day, namely, that if a product was advertised it must be good. To advertise a medicine all over England, the minimum sum required, he said, was £800 or £900 a year; to advertise it well cost £1,500. Obviously, he explained, a bad medicine could not last long.† Alas, the facts of history are against him.

Spilsbury was inspired to defend the empirics by the controversy which followed the death of Oliver Goldsmith, who had consumed injudicious quantities of Dr James' Fever Powder. The fault lay not in the specific, said Spilsbury, but in 'the little sense and judgment in the poor head of that great man once bred a physician.' As well, he argued, might the law prohibit muskets because sometimes accidents happened.

In the same pamphlet Spilsbury took the opportunity to

---

* *Medical Essays.*
† *Free Thoughts on Quacks and Their Medicines* (1776).

publicise his dispensary for the poor, whom he treated gratis.
The poor did not obtain their scorbutic drops without their
proper share of form filling, however. The application form ran :

The under written .... by trade ....
in the parish of .... in the county of ....
declares that .... has for these .... past laboured
under a .... attended with .... for which
.... has been .... treated ....
without effect. Wherefore, having been advised to try the use of
Spilsbury's Anti-Scorbutic Drops and being unable to afford paying
the Price at which they are fixed, humbly craves the Indulgence
of .... being admitted at the said Francis Spilsbury's
Dispensary as a PAUPER; and, upon producing a CERTIFICATE
duly authorised by the Overseer of the Parish aforesaid, as a Voucher
of .... actual and truly indigent circumstances, thereby
to enjoy the Benefits accruing from the charitable Distribution of the
said Drops so generously offered by the Author in his INVITATION
TO THE POOR of the 12th March 1775, in Consequence of which
.... is encouraged to make the present Application and
petitions for obtaining the DROPS GRATIS. Dated this ....
day of .... in the year 1777.
Signed in the presence of the following :

Another specimen form, intended for the use of the not
altogether destitute, was as follows :

Anno 177–   No.
This Day .... by trade .... was admitted
to the Indulgence of .... Shilling per *every Bottle* of
our ANTI-SCORBUTIC DROPS on account of h—— unfavourable
circumstances.
Recapitulation :
This Grant good for .... Bottles
Renewed for .... ditto.
Disorder ....
Patient entered ....
Discharged by reason of .... on .... day
of ....

Cure perfected   in .... weeks
                 with .... bottles

Spilsbury published a good many testimonials from persons
who had seen holes in their legs vanish after suitable treatment.
It is quite possible that these testimonials were also obtained on

forms designed for the purpose. A practitioner as conscious of his own rectitude as Spilsbury claimed to be would hardly have demanded the filling in of a testimonial before starting the cure; a practice not unknown during the century.

In 1785 Spilsbury lent the vigour of his pen to fighting a vicious Parliamentary measure designed to embarrass the long-suffering race of medicine men. 'Let Britain talk no more of virtue, honour, valour, humanity, charity or whatever ennobles man, exalts a State or dignifies a King,' he exclaimed. The reason for this outburst was that Spilsbury's Anti-Scorbutic Drops and many other sovereign remedies were now faced with the imposition of a stamp duty. To such depths had England sunk that a King should 'sign an act that when his subject was bit by a mad dog it demanded a tribute from the terrified sufferer or no medicine to heal his wound.' William Pitt would 'wrest a tax from the helpless female servant who, because of the imbecility (*sic*) of her sex demands the friendly aid of medicine at certain times.' Even worse, the measure would encourage the spread of the French pox. 'Would Rome have thus chid her sons who had indiscreetly sacrificed to Nature's laws?'*

But the quacks had their revenge. Forced, in due course, to carry an official stamp on their products, they pointed to it as a sign that these had the approval and recommendation of the Government.

Many physicians were willing, unofficially, to prescribe secret remedies if the patient professed faith in them. This course was legitimate, says Thomas Percival in his *Medical Ethics,* so long as the patient was first 'apprised of the fallacy of his expectations.' In such instances, he argues, 'some indulgence seems to be required of a credulity that is insurmountable, and the patient should neither incur the displeasure of the physician nor be entirely deserted by him.'

There were undoubtedly a few well-advertised remedies which had virtue in them, and which survive, in modified form, in our own days. One or two of them were marketed, covertly, by orthodox physicians. Dr John Brown, originator of the 'Bruno-nian' system, refused an offer from a group of speculators to lend his name to a pill, although by so doing he would have lifted himself out of financial difficulties.

When Edward Jenner published a book dealing with an

* *The Power of Gold Displayed.*

improved preparation of tartar emetic, John Hunter wrote to him :

'Do you mean to take out a patent? Do you mean to advertise it? Or do you mean to let it take its chance? I approve of it much and will do all in my power to promote the sales. I would also advise you to burn your book or you will have all the world making it.'

Hunter also suggested finding a better name for the product— 'Let it be called Jenner's Tartar Emetic.'

Drewry Ottley, an early biographer of Hunter, mentions this as 'an example of that want of professional feeling occasionally displayed by Hunter.' Others consider that Hunter was merely being facetious. Jenner made no attempt to exploit the preparation.

Attempts to persuade Parliament to legislate against quacks usually met with little encouragement. The law-makers and the intellectuals of the day held no high opinion of orthodox medicine and, as a rule, were quick to suspect attempts by its warring branches to enrich themselves at each other's expense. A little quackery, they thought, was no bad thing if it helped to ginger the gentry with the gold-headed canes.

Even the insolences perpetrated by the Scots universities—as when Edinburgh made an illiterate brush-maker a doctor of physic and St Andrews awarded a degree to a stage doctor— failed to arouse indignation in responsible quarters. At one time an attempt was made to enlist the support of Dr Adam Smith, the political economist, in the campaign against 'quack' doctors from Scotland, but he professed himself unable to see what all the fuss was about. 'Do not all the old women in the country practise physic without exciting a murmur or a complaint? And if here and there a graduated doctor should be as ignorant as an old woman, where can be the great harm?' he asked. No university, in his view, could be certain that a man was fit to practise physic. If the graduates of Oxford and Cambridge had been able to maintain their monopoly, the cost of feeling a pulse would have been doubled or tripled; hence the Scots invasion served 'as a corrective to what would otherwise soon grow up to be an intolerable nuisance, the exclusive and corporation spirit of all thriving professions and of all great universities.'*

* John Thomson: *Life of William Cullen.*

XII

SLINGS AND ARROWS

As if Sydenham had never lived, the theory-spinners continued to hatch out frail and dubious hypotheses and then struggled to nurture them to lusty lunacy on carefully selected facts.

The more far-fetched a theory was, the more fiercely it was defended. Sooner or later, another savant would be found to be working on parallel lines, but instead of being hailed as an ally on the road to ultimate truth, or even claimed as a disciple, he would be attacked as a pirate and plagiarist. Pupils assailed their masters, masters savaged their pupils. Universities were ravaged by feuds and boycotts, careers were blasted.

A sad bibliography could be compiled of all the angry pamphlets and counter-pamphlets, tracts, remonstrances, lampoons and scurrilous parables published by doctors during this excitable century. Even the wiser men of medicine stooped to the incivilities of the lunatic fringe. Both Hunters quarrelled with the Monros of Edinburgh, and also quarelled with each other.

When setting out to deflate an opponent it was customary to say how willingly one would have declined to notice his existence, but that his tactics, reflecting as they did on one's candour and veracity, allowed no other course to a man of honour than to attempt a reply. The way was then cleared for impugning the other man's good faith, education, morals and degrees. A notable piece of medical Billingsgate is the following, from the pen of Dr John Brown, who was describing a theory of 'spasm' put forward by Dr William Cullen:

'This brat, the feeble, half-vital, semi-production of frenzy, the starveling of strained systematic dullness, the forlorn outcast of the fostering care to which it owed its infect vitality, was now to be pampered by a crude and indigestible nutriture, collected from all the materials which had composed the several fabrications of former erroneous systems, was to be decorated with every foreign plumage, and in this its totally borrowed and heterogeneous form, instead of the hideous caricatura which it was, contrived to excite the derision of mankind, it was to be ostentatiously obtruded upon the world as a new and respectable doctrine, and held up, forthwith, as the formidable rival of a splendid system.'*

This was how Dr Brown discussed the work of a man who had gone out of his way to befriend him. Perhaps he had a still sharper style for a life-long enemy. Dr Brown's own medical theory (he believed that illnesses were caused as much by debility as by excessive vitality) split the profession into bickering and contemptuous factions, not only in Britain but in Europe. In 1802 so violently did the students of Gottingen University dispute the Brunonian issue that they fought for two days in the streets, not without assistance from their professors, until the authorities broke up the battle with the aid of a troop of Hanoverian horse.

Dr James Gregory had the reputation of being Edinburgh's most rabid controversialist. Mere pamphlets did not content him; he published some eight quarto and octavo volumes of between 300 and 500 pages, stuffed with attacks on individuals and corporations. For defaming two colleagues he paid damages of £500 and costs; for beating another colleague with a stick he was fined £100. A great deal of his energy was spent abusing John Bell, the surgeon, who was foolish enough to attempt to answer the torrent of 'defamation, ribaldry and obscenity' volume for volume. In one of his works Bell likens Gregory to 'one who tumbles for the amusement of a mob and for his last greatest feat stands on his head, wagging his heels in the air, quite unconscious that the mob has gone by.'

So pleased was Dr Gregory with his pamphleteering style that he distributed copies of his attacks to all the leading families of Edinburgh, pushed them through the windows of post chaises, posted copies conspicuously at every other corner of the city, and pinned them to the doors of Bell's lecture hall and operating rooms.

It was, of course, the custom for devotees of other arts than that of medicine to belabour each other in print, but the doctors set a standard of venom hardly matched even by the Puritan pamphleteers of the previous century. In the next century

* *Observations on the Present System of Spasm* (1787).

acrimony was to grow still sharper with the advent of medical journalism.

The Royal College of Physicians, instead of setting an example in these matters, was perennially involved in an undignified domestic conflict. Its licentiates grumbled, with some justification, that the College was run for the exclusive benefit of the fellows, who looked upon them as an inferior race. The dispute was aggravated by the activities of Dr Isaac Schomberg, of German origin, who in 1746 incurred the censure of the College for unlawfully practising in London. He disguised neither his contempt for the College nor his intention to continue in practice, and there was sporadic litigation between the parties for the best part of a decade. In 1753 the eccentric president of the College, Sir William Browne, published *A Vindication of the Royal College of Physicians,* putting forward evidence against Schomberg which, he said, should have been heard at a recent legal hearing. After flailing the presumptuous alien with the usual Greek and Latin texts, he quoted from the statutes of the College a clause which called for 'the admission of those only to be fellows who, being graduates of Oxford and Cambridge, besides approved learning and morals, have also agreeable and sociable dispositions.' Schomberg clearly did not come into the latter category. His actions went to show, said Sir William, that whoever nibbled at the noble statutes of the College was like a viper nibbling a file—he could only draw blood from himself. By Sir William's computation Schomberg now owed the College more than £1,000 in respect of his 17 years unlawful practice at £5 a month.

The pamphlet incensed the licentiates, who now supposed themselves to be excluded from the College because of their dubious morals and unsociable dispositions. Year after year the strife continued, reaching a climax in 1767. The fellows were dining behind locked doors in the College in Warwick Lane when a large body of angry licentiates descended on the building, breaking the windows with their canes. A locksmith whose services they had suborned picked the locks of the doors and they burst in on the banquet. Never had so many gold-headed canes been flourished in fury. Soon afterwards, at the anniversary meeting of the College, the licentiates again massed for the attack. A locksmith was offered ten guineas and an indemnification of £300 if he would force the gates, but he declined. Later the College obtained a court ruling that the licentiates were in the wrong.*

The town laughed heartlessly. How those physicians hated each other! It remains to be added that Schomberg, when his principal opponents had died off, became a fellow and in due course a censor, of the College he had covered with abuse.

At the close of the century the Royal College had an opportunity to honour itself by honouring Edward Jenner, at a time when universities and academies all over the world were hastening to heap distinctions on him, but it successfully resisted the temptation. Why should it admit to its fellowship a mere country surgeon whose degree had been granted by the suspect university of St Andrew's? It was true that the University of Oxford had so far forgotten itself as to award him a degree by diploma, but if Dr Jenner wished to become a fellow of the College he must sit the examinations like everybody else. Jenner did not care whether he became a fellow or not. He said he would not start mugging up the classics at his time of life for all John Hunter's museum.

The fellows of the Royal College saw the century out, aloof, scornful, and not a little resentful that their efforts to keep the profession dignified should have met with so little sympathy. It was true that knighthoods and baronetcies came their way in some profusion, but these distinctions were now being bestowed on surgeons. In the Upper House soldiers and sailors rubbed shoulders with lawyers and churchmen. Was no physician worthy to mingle with them?

In fact, no peerage was bestowed on a medical man until 1897 —and then the recipient was a surgeon.

* *Annual Register*, 1767.

XIII

'SUBJECTS' FOR SALE

ONE of the deepest rifts ever created between the medical profession and the public was caused by the passion for dissection which gripped surgeons and their pupils at the end of the eighteenth century. This rift had been widening slowly since the days of Cheselden. As the new century came in the battle for human bodies—or 'subjects,' as they were known in the trade—produced some of the most macabre episodes to be found in social and criminal annals.

The body-snatchers, most of them part-timers, were recruited mainly from the less fastidious in the ranks of grave-diggers, hearse-drivers, sextons, coachmen and professional mourners. There were two principal methods of obtaining subjects: by surreptitiously disinterring the newly dead or securing custody of bodies before burial by such tricks as impersonating relatives. Dickens's Jeremiah Cruncher, bank porter by day and purveyor of scientific goods by night, is a fair example of a resurrectionist.* Not every Mrs Cruncher necessarily disapproved of her husband's midnight fishing expeditions.

The Government, knowing that public opinion was against 'mangling' of the dead, winked at the collusion between surgeons and body-snatchers. The Law did its best to shut its eyes and stop its ears. Its servants who stumbled across evidence of grave-robbing were congratulated on their alertness and told to forget what they had seen. The view of authority was simple: so long as the violation of graves was decently and quietly done, what did it matter?

Among the qualities required in a successful resurrectionist were strong arms, a strong stomach and an eye for country. Before beginning to dig, he would memorise the position of such

* *A Tale of Two Cities.*

objects as twigs, flowers and pieces of shell which might, or might not, have been set out in a deliberate pattern. He would also search carefully for a spring gun, and if he found one, neutralise it. The method of obtaining the body was to uncover the head of the coffin, piling the earth on to tarpaulin sheets, and then, with the aid of a special grappling instrument, snap off half the lid, thus making it possible to tie a rope round the neck of the subject, which was forthwith hauled out of its coffin and up to the surface. The corpse was stripped, so that there could be no prosecution for theft of clothing, put in a sack and the grave refilled. The whole operation had to be performed in silence and all the tell-tale evidence restored. One zealous resurrectionist is said to have raised two bodies in this manner in one and a half hours. With such skill were graves restored that many a mourner who prayed for the resurrection of a lost one did so unaware that the lost one had already been resurrected.

Accidents, of course, sometimes happened. One day in 1776 two Customs officers saw a coach being driven precipitately across London at four in the morning. Suspecting that it contained smuggled goods they ordered it to halt, enforcing their demand with pistols. Two men leaped out and ran away, leaving the coachman to explain the presence, inside the coach, of the naked bodies of an elderly man and woman, each with a rope round the neck. It turned out that they had been abstracted from a paupers' grave in Shoreditch and were on their way to St George's Hospital. In London the quick rode by day and the dead by night.

A few days after this incident the remains of more than a hundred bodies were found in a shed in Tottenham Court Road. According to the *Annual Register* they were 'supposed to have been deposited there by traders to the surgeons.' The discovery caused a big outcry. Next year a grave-digger and a woman assistant, convicted of grave-robbing, were sentenced to six months' imprisonment. Each was to be severely and publicly whipped on the first and last day of the sentence, but by Royal order the whipping was cancelled, as it was thought likely the mob would have lynched the offenders.

One who had a narrow escape from being hauled up before the Lord Mayor as a resurrectionist was George Crabbe, who came to London in 1777 to pursue his medical studies. Happening to open a cupboard in his lodgings, Crabbe's landlady found a dead child in it. Unfortunately she got the idea that it was a child she had had the misfortune to lose a week before. 'Dr Crabbe had dug up William; she was certain he had; and to the Mansion House he must go.' Somehow Crabbe contrived to exculpate himself.* Incidents of this type did much to bring about strained relations between landladies and medical students.

John Hunter took many a calculated risk to obtain a coveted subject. In 1783 Byrne, the Irish giant, was dying and Hunter set his man Howison to watch him. Whether or not Byrne had sold his body in advance to Hunter is not clear; what is clear is that he had a horror of dissection. Finding that Howison was shadowing him, he left strictest orders that his body was to be guarded day and night and then sunk at sea in a lead coffin. After the giant's death Howison prowled round until he found where the undertaker's guard drank when off duty. Hunter then went along, made contact with one of them, and offered £50 for the body. The man said he would have to ask his mates and came back with a demand for £100. When Hunter agreed, the guard regretted the modesty of their demand and eventually worked the figure up to £500. In the dead of night the body was removed by hackney coach and then transferred to Hunter's personal carriage. Fearing a hue and cry, Hunter had the body boiled down that same night.†

It was no time to worry about ethics when a giant's body was to be won. In Dublin, when the great Corney Magrath died, Dr Robert Robinson cautioned his class against trying to snatch the body, but added that if, against his express wish, they persisted in doing so, they should be careful to strip off its clothing. The hint was not lost. Four students, disguised, joined the wake in the giant's lodgings, doped the whisky with laudanum and carried back the body to Trinity College. When, next day, the giant's friends applied to the Provost for the body, Dr Robinson explained that such was the students' professional zeal that already dissection was far advanced. The Provost was left to pay off the mourners and Dr Robinson went away chuckling, 'Divil a knife's in him yet.'‡

It was the multiplication of medical schools, in the early nineteenth century, that increased the demand for 'subjects' and

* *Life and Poetical Works of George Crabbe*, by his Son.
† Drewry Ottley: *Life of John Hunter.*
‡ Sir A. Macalister: *Dr James Macartney.*

encouraged the most vicious members of the community to take a hand in the resurrection game. Since they observed neither the rules nor the decencies, they were treated by the courts as the criminals they were; a development discouraging to the more conscientious body-snatchers, who withdrew from what, in their eyes, had now become a degraded trade.

Whether the purveyors were respectable or otherwise the medical schools still required subjects, and were ready to take outrageous risks to get them. 'It is distressing to men of good education and character to be compelled to resort for their means of teaching to a constant infraction of the laws of the country and to be made dependent for their professional existence on the mercenary caprices of the most abandoned class in the community,' said the Select Committee on Anatomy in 1828. Yet few surgeons and pupils lost any sleep over the traffic; to judge from medical reminiscences this fraternisation with the underworld seems to have rested lightly on their shoulders. Graveyard raids were the sort of lark in which a man showed his spirit and audacity. The public saw that surgeons and rogues were in conspiracy against them, and the surgeons and rogues, knowing that they were looked on as pariahs, were spurred to fresh audacities against the community.

The director of an anatomy school could not afford to have a conscience about the source of subjects. His students would complain if there were not enough to go round and would mock him for lack of enterprise, or parsimony, or both. The more uncouth pupils would get the school a bad name by carousing and idling until the trade in subjects improved; the more ambitious would go to other schools, if necessary on the Continent.

Bransby Cooper, nephew of Sir Astley Cooper, has told how the resurrection men would wander round the dissecting rooms at the start of a new session, bowing to the lecturers and demonstrators. Then one of them would say to the superintendent : 'Well, Mr —, what does Sir — mean to stand this season?' The conversation would continue :

'Oh, I don't know, Murphy—whatever's fair. What will you take this morning?'

'Nothing, I thank you, Mr — but I don't mean to work this season without I get ten guineas for a subject.'

'Oh indeed, well we don't mean to go more than eight.'

Resurrection men at work. From G. W. M. Reynolds' *The Mysteries of London*

'Then you may go and tell Sir —— that he may raise his own subjects for not one will he get from us.'*

After perhaps a month the resurrectionists would return and begin the bargaining again.

About 1800, when there were some 300 students dissecting in London, the price of a subject rarely exceeded one or two guineas. Twenty years later there were 1,000 students and the price had shot up to eight, ten and even fifteen guineas. Some of the cost had to be passed on by the schools to the consumer, with the result that 200 students annually preferred to prosecute their studies in Paris, where a subject cost a few francs only. (Exhuma-

* *Life of Sir Astley Cooper.*

tion in France was almost unknown. Those who died in hospitals and were unclaimed within 24 hours were automatically sent for dissection. The *Chef des Travaux Anatomiques* drove the bodies in a discreet covered carriage in the small hours to the various anatomy schools. Doubtless the violent controversy over body-snatching in Britain was thought to be just another manifestation of British hypocrisy.)

Sir Astley Cooper's band of resurrectionists were reputed the most resourceful. He spent hundreds of pounds supporting their families when the breadwinners were jailed. Sometimes they would obtain for him, as a special assignment, the bodies of former patients on whom he had operated, in order that he could check on the cause of death. It was customary for doctors to inform Sir Astley when one of his patients died, in order that he might make such plans as he thought fit.

Before the Select Committee on Anatomy Sir Astley made his famous boast :

'The law does not prevent our obtaining the body of an individual if we think proper; for there is no person, let his situation in life be what it may, whom, if I were disposed to dissect, I could not obtain.'

Sir Astley told the Committee how, at one period, 'an individual possessing considerable talents' tried to establish a monopoly in the body-snatching business. If he found rival gangs at work he would burst into their storehouses and spoil their subjects for dissection, or excite a public riot against them. Joshua Brookes, another witness, formerly a lecturer in a school in Blenheim Street, described how the mob broke into his house and hacked to pieces a subject for which he had paid eight guineas the night before. On another occasion, because he refused to pay a *douceur* of five guineas at the start of a lecture season, a gang came at dusk and laid two subjects in an advanced state of decomposition in the roadway near his premises. Two young ladies stumbled over them; and the result was a riot in which his establishment narrowly escaped being sacrificed to popular fury.

Sir Astley Cooper's indulgence towards the resurrection men seems to have been carried to curious lengths. One day in 1814 his nephew Bransby Cooper, then a surgeon in Wellington's army in Spain, received a furtive and unprepossessing caller who produced a letter from Sir Astley reading : 'Butler will tell you the purpose of his visit.' Invited to explain, Butler said he had

come to Spain to collect teeth for dentists. He had travelled from
Lisbon on foot or riding in bullock wains, but so far had been
unlucky in his quest. 'Oh, sir,' he exclaimed, 'only let there be a
battle and there'll be no want of teeth! I'll draw them as fast as
the men are knocked down.' Out of respect for his uncle,
Bransby Cooper refrained from booting this jackal (a one-time
porter of St Thomas's) from the camp. Noticing that the man
had a physical complaint, he performed an operation on him,
then gave him money and sent him away. Two years later Butler
wrote to him expressing thanks for saving his life, and mentioning
that he had made £600 out of his Peninsula adventure. Two
other resurrectionists, Ben Crouch and Jack Harnett, also made
a fine haul of teeth, and much else, from the Peninsula. At this
period teeth were in heavy demand for riveting to dentures.
During the next decade many a citizen sported 'Waterloo teeth.'

Any honour that might have existed among body-snatchers
eventually faded. An operator would demand fees for 'exclusive
services' from as many schools as possible. A gang might deliver
a body to one school, receive payment, then burgle the premises,
abstract the body and sell it elsewhere the same night. Joshua
Brookes was awakened one night by a man who offered him a
subject. Without inspecting it, he paid over part of the fee and
then kicked the parcel down a flight of steps into his dissecting
room. As he went back to bed he thought he heard noises from
the package and went to investigate. In his cellar he found,
standing beside the empty sack, a dazed man who explained he
had been parcelled up when drunk. Suspecting a plot to get
money from him, Brookes summarily turned the subject into the
street. The incident goes to illustrate the casual manner in which
many anatomists were prepared to accept their raw material.

Two anonymous body-snatchers gave evidence before the
Select Committee. 'A.B.,' believed to have been Ben Crouch,
who was not without a reputation as a pugilist, explained that he
had withdrawn from the business because all the burial grounds
were too well watched. He had served six months' imprisonment
and had been shot at from two yards distance. Some grave-
diggers, he said, were refusing bribes of £100 to look the other
way, preferring a steady job to the dismissal that would follow
detection. He preferred to exhume the bodies of the poor because
they were buried in readily accessible stacks; he had not been
able to raise more than half a dozen wealthy persons.

E

'C.D.' (probably Butler) said he had supplied subjects from 1809 to 1813.

'Will you state to the Committee what was the number of subjects you supplied to the anatomical schools in 1809–1810? — The number in England was, according to my book, 305 adults, 44 small subjects under three feet; but the same year there were 37 for Edinburgh and 18 we had on hand that were never used at all.

'At what price on the average were these subjects delivered? — Four guineas, adults. Small ones were sold at so much an inch.'

The game had indeed grown difficult. Citizens who had spent weeks watching at the bedside of a relative grudged having to spend chilly nights at his graveside, and loosed off their blunderbusses on the least suspicion of interference. In some areas the militia were ordered out to keep watch over the burial grounds. The wealthier classes buried their dead in lead coffins, at twice the normal depth, and erected iron railings round the grave.

In Scotland religious feeling against tampering with the dead was stronger than in England (it was 'remarkable and unaccountable,' according to one medical witness before the Select Committee). The anatomy rooms of Edinburgh were watched by detectives hired by the civic authorities and all visitors of questionable appearance were shadowed. As a result the resurrection men who had fled from London to the north, hoping for easier pickings, began to take ship for Ireland or to operate on the Borders.

Granville Pattison, a Maryland surgeon who had studied at Glasgow University, told the Select Committee that it was customary in his day for students to obtain their own subjects. 'Every teacher had what he called his private party; this consisted generally of eight students.' Pattison knew what it was to be shot at and stoned during his forays. Once he was arrested by the police and tried like a common criminal in Edinburgh, 'a man sitting on each side of me with a drawn bayonet.' His acquittal cost him £520. Asked how subjects were obtained in America, he explained that although exhumation was illegal the authorities in cities like Philadelphia and Baltimore would allow discreet resurrection by students from the potters' fields on the civic outskirts.

In Edinburgh for some years the schools of Monro and Barclay had a gentleman's agreement to share the supply of subjects. This was upset when the thrusting Robert Liston arrived on the scene, bringing with him Ben Crouch. It was customary in

Robert Knox's traffic with Burke and Hare inspired this cartoon in
Noxiana (1829). The caption, adapted from *King Richard II*, ran:

Know'st thou not any, whom corrupting gold,
Would tempt unto a close exploit of death?

I know a discontented Irishman,
Whose humble means match not his haughty mind;
Gold were as good as twenty orators,
And will, no doubt, tempt him to anything.

Edinburgh for one grave-robbing party to have a look-out man who would watch for rivals and establish a claim to a grave by standing astride it. Between them Liston and Crouch tried to hustle a rival look-out man from a grave, but he presented a pistol at them. Liston withdrew after an altercation.*

One lecturer, described as 'a Napier in action,' had to flee from a churchyard on being detected, but before leaving he picked up a subject under each arm and carried them off into the garden of an institution nearby.†

Immense pains would be taken to secure the body of anyone who had succumbed to an interesting disease. A country lad who died from hydrocephalus was interred in an exposed cemetery on the Firth of Forth and watchers were set over his grave every night. Bribes and offers of whisky were refused. One afternoon two well-dressed gentlemen arrived in a carriage at the nearby inn and told the attendant that they were expecting a parcel. They went away and presently two men in livery arrived with a large bundle. Soon afterwards the gentlemen returned and drove away. They had performed a quick-change act and disinterred the body at twilight before the watch arrived.‡

Amédée Pichot, biographer of Sir Charles Bell, tells how in 1823 he accompanied a friend to Edinburgh Infirmary to entrust into its care a former actor called Berry, who had almost drunk himself to death. On leaving they were accosted by a well-dressed, bland young gentleman. 'You have, I see, left poor Berry within,' he said. 'He is booked, and will not live a week. I'll give you three guineas for him—more than so miserable an object is worth and considerably less than a funeral will cost.' The offer was declined. Berry died after ten days and was buried. No doubt, says Pichot, he was lifted the same night.

Those who died forgotten in Edinburgh institutions were liable to be befriended ere they were cold by such characters as Andrew Lees, who specialised in impersonating bereaved relatives, and had the gift of weeping on demand. His accomplices included a man resembling a Methodist preacher, demure and saintly. The gang sometimes co-opted prostitutes to carry through impersonations.

Dr J. Paterson, who had a practice on the Ayrshire coast,

* Sir Robert Christison: *Autobiography.*
† Henry Lonsdale: *Life and Writings of Robert Knox.*
‡ Ibid.

sought to help his pupils by smuggling bodies over from Ireland. At first he tried to import his goods by normal methods, but the Customs imposed a 'downright despotic tax' on them. The doctor complained, moreover, that 'a still greater obstacle was the antipathy of the Customs officer to inspect subjects.' High-handedly, the officer would order the 'perishable goods' to be interred. Hence it became necessary to arrange private landings. Sailors from the limestone boats, knowing the doctor's require-ments, would approach him with, 'Do you wish to have a stiffin?'*

In one respect at least the task of the body-stealer was made more difficult in Scotland: when a person died in hospital a relative's permission had to be obtained before dissection could be authorised. It was otherwise in London. Sir Robert Christison has told how, at St Bartholomew's, there was an indecent race between students and relatives for the still warm subject. Dis-sectors would begin to use their scalpels when the blood was still fluid. Once Christison, fearing that the subject was still alive, grabbed the knife from the operator.†

In Ireland the main source of subjects was Bully's Acre, the burial ground for Dublin's teeming paupers. It provided work for some 50 resurrectionists, whose task was made easier because there was no organised watch. Scandalised by the in-and-out-traffic at Bully's Acre, a number of citizens formed the Humane Society of St John 'to protect the remains of our poor fellow citizens.' This organisation incurred the anger of Dr James Macartney, Professor of Anatomy at Dublin University, who said its activities would merely serve to raise the price of subjects and ruin the medical school. He also pointed out that very many of those who complained about the operations of the resurrection men 'carry in their mouths teeth which have been buried in Hospital Fields.' Happily for science, the watchmen employed by the Humane Society of St John proved as corruptible as all the others and joined in the disinterring with a will.‡

A flourishing export trade in subjects is said to have been organised in Dublin by William Rae, a Scots naval surgeon on half-pay who gave ships' captains a percentage on all cadavers carried. Some were shipped in brine as prime pork, some were designated as bodies of animals *en route* to museums and others

* *Report of Select Committee.*   † *Autobiography.*
‡ Sir A. Macalister: *Dr James Macartney.*

were shipped in piano cases. The traffic caused offence not only to Customs officers. Once at least the stench of ill-preserved bodies forced passengers to leave a vessel at first landfall, rather than continue to their booked destinations.

The same hazard was encountered by land travellers, who grew to look askance on passengers who joined coaches at the last moment with large bales. At Carlisle, in the days when the Scots anatomy schools were hard put to get subjects, many an inquest was held on bodies removed from the luggage compartments of coaches, and the jury's verdict of 'found dead in a box' was a standing joke in those parts.

The critics of anatomy fell into many classes. There were those who held that dissection was unnecessary; there were others who thought that it might be necessary but that there was too much of it. Some were in favour of anatomising other people but not themselves or their near relatives. Others said they would be in favour of anatomy if they could be assured that the remains would be reverently handled and a service conducted over what was left. The difficulty here was that surgeons had a passion for removing organs and preserving them in pickle, as hinted in Thomas Hood's ballad 'Mary's Ghost' :

> 'The arm that used to take your arm
>   Is took to Dr Vyse,
> And both my legs are gone to walk
>   The hospital at Guy's.

> I vowed that you should have my hand,
>   But Fate gives us denial;
> You'll find it there at Mr Bell's
>   In spirits in a phial . . .

> The cock it crows, I must be gone.
>   My William, we must part;
> And I'll be yours in death although
>   Sir Astley has my heart.'

Those who based their opposition to anatomy on religious grounds held that it was impious to mutilate the image of God and to pry among man's organs for the secrets of life. Lingering in their minds, no doubt, were ancient taboos about touching the dead. 'Curs'd be him who moves my bones' seems to sum up this attitude; but such critics were often quite happy to let the

'That's the body I want.' A surgeon identifies a former patient resurrected for him in a church. From G. W. M. Reynolds' *The Mysteries of London*

surgeons cut up corpses imported from abroad. There was also a widespread notion that the anatomist's audacities were going to make for an unseemly and confusing state of affairs on the day of Resurrection, when mortal bodies were due to be reunited to their departed spirits. The air would be thick with kidneys and lungs flying from their pickle and joining up again with their parent skeletons. Those who objected on these grounds seemed unconcerned about the difficulties of reassembling those untold millions who, since human life began, had been picked clean by worms and fishes.

Family feeling for the dead was probably the strongest reason of all for opposing dissection, and even autopsy. To such a fervent anatomist as John Hunter this attitude was as incomprehensible as it was anti-social. Once, when a householder resolutely refused to allow a post-mortem on a member of his family, Hunter exclaimed : 'Then, sir, I heartily hope that you yourself and all your family, nay all your friends, may die of the same disease, and that no one may be able to afford any assistance.' Faced with similar opposition, Sir Astley Cooper would say : 'Life depends on the integrity of organs which are enclosed in cavities and consequently concealed from view; and the derangement of these by disease cannot possibly be understood unless the dead body be opened and examined.' If this argument failed, his resurrection men would not.

In the main, surgeons were willing to respect the reluctance of individuals to have their relatives dissected, as distinct from opened. Pressure of family opinion was one of the reasons why surgeons themselves did not leave instructions for the dissection of their bodies. An anonymous doctor explained in the *Morning Herald* of March 24, 1828 :

'Were it left to the practitioners only, they would almost unanimously declare their willingness to be dissected after death; but is it to be supposed that their wives, their children or relations, who are not in the profession, and who are no more interested in the cause of anatomy than the public in general, would submit to it?'

Nevertheless, those who countenanced dissection were constantly taunted with being afraid to offer their own bodies for the purpose. A Member of Parliament told the strange story of Sir William Myers, mortally wounded at the head of the Fusiliers brigade at Albuera. To his surgeon he said : 'As you know I have always insisted upon the surgeons of my regiment and of my brigade having the right to examine the bodies of all the men who died in quarters and that I frequently attended myself to countenance the proceeding. I have, I confess it, a prejudice against being opened of which I am ashamed but which I cannot get the better of. Promise me that it shall not be done.' The surgeon promised and shook hands.*

The anti-anatomy agitators had another favourite argument : that the constant 'junking up' of bodies encouraged atheism and materialism in the medical profession. This notion led two clergy-

* Commons, Feb. 27, 1832.

men into committing egregious follies in Dublin in 1825. A young pupil of Dr James Macartney declared, on his death-bed, that he was an atheist. He was said to have formed these views while studying anatomy at Trinity College, Dublin and to have declared, 'No one could be a physiologist without being a materialist.' Just before his death, however, he rediscovered his faith.

Two clergymen of the Established Church, one of them a baronet, at once began an investigation of Macartney, who was a Unitarian. Sir F. Blosse attended the Professor's lectures and tried to pump the students for evidence which could be used against him. In his enthusiasm he penetrated into the anatomy rooms, where the sight of flayed and half-dissected bodies 'filled him with horror and he became convinced that one who had to teach such subjects in such a place must be capable of any extreme of immorality and materialism.' Hearing that the students remained loyal to their teacher, Archbishop Magee sent a clothes basket full of tracts for distribution to them as they left their lecture-room. Macartney was formally arraigned for spreading infidelity and immorality, but his accusers could produce nothing more than diatribes. Powerful evidence was given for Macartney, showing that his lectures had no materialistic tendency, but rather the opposite. Then it turned out that the dead youth had been reading Voltaire and other French writers, long before he came under Macartney's influence. The Professor was honourably acquitted. His trial was widely reported in the British Isles, and even on the Continent. Public opinion seems to have been largely on the Professor's side. There were anatomists ready to proclaim that dissection tended to increase reverence for the divine mysteries and in some instances they were undoubtedly right; nevertheless, the view that anatomy brutalised its practitioners continued to be widely cherished. Many believed this to be the reason why surgeons were not called for jury service; anatomy had rendered them too hard-hearted for the social duties and responsibilities of a citizen. The truth was simple and less sensational. Surgeons were excused jury service because they had to be always ready for emergencies.

The surgeons' case for conducting dissections was strong and simple. If a knowledge of anatomy was to be possessed it could be obtained in only two ways: by dissecting the dead or mangling the living. When Sir Astley Cooper was asked whether a surgeon could operate on the living without gaining experience on the dead, he replied : 'He must be a blockhead if he made the attempt, and the practice of the most sensible and the most expert surgeons in London has been to visit the receptacles for the dead for the purpose of performing the operations which they were about to execute upon the living, if the operations were in the least novel.' In his view each student who intended to be a surgeon (and nine-tenths of medical men at this time practised both physic and surgery) required to dissect at least three subjects —'a half-anatomist is a most dangerous surgeon.' Because of the gain in anatomical knowledge surgeons were performing more, and easier, operations. 'Anatomy,' he said, 'is our polar star.'

The State, while refusing to regulate the supply of bodies, demanded a full knowledge of anatomy in the surgeons it employed in the Army and Navy. The courts, moreover, were never backward in awarding damages against surgeons who were shown to have an inadequate knowledge of the interior of their patients. Yet, as Professor G. J. Guthrie, a future President of the Royal College of Surgeons, pointed out in a pamphlet :

'The jury who award damages against a surgeon on account of his ignorance of anatomy will, in their several other capacities of churchwardens, overseers of the poor and governors of hospitals . . . take all possible pains to prevent perhaps the very same man from obtaining that knowledge (which is only to be gained by dissection) and which they have just punished him and would punish him again for not having acquired.'*

The *Quarterly Review* considered that, if surgeons were to be prevented from dissecting, surgery must go back a thousand years. As the brush was to the painter and the saw to the carpenter, so was the scalpel to the surgeon. All too many doctors were practising surgery who had never opened a body. 'If your bladder bursts because your surgeon cannot pass the catheter, or your strangulated hernia mortifies because he cannot release it by an operation—do not complain; it is not *his* fault, but *yours*.'†

John Abernethy, the surgeon, used to tell his students a cautionary tale about an apothecary whose knowledge of anatomy was deficient. One day this fumbling fellow was called to an Army major whose jaw was in the habit of becoming dislocated when he laughed too uproariously. The apothecary tried to move the jaw in the wrong direction, which produced such violent

* *A Letter to the Home Secretary* (1829).
† January, 1830.

protests from the victim as to suggest that he was out of his mind.
Well aware how to treat a madman, the apothecary sent for a
strait-waistcoat and prepared to blister his patient's head. With
the utmost difficulty the major was able to obtain pen and paper
and write 'Send for the regimental surgeon.'

It was the view of most medical men that the bodies of the
friendless poor should be set aside for dissection, plus those of
criminals, and the army of those 'found dead.' The reaction of
many citizens was 'Why pick on the poor?' In Parliament a Mr
Hunt said that if this were done he would move to include the
bodies of 'those rich paupers, the pensioners on the Civil List.'
The poor found themselves befriended in some unlikely quarters.
In practice, as the profession did not fail to point out, it was the
poor who suffered most from the ravages of body-snatchers; the
bodies of the rich were guarded by stone and metal. A Member
called Leycester thought it would be a source of satisfaction 'to
those whose last moments received consolation from the public
charities to know that they were able after death in some measure
to repay the debt they owed to those who administered comfort
to them during the last stage of their existence.' The rich, he said,
would always have their fully trained surgeons. Limiting the
supply of subjects simply meant that those who practised on the
poor would be half trained.

Great ingenuity was shown in both Houses in discovering
reasons for doing nothing. Sir J. Yorke thought that more use
should be made of suicides' bodies, only to be confronted with
statistics showing that, contrary to popular belief, the suicide rate
in Britain was low compared to that of the Continent. Other
Members contended that the surgeons ought to be able to make
do with the bodies of criminals. It was explained to them that
whereas in 1733 there was one execution to 10,000 of the population of London and Middlesex, the rate for the 1820s was only
one in 70,000. A Mr Pelham thought that any necessary knowledge of anatomy could be picked up, as of old, on the battlefields, and a Mr Perceval suggested that a ban should be imposed
on anatomy for two years, with a view to putting resurrectionists
out of business; meanwhile any necessary anatomical research
could be done on animals. Many Members pointed out that Dr
Azoux of Paris had invented an artificial corpse of complete perfection. It had 1,244 parts, all removable, and cost only £120.
Yet the Astley Coopers still demanded human flesh.

In the proposal to empower relatives to assign bodies for dissection several Members detected a grave risk. 'There were those in great cities,' said a Mr Fane, 'who did not scruple to barter the chastity of their daughters. Why therefore should it be supposed that there were none brutal enough to sell the bodies of their own children to the surgeon?' Lord Wynford was worried at the risk of men 'in a moment of excitement or intoxication engaging to sell their bodies to the Jews.'

Another peer, Lord William Lennox, was anxious to stop surgeons and students taking bodies or parts of bodies home to their lodgings. He was told that this would be unfair to country practitioners who liked to brush up their knowledge from time to time on a subject.

When all other arguments failed, Members had another weapon to throw at the surgeons: the notorious levity with which, as they alleged, anatomies were carried out. The conduct of students in the dissecting rooms, said Mr Hunt, was 'too disgusting to describe even in an assembly like that, composed as it was entirely of men.' It was a point on which members of the Select Committee were not wholly at ease. Dr Southwood Smith was asked: 'When dissection takes place in a school, is the examination conducted with decorum and is all indelicacy and levity discountenanced among the students?' He replied guardedly: 'In general I think it is; and I think more so than it was.'*

A pamphleteer calling himself 'Medicus' was quite sure that a medical student did not approach his dissection as he did his prayers. 'Who in his sober hours that is at all acquainted with the treatment of medical students towards the dead would not shudder at the thought of being dissected?' he wrote. Was it not the fashion to use skulls for sugar basins and drinking cups—'a far more appropriate badge for the murderer and the assassin.' It was well known, he said, that many eminent anatomists kept vultures to dispose of human offal. He was one of many who were prepared to tolerate anatomy only if all the pieces were put

---

* If a medical contributor to *Punch* in 1842 is to be believed, November the Fifth in a dissecting room provided the ultimate in saturnalia. His 'Directions to Medical Students' include the following: 'If you owe a new man a grudge, who chances to be dissecting the lungs and mediastina of a recent subject, place a sixpenny maroon in the cavity of the thorax. Light it and walk off—a singular effect will be produced.'

back in the coffin afterwards, ready for the Great Resurrection.*

The first Anatomy Bill, designed to regulate the supply of subjects, was stifled by Parliament in 1829. Even while the niceties of the issue were being debated, Burke and Hare were busy perpetrating their classic crimes in Edinburgh. These have been described so often that they need only brief recapitulation here. The two Thugs, despairing of obtaining bodies the hard way, found it easier to suffocate their victims and carry their still-warm bodies round to the anatomy schools. Fifteen times they were lucky; but their sixteenth murder led to their undoing. Hare turned King's evidence; Burke was hanged and anatomised. In the opinion of the Edinburgh mob, another who should have gone to the gallows was Robert Knox, principal client of the murderers. The popular attitude was summed up in the jingle :

> 'Burke's the butcher, Hare's the thief,
> Knox the man that buys the beef.'

A committee of professional men, on which doctors were represented, sat to decide whether Knox was to blame. They held that, while he himself had no knowledge of what was going on, he had allowed too much latitude to his assistants and door-keeper. They conceded that it was common practice on the part of anatomists not to ask too many questions about the source of subjects, lest the touts went elsewhere; nevertheless the notoriously bad character of the persons engaged in the traffic 'undoubtedly demanded greater vigilance,' especially as the bodies supplied by Burke and Hare had never been interred.

Knox regarded himself as a wronged man. He went about the city in a military cloak, with sword, pistols and dirk under it. His 400 pupils stood solid behind him. Once when the yells of the mob reached his lecture-room he said : 'Gentlemen, you are disquieted by these noises to which no doubt you attach a proper meaning. Do not be alarmed. It is my life, not yours, they seek. The assailants of our peace may be big in menace but they are too cowardly in act to confront such a phalanxed body of gentlemen as I see before me.' The cheers which greeted these remarks served, temporarily, to silence the mob.

According to Knox's biographer, Henry Lonsdale, 'anatomy was not an ordinary occupation or mere intellectual pastime with Knox but viewed by him as an object of high philosophic re-

* An Exposure of the Present System of Obtaining Bodies (1829).

search.' In his passion to impart his enthusiasm, he would spend up to £800 a year out of his own pocket for subjects. The view of a medical contemporary, Sir Robert Christison, was that Knox, 'a man of undoubted talent but notoriously deficient in principle and heart, was exactly the person to blind himself against suspicion and fall into blameable carelessness. But it was absurd to charge him with anything else.'* Many of his professional colleagues who condemned him would have done better to recall the narrow escapes they themselves had undergone in this lawless traffic.

Parliament did not stir itself again until the operations of another murder gang were exposed, this time in London. One November night in 1831 three men called on the porter at the dissecting room at Guy's offering him a youth's body, which he declined. It was also rejected at Grainger's anatomy school. The three then hawked it at King's College, where there was a long argument about whether it was worth nine or ten guineas. Suspicions were aroused because the body was fresh and had a swollen jaw and bloody eyes. The teeth had already been abstracted. The three men, John Bishop, Thomas Williams and James May, were tried for the murder of the youth and another person unknown. It turned out that Bishop and Williams hung their victims upside down in a well while making plans for their disposal. Bishop in a confession said that although he had trafficked in between 500 and 1,000 bodies he had not murdered any persons other than those stated in the indictment (rumour said that he had accounted for upwards of 60). Thirty thousand persons watched the execution of Bishop and Williams.

Memorials urging reform were now reaching Parliament thick and fast. One of them was from Professor James Macartney, who urged that all anatomy schools be closed until popular fury had subsided. He had gathered the signatures of nearly 400 persons who were willing to donate their bodies for dissection, including those of Spurzheim, the phrenologist, and Robert Owen, the philanthropist. Naïvely, Macartney urged that 'an Act be passed declaring that the dead body is not dishonoured by dissection.' John Abernethy suggested an amendment to the burial service; instead of 'we therefore commit his body to the ground' why not say 'consign his body to the enquiries of the learned?'

* *Autobiography.*

Only a few days after the execution of Bishop and Williams a new Anatomy Bill was introduced into Parliament. This time it reached the Statute Book. It empowered the governors of public institutions to assign bodies, at their discretion, for dissection, and introduced a tight system of licensing and inspection.

It was a long time before the public lost their distrust of the surgeons. The year 1832 was a cholera year. At Manchester the mob got the idea that the cholera hospital was being run by the surgeons in order to provide themselves with subjects (a boy's corpse had been found buried without its head). They forced the hospital gates, carried away a number of patients and encouraged the others to go home. Many who did so died on the way. Four troops of the 15th Hussars under Lord Brudenell (later Earl of Cardigan, who led the Charge of the Light Brigade) arrived to restore order. There was a similar riot at Paisley.

It was perfectly true that the bodies of cholera victims found their way to the anatomy schools, irrespective of the appalling danger to the dissectors and the community at large. Many students contracted fatal infections when handling such material. Robert Knox's tables were well supplied at this period by plague victims.

For several years after the passing of the Anatomy Act surgeons would be stopped in the street by ingratiating ruffians who would say, 'I was one of them, sir, who lost work by the Anatomy Act.' Still loyal to those who had kept them supplied in the difficult days, the surgeons would hand over an appropriate gift.*

From this remove, it seems an incredible chapter in our history. Today few know or care how the medical schools obtain their subjects, and the traffic is carried on with much circumspection. It is unlikely, however, that the general attitude to anatomy has basically changed. A whiff or two of scandal would be enough to work up the public to a pitch of indignation comparable to that which animated their forefathers. The attitude of the ordinary man would be: 'I don't care who they practise on so long as it isn't me or mine.'

---

* J. F. Clarke: *Autobiographical Recollections.*

XIV

'AN INSUFFERABLE CAD'

A REPUTATION for wildness still clings to the medical student, even in these regimented days. In every school are a handful who make conscientious efforts to live up to the legend, like Yeomanry subalterns at summer camp.

This notoriety was built up in the latter part of the eighteenth century and consolidated in the first half of the nineteenth. During these hundred years or so the medical student was a pariah. Not only was he an unrepentant grave-robber, but a swaggerer and a drunkard. He was not beyond suspicion of practising vivisection. He was a patron of pawnbrokers, but not of launderers. Shopkeepers snubbed him. When really hard up, he would pick up a shilling or two by pulling the teeth of paupers. As if liquor was not enough to corrupt him, he indulged in unseemly 'laughing gas' revels or ether 'jags.' Periodically, he joined with his fellow ruffians in a great baying herd and they all ran shouting to assault the ruffians of a rival hospital, thus providing a crop of new cases for their respective casualty wards. It was inconceivable that this seedy young bear could ever develop into a grave and revered physician. But often he did; and if he did not, he became a creditable surgeon-apothecary.

There were many excuses to be made for the medical student, but few people were willing to listen to them. While other young men of his age were learning law, or struggling with Hebrew, he was faced with the raw stuff of life and death. He saw revolting sights and worked amid foetid stenches. Daily, in those times before anaesthesia, he watched human beings undergoing pain that few human beings are called upon to suffer today, and he knew that he himself must some day inflict such pain. His masters moved calmly and apparently unaffected amid these racking scenes and it was up to him to reach the same level of hardihood.

It was no easy struggle. At Edinburgh the young Charles Darwin watched two bungled operations on children and rushed out before they were completed—'the two cases fairly haunted me for many a long year.' The tougher spirits learned to mask their feelings by crude jests, as soldiers will amid carnage, or to soften the sharp edges of recollection with drink. Somehow or other, the mind had to be purged of horrors, but nobody must suspect that such was the purpose of a carousal.

A small proportion of students came from wealthier metropolitan homes and were able to fall back on the social life to which they were accustomed. Others boarded with surgeons who kept a cautionary eye on their habits. *The Lancet*, which first appeared in 1823, published advertisements like these :

'One or two MEDICAL STUDENTS of retired habits may be accommodated with board and lodging in the house of a surgeon in a pleasant and airy situation.'

'A SURGEON residing in a large and airy house situated in a very genteel street . . . is desirous of accommodating two or three MEDICAL STUDENTS with BOARD and LODGING. He will be happy to assist them in their studies and his books will be at their service.'

Other students, again, were put firmly in the care of family friends. Mary Braddon, in her novel *The Doctor's Wife,* introduces a young doctor of 22 who, after 'the fiery ordeal of two years' student life at St Bartholomew's' was still 'almost as innocent as a girl.' This was because his father had planted him 'during those two awful years in the heart of a quiet Wesleyan family in the Seven Sisters Road and the boy had enjoyed very little leisure for disporting himself with the dangerous spirits of St Bartholomew's.'

John Keats, who lodged in Dean Street, near Guy's, also survived the 'fiery ordeal' without moral dilapidation. It is a fascinating thought that he probably helped to dissect bodies supplied by Sir Astley Cooper's resurrection men.

Students without friends, influence, money or the consolation of a divine muse soon tired, in their leisure moments, of looking at their own blood under a microscope or dissecting pigs' eyes from the butcher, and set out to conduct such roysterings as they could afford. As they could afford very little, they fell into low company. Not the least factor which cut them off from polite society was the aura of the death-house they carried with them.

The authorities offered students no facilities for recreation, so for the sake of economy and convenience, and for sheer devilry, many of their revels were held in the dissecting rooms. In such ways, as Sir Squire Sprigge has said, they achieved 'a familiarity with repulsive objects which effectually did away with a proper respect for the decencies of life.' This led to a 'regular and accepted tone of low shiftlessness, which tone it became almost necessary for each man to assume if he had it not and an act of *esprit de corps* to transmit to his juniors.'*

The medical student needed little encouragement to show off in public. Many people have suffered from the type of conversation which distressed Mr Pickwick on that Christmas morning when he found Bob Sawyer and Benjamin Allen breakfasting in his inn.

'Nothing like dissecting, to give one an appetite,' said Mr Bob Sawyer, looking round the table.

Mr Pickwick slightly shuddered.

'By the bye, Bob,' said Mr Allen, 'have you finished that leg yet?'

'Nearly,' replied Sawyer, helping himself to half a fowl as he spoke. 'It's a very muscular one for a child.'

'Is it?' inquired Mr Allen, carelessly.

'Very,' said Bob Sawyer, with his mouth full.

'I've put my name down for an arm, at our place,' said Mr Allen. 'We're clubbing for a subject, and the list is nearly full, only we can't get hold of any fellow that wants a head. I wish you'd take it.'

'No,' replied Bob Sawyer, 'can't afford expensive luxuries.'

And so on. Later Bob Sawyer 'related with much glee an agreeable anecdote, about the removal of a tumour on some gentleman's head; which he illustrated by means of an oyster knife and a half-quartern loaf, to the great edification of the assembled company.'

Dickens did not enlarge on life in his portrayal of Bob Sawyer, according to Sir Ernest Morris, historian of the London Hospital, who says that the medical student of the period was 'generally as insufferable a cad as can be imagined.'

If little complaint was heard in those days about medical students larking about with hospital nurses, the reason was not hard to discover: all too many of the nurses of the day were

* *Life and Times of Thomas Wakley.*

The Medical Student

elderly harridans unlikely to appeal even to the least fastidious student.

Ill discipline of students in hospitals had caused concern to many a board of governors. In the London Hospital, during the middle years of the eighteenth century, students took it upon themselves to invite their friends along 'to see the show,' infiltrating them into the operating room where some wretch was being held down under the saw, or introducing them to patients with spectacular diseases. These patients would consider themselves fortunate if the visitors did not try to improve on their treatment. When the entertainment was over hosts and guests would carouse within the hospital walls and those visitors who were unable to go home would be tucked up in vacant beds in the wards. This kind of abuse, says Sir Ernest Morris, was stamped out in the early 1760s.

Much of the blame for these follies, in the London Hospital as elsewhere, lay with the physicians and surgeons to whom the students looked for instruction. Aloof and orgulous, they felt that the maintenance of their dignity was of more importance than the imparting of information; and their knowledge of their art was not always such as to encourage them to make unnecessary pronouncements. When John Hunter sought to stimulate his colleagues at St George's Hospital into addressing students, one of them retorted that 'he did not choose to lose any reputation he might have in surgery by giving lectures.' A student's request to be told the nature of a patient's disease might be met with a reply like, 'I am sure I do not know, do you?' Favoured protégés of the eminent would be granted a little more information, as some return for the hundreds of guineas paid, but the unprivileged and unattached had little choice but to stand silent or be snubbed, or to try to pump the house surgeon afterwards. Only those avid for knowledge and advancement could remain undiscouraged. This off-hand treatment of pupils lasted until the nineteenth century was far advanced. 'I cannot recollect having got a single useful lesson in the treatment of disease from the three physicians of St Bartholomew's Hospital,' writes Sir Robert Christison, referring to the 1820s. Sir James Paget, who was a student in the same hospital in the 1830s, says: 'For the most part the students guided themselves or one another to evil or to good, to various degrees of work or of idleness.'* No one was, in any sense, responsible for them.

Besides the medical schools attached to certain hospitals, there were private schools which provided good solid cramming for those willing to be crammed. There was no means, however, of enforcing either attendance or discipline. If the proprietor took a strong line, his students would transfer their patronage elsewhere.

Lecturing to a restive audience of medical students was an ordeal akin to that faced by the dedicated few who presume to teach juvenile delinquents in the 'blackboard jungle' of modern America. During the opening catcalls the lecturer would notice without surprise that the demonstration skeleton had been assembled in such a way that the legs were where the arms ought

* *Memoirs and Letters* (ed. Stephen Paget).

to be, and *vice versa*. His introductory remarks would be interrupted by the noisy arrival of roysterers who had been up all night, bringing with them door-knockers, mice and musical instruments, with bad fruit or fireworks according to season. An unpopular lecturer might have to close his books and walk out for half a dozen periods in succession until his audience tired of baiting him. It was small wonder that those who were supposed to lecture often passed on the disagreeable task to their inferiors.

From time to time *The Lancet* dropped hints that the dignity of the profession would be improved if students refrained from keeping their hats on during lectures, or wearing their 'elegant dissecting gowns.'

Rude pranks were seldom attempted on men with the authority of Sir Astley Cooper, who could hold as many as 400 students spellbound. John Abernethy, too, had a strong grip on his class and would invite idlers to walk out if they found the lecture uninteresting. The great John Hunter, however, cut a poor figure at the rostrum; he was self-contradictory, he was imprecise, and sometimes, forgetting the line of his thought, he had to ask his class to cross out what they had written. Of Hunter's class, Abernethy said : 'The more humorous and lively members of the audience would be tittering, and the more sober and unexcitable quietly dozing into a nap; whilst the studious and penetrative few appeared to be seriously impressed with the value of Mr Hunter's observations and inquiries.'* George Dermott, lecturer in a private school in London, had his own way of breaking the *ennui* engendered by a long lecture. When the class grew restive he would cease demonstrating and give the soliloquy from *Hamlet* or the death scene from *Richard III*.†

There were lecturers on midwifery who held their students' attention by keeping up a bawdy commentary. 'It was not, generally, thought amiss that one of my teachers told many stories, some of which were obscene, some very nasty,' writes Sir James Paget. 'Perhaps some thought them fairly balanced by the care with which, in telling the uses of every part and the advantages of every arrangement of parts, he used the methods of the natural theology then popular.'

The extent to which lecturers joked and truckled with their students deeply offended young Henry (later Sir Henry) Acland,

* George McIlwain: *Memoirs of John Abernethy*.
† J. F. Clarke: *Autobiographical Recollections*.

when undergoing his medical studies in London. 'The notion of a master being cheered by his pupils is enough to sicken an Oxford man at once,' he wrote.*

Often, the ill-discipline which marred lectures was carried into the operating theatre. If the case was an unusual one, and the surgeon a man with a reputation, the students would surge in from lecture, pothouse or dissecting room, with as little regard for humanity as for hygiene. So thickly would they cluster on the floor that the surgeon would have to part them to get at the patient, who would judge the gravity of his condition by the size and excitement of the audience. *The Lancet* in 1825 published an account of the scenes which preceded a difficult operation at the Middlesex Hospital. 'Keep back, gentlemen,' said the senior surgeon to the students who jostled round the patient in the ward. 'You are not gentlemen if you do not keep back.' When this had no effect, he said, 'Well, then, if you won't keep back we must go up into the theatre, I suppose.' In the theatre the jostling was repeated. Students came down from their seats and crowded round the table until the floor was covered. From behind came cries of 'Heads! Heads!' Amid the noise *The Lancet's* representative was unable to hear the surgeon's whispered instructions.

It is probable that fewer students would have idled their time away if they had anticipated any serious trouble in passing their examinations. They knew that only low standards were required and that no serious precautions were taken against impersonation or cribbing. In Dublin, Professor James Macartney set his face against the system whereby medical teachers, having received their fees, gave certificates of attendance at lectures whether or not such attendance had been put in. Not all absentees were necessarily idling in pothouses. Macartney's biographer, Sir Alexander Macalister, says he knew of several young men who worked for the whole of their student career as nine-to-five clerks in the Royal Bank. One of them passed the examinations of the College of Surgeons without having seen an operation performed.

For the conscientious, *viva voce* examinations held all the terrors that they hold today, especially if such a tyrant as Abernethy was the questioner. But there were young men who were not ashamed to show their spirit, to judge from the following exchange said to have occurred between Abernethy and a student:

* J. B. Atlay: *Henry Wentworth Acland.*

'What would you do if a man was brought to you with a broken leg?'

'Set it, sir.'

'Good, very good. You're a very pleasant, witty young man; and doubtless you can tell me what muscles of my body I should set in motion if I kicked you as you deserve to be kicked for your impertinence.'

'You would set in motion the flexors and extensors of my right arm; for I should immediately knock you down.'*

For the mass of students there was little hope of reaching the top of their profession, and they knew it. In the medical world, as in the military, a man rose by favouritism or something very like purchase, or both. Many of the best-known physicians and surgeons had obtained their coveted appointments in hospitals by paying large fees, as pupils, to the previous incumbents, on the unwritten understanding that they would step into the posts later; others had secured the posts by family influence. For the unprivileged, the prospect was that of setting up as apothecaries in small towns or villages, and as most of them had already served as apprentices to apothecaries they well knew the limitations of such practice. This was just another reason for not exhausting one's brains in an effort to acquire knowledge. It was the inequity of this system, and its stultifying effect on students, that roused the anger of Thomas Wakley, of *The Lancet*.

Edinburgh had perhaps the rowdiest medical students of any city outside London. Robert Knox's loyal young men were always ready to crack the heads of the citizens, and so were their successors. In 1838 occurred a famous affray which began with street boys snowballing the students. Police could not restore order, but night brought temporary truce. Next day, when hostilities were resumed, the students held out in their quadrangle, until the 79th Highlanders were called down from the Castle, each man with 40 rounds of ball cartridge. The students 'cordially cheered' the military but refused to yield to the police. Reports of this affray reached Paris, where Louis Philippe's nervous ministers are supposed to have enquired whether the outbreak was part of a revolutionary movement among the university students of Europe.

In Louis Philippe's capital the medical students of this period were described by young James Paget as 'the most ruffianly, ill-

---

*J. C. Jeaffreson: *A Book About Doctors.*

looking set of fellows I ever saw.' English students were bad
enough, he admitted, 'but here you can conceive nothing so out-
rageously vulgar as their appearance—wooden shoes, ragged
coats, and unwashed and unshaven faces are the ornaments of
the large majority; and really, but that I rather like to appear as
as Englishman, and if possibly as a gentleman, I might fairly
have left my two best suits of clothes, and nearly all my linen, at
home, without losing any of the respectability of my professional
appearance. It is annoying to see, too, how readily Englishmen
fall into these customs—it is often difficult to distinguish them
except by language.* Young Paget was a high-minded and somewhat priggish young man. He was able to do something to
improve the behaviour of his contemporaries in the 1840s, when
the hospitals began to arrange for students to live in, or near, the
premises. Appointed warden of the hostel of St Bartholomew's,
he spent much time curbing and rebuking the more profligate
figures. One of them, whom he reported to be 'idle, dissolute,
extravagant, vulgar and stupid,' with a predilection for the turf,
was, according to Paget's biographer, later hanged for murder.
This appears to have been Dr William Palmer, the Rugeley
poisoner.

In 1841 the ever-zealous Henry Acland, one of the few medical
students to attend prayers in Westminster Abbey at a quarter to
eight every morning, wrote a pamphlet asking for a fair deal for
his fellow students. 'Why,' he asked, 'have the youth of a profession second only to one in blessedness never received till these
few years one act of gratitude? Why have men been pleased to
say we were ever drowning and have never thrown so much as a
straw to save us?'

It was a fair question.

* *Memoirs and Letters.*

XV

WAKLEY FIGHTS THE HYDRA

THE medical profession could hardly expect to pass unchallenged through the age of reform.

In 1800 anyone who thought, like Laurence Sterne, that there were worse occupations than feeling a woman's pulse could call himself a doctor, even if he had done no more than devil behind an apothecary's counter for a few months. Anybody could cut off anybody else's leg, without legal penalty. Within the British Isles were nearly a score of authorities, including the Archbishop of Canterbury, with powers to license practitioners in physic and surgery, but any amateur was at liberty to thumb his nose at them and put up his own brass plate, red lamp or mortar and pestle. Many a surgeon-apothecary, or general practitioner, looked on diplomas as mere pedantry.

In London the Royal College of Physicians had neither the money, the will nor the energy to prosecute unlicensed practitioners. When its spokesmen were asked why the College left the populace to the mercy of quacks, they said they regarded the moral disapproval of the College as its most powerful weapon, or retorted that the Government had sanctioned quackery by clapping a tax on patent medicines.

Just before the new century came in the unhappy and impecunious Company of Surgeons had hatched a pretty plot. Through mismanagement and dereliction the Company was moribund, if not legally extinct, but the resourceful master, wardens and assistants, unwilling to concede defeat, slid a Bill into Parliament with the object of building a Royal College on the ruins. This Bill had passed a negligent Commons and had been twice read in the Lords before the commonalty of surgeons—that is, the members whose fees supported the Company—realised what was happening. They then scented a plot to trample on their rights and privileges, in so far as they had any. An unexpected champion appeared in Lord Thurlow, who told his fellow peers that never had there been such an attempt to take Parliament by surprise. He described the Bill as 'a miserable and wretched performance, in which the arrogance of the provisions maintained an equal contest with their absurdity.'

Here, he said, was a body which sought to ban its members from midwifery, physic and pharmacy, yet its examiners wanted the power to pass or reject practitioners in pharmacy for the Dominions and all surgeons of the Navy and Army, in whom a knowledge of pharmacy was essential. Because of Lord Thurlow's contumely, the Bill was thrown out. The plotters were not unduly discouraged; what they failed to obtain from Parliament they won by charter from George III. Thus, in the year 1800, the Royal College of Surgeons was born.

The College had no legal powers. If it was to have any influence for good on the profession of surgery, it would have to do so through exercise of moral strength. Unfortunately, it failed completely to profit by the disasters which had overtaken the other Royal College, and all too soon found itself involved in disputes with its commonalty even more farcical than those which had led to the storming of the College of Physicians by its furious licentiates. In no time at all, it became, in the words of a medical historian, 'a close and irresponsible oligarchy, obstructive and insolent.'*

A more significant event than the founding of the Royal College of Surgeons was the passing of an Act in 1815 (approved, as its critics pointed out, late at night in a thin House) which gave the Society of Apothecaries not only the right to examine all apothecaries in England and Wales, but to bring actions against those who practised pharmacy without its licence. The Society, which was not wholly guiltless of the complacency which besets Worshipful bodies, had been jockeyed into action by some of its more vigorous members, called together by advertisement. They were anxious, not only to protect their own reputation, but to check the inroads of the new class of chemists and druggists, who were clamouring for the right to prescribe, just as the apothecaries had done in an earlier day.

The 1815 Act was a considerable triumph for the apothecaries. It meant that the Government, in its first attempt to regulate the

* J. F. Clarke: *Autobiographical Recollections.*

medical profession, had by-passed the ancient College of Physicians and the upstart College of Surgeons, ignored the universities of Oxford and Cambridge, and vested control of the great mass of practitioners in what had once been regarded as a society of shopkeepers. Under its provisions the Society could demand from its entrants certificates of instruction and of attendance at hospitals. To meet these demands the medical schools had to reorganise and rationalise their teaching and many new schools sprang into existence. Students who had secured the licence of the Society were at liberty to try for the diploma of the Royal College of Surgeons, as a large proportion of them did.

'In the near future,' as Elie Halévy wrote, 'the practice of medicine would no longer be divided between an oligarchy too exclusive and too confident of its privileges to be industrious, and a proletariat of practitioners who offered no proof of necessary scientific equipment.' But there were many battles still to be fought.*

In 1818 a Bill was brought into Parliament 'for the better regulation of surgery in the United Kingdom,' the idea being that no one should be allowed to practise without a testimonial from an established college of surgery. This measure was roughly handled, the Commons suspecting that the promoters were less concerned with saving the public from quacks than with establishing a fee-snatching 'ring.' One member said that the surgeons ought to have more pride than to apprehend competition from pretenders. Sir Charles Monck recalled that Parliament had recently abolished restrictive practices laid down for the protection of certain mechanical trades in Queen Elizabeth's reign; why allow the surgeons to reverse this liberal policy? A soldier member thought it would be as sensible to rule that all surgeons should pass through a certain turnpike and pay a toll in order to qualify them for their profession.

For many years the proletariat of medicine railed impotently at the arrogance of the aristocracy. Then came the fire-brand Thomas Wakley, with his truculent journal *The Lancet,* to canalise old grievances and publicise new ones. Wakley had been a student at the Combined Hospitals of Guy's and St Thomas's, and also at the private anatomy school in Webb Street. Like many reformers he continually overstated his case and was never happier than when 'all the slanderous tongues of the hydra of

* *A History of the English People in the 19th Century.*

aristocratic indolence' were loosed at him. Many times he fell foul of the courts, but usually he emerged on the winning side, and when he did not his opponents received only derisory sums. The ordinary public, as well as the students and the under-privileged of his profession, were strong behind him.

There was much to rouse Wakley's anger. In his own student days he had seen the elect of the Colleges preserving among themselves and their relatives the profitable hospital appointments, charging high fees for instruction they frequently failed to give, and indulging in 'hole and corner' surgery—that is, conducting operations and the all-too-frequent autopsies which followed them with a minimum of publicity.

Wakley's first shot in the offensive was to print without permission the lectures delivered by such eminent surgeons as John Abernethy, at St Bartholomew's, and Sir Astley Cooper, at Guy's. His justification was that, thanks to an 'infamous by-law,' the hospital lecturers had 'secured for themselves a monopoly of lecturing to students in surgery and have therefore excluded the profession and the public from all the benefits of competition.' The eminent lecturers who saw their words in print, complete with asides and not always decorous jokes, tried strenuously to trace and discredit *The Lancet's* reporters. Abernethy took it hard. He called, without success, for 'the hireling of *The Lancet*' to stand forth, or to see him privately. He appealed to honour and decency. Lights were turned out and note-taking was forbidden, but somehow the lectures, which were reported by senior students, still found their way into *The Lancet*. In the courts, on two occasions, Abernethy claimed copyright protection, but it was ruled that the lectures were public property. Sir Astley Cooper felt less strongly on the matter; he was able to persuade Wakley to take his name off the reports, thus saving himself from any charge of self-advertisement.

Even more alarming to the hydra of aristocratic indolence was *The Lancet's* practice of reporting on the conduct of individual operations in the London hospitals, with copious censure for what it held to be slipshod work. This, said the aggrieved surgeons, was a gross invasion of professional privilege. If a patient died, the surgeon suffered anguish enough in the theatre without having his misfortune sarcastically described in the public prints. But Wakley denied that 'the sufferings of the patients in public hospitals are the private property of the surgeons, and that men who are paid for performing a duty, who derive enormous incidental profits from the appointment in the sums which they levy upon medical students, have a right to conceal from the public the manner in which that duty is discharged.' And, on another occasion : 'Shall an unfortunate individual cut off in the prime of life die unnoticed? . . . And were not hospitals founded and endowed for the relief of the poor alone and not for the emolument of mischievous imbecility?'

It was a nasty period for the less-than-brilliant surgeon. He did not know which of his pupils round the table might be *The Lancet's* man and it must have seemed that he was performing his operation as publicly as if he were in Piccadilly. In 1828 Wakley overshot himself when he published a prejudiced account of a 'murderous' operation for the stone at Guy's, the surgeon being Bransby Cooper, nephew of Sir Astley. Cooper was said to have taken nearly an hour to perform what should have been done in a minute; and the patient died. The report, which failed to make allowances for certain difficulties of the operation, was written on a note of sustained sarcasm, beginning, 'It will doubtless be useful to the country "draff" to learn how things are managed by one of the privileged order—a hospital surgeon—nephew and surgeon, and surgeon because he is a nephew.' It quoted the anxious asides of the surgeon and the appeals of the patient to desist from further exploration.

Bransby Cooper served a writ and the public prepared for excitement; there was no doubt that they were on Wakley's side. Instead of the £2,000 damages he claimed, Bransby Cooper was awarded only £100, which well-wishers cheerfully paid on Wakley's behalf. Many of these hospital reports were thoroughly unfair, but they probably did much to sharpen the conscience of the more laggard members of the profession.

Though it often complimented Sir Astley Cooper on his skill and fair treatment of students, *The Lancet* never ceased to criticise the system of nepotism of which he was allegedly the king-pin. Once, answering a charge that he had aspersed his fellow surgeons, Sir Astley exclaimed : 'Are they men whom I could possibly feel disposed to injure? Is not Mr Green my godson, Mr Tyrell my nephew, Mr Travers my apprentice, Mr Key my nephew, Mr Cooper my nephew?' (The first three were surgeons at St Thomas's, the last two at Guy's.) This rash defence with all its implications was exploited to the full by Wakley. It

was perfect proof, he said, of the existence in a public institution
of a privileged fellowship linked by consanguinity and avarice.
(Sir Astley himself had been apprenticed at one time to an uncle
at Guy's.)

Wakley attacked, with good reason, the way in which physicians and surgeons canvassed for hospital appointments—'by
beating up the quarters of their brewers, their bakers, their tailors,
and their other tradesmen.' It was only too true that hospital and
dispensary appointments were obtained through the votes of those
who had no means of assessing medical qualifications, but who
were flattered by visits from fellows of proud colleges and enjoyed
keeping them in suspense. For a man who liked to think of his
profession as a dignified and liberal one, this hat-in-hand solicita-
tion could be an acute ordeal. Sir George Lefèvre tells how he
went round greengrocers and cheesemongers, praising stuffed
parrots, sampling currant puddings and generally undergoing all
the humiliations of a Parliamentary candidate.* Faced with
intolerable condescension by a greengrocer, a canvasser could
always pretend, as Dr William Barrowby, of St Bartholomew's,
once pretended, that he had called to buy a pound of plums. In
1814 Sir Charles Bell reluctantly began to canvas for a post at
the Middlesex Hospital. 'I have many opponents,' he wrote, 'and
must come in on the shoulders of the nobility!! We are not
permitted to canvas yet for eight days, but then I am told I have
600 people to visit.' In due course he was falsely accused of trying
to bribe down opposition.†

The contemptuous way in which medical students were treated
in the wards by their masters was another of Wakley's running
grievances. Post-mortems were held at unadvertised times in a
room to which it was necessary to pay to be admitted, and the
organs were liable to be taken away without comment. In 1824
Wakley took credit for the fact that clinical lectures both in
medicine and surgery were about to be started at St Thomas's
and Guy's. Furthermore, 'the surgeons in passing through the
wards will be required to make observations to the students in an
audible voice upon every case of importance; consultations as to
the propriety or impropriety of operations are to take place in the
operation theatre in the presence of the assembled students; and
the surgeons will be further required to make remarks in the

* *The Life of a Travelling Physician.*   † *Letters.*

theatre on any important circumstances which may arise in the
performance of operations.'

For the Royal College of Surgeons, whose licence he held,
Wakley reserved his purest vitriol. It was the chronic complaint
of those who paid their fees to the College that their resources
were being used to keep their self-styled betters in luxury, that the
wonders of the John Hunter museum were locked away for eight
months in the year, that the library was as jealously guarded as
any collection of *erotica,* and—most bitter complaint of all—
that the members were not allowed to use the front door of the
College in Lincoln's Inn Fields. On one occasion *The Lancet*
described the College as 'this sink of infamy and corruption, this
receptacle of all that is avaricious, base, worthless, and detestable
in the surgical profession.' The rulers were 'benighted buzzards'
seeking to preserve themselves from contamination with 'the
Democracy of Surgery.' A contributor to the paper said : 'They
take our money, give us *ex-post facto* laws, lock up our property,
insult us with mock orations, live at our expense and refuse to call
us by our proper names.'

Under this fire the College of Surgeons still strove to preserve
what it supposed to be the dignity of the profession. Many of the
dissentients, it considered, were mere man-midwives, corn-cutters
and drug pedlars. What it failed, or refused, to admit was that
only a trivial proportion of practitioners could hope to live by
pure surgery.

All Wakley's attacks on the medical oligarchies were coupled
with assurances that the country's general practitioners (this
phrase was used by *The Lancet* in its earliest days) were noble
fellows, the worthy heirs of Hippocrates. 'The public are grossly
imposed upon by the belief that the physician has a greater
medical knowledge than the general practitioner, when it is a
notorious fact that nine-tenths of the physicians have infinitely
less chance of observing diseases than the general practitioners,'
wrote Wakley in 1827. He held that the division of the professional into the largely social strata of physicians, surgeons and
apothecaries was absurd.

In the late 'twenties, with the encouragement of *The Lancet,*
indignation meetings of general practitioners were being held in
London and elsewhere. Their object was to draw up qualifications to be demanded from the profession as a whole and to effect
reform of the Royal Colleges. The sight of masses of its licentiates

plotting with a view to overthrowing it did not worry the College of Surgeons, nor did an attempt to persuade Parliament to abrogate its charter. In 1831, however, the war came home and the College witnessed a scene comparable to that which occurred in the College of Physicians in 1767. There had been a ban on surgeons of the Royal Navy attending the King's *levée,* and in protest against this Wakley organised a disturbance at the Hunterian oration, followed by another scene a week later. Some hundreds of surgeons clamoured outside but could not effect an entry. Eventually Bow Street officers were called in and made a rush at the protesting Wakley. His supporters rose to his protection and a fierce scrimmage ensued before he was ejected.

In the following year, at the instance of Charles (later Sir Charles) Hastings, a group of general practitioners met at Worcester to found the Provincial Medical and Surgical Association. Its objects were to disseminate information, to investigate diseases, to strengthen the standards of the profession and to maintain its dignity. This body was to become famous under the new name which it assumed in 1856: the British Medical Association.

In 1834, when the Government appointed a Select Committee on Medical Education, the president of the Royal College of Physicians, Sir Henry Halford, was pressed to reveal why the fellowship was reserved for graduates of Oxford and Cambridge, when there was no mention of any such restriction in its original charter or in the Act of Parliament confirming it. He maintained that there was in fact no restriction, but that there was 'a certain preference' for graduates of Oxford and Cambridge because of the 'moral and intellectual trial' they had undergone at those universities. Certainly any young man who resisted the temptations of Oxford and Cambridge in those days deserved his reward in life; but presumably this is not what Sir Henry meant.

Sir Henry pointed out that licentiates had to wait ten years before they could be considered for fellowship status, in order that they could 'give a proof of their moral qualifications as well as their intellectual ones.' Pressed for figures, he said that in the last 63 years only 19 licentiates had been made fellows, seven of them in the last 10 years. It was probable, he admitted, that more than 19 licentiates practising in London during those 63 years had been qualified by their moral behaviour to be ranked as fellows, but he blamed the acrimony of the disputes between licentiates and fellows for the fact that no more had made the transition. Sir Henry then tried to show that the licentiates were missing nothing by not becoming fellows. 'They have been able to make their fortunes just as well as the fellows have'; they were as capable of becoming royal physicians or of securing hospital appointments. Nor would Sir Henry admit that the College was a repository of religious intolerance : 'we have dissenters among us as well as members of the Church of England. We have no oath by which they are excluded.' Not even Roman Catholics were barred. But he agreed that in practice the fellowship was very much reserved to members of the Church of England, because of the preference shown to Oxford and Cambridge.

The evidence before this Select Committee showed that the censors of the College still went out three times a year with wardens of the Apothecaries' Society to examine drugs in the shops of apothecaries and druggists. It was an unpopular task. One witness said he was ill for a week after tasting so many medicines. An offending dealer might be 'remonstrated with' or have his drugs thrown into the street in the old contemptuous manner.

One witness was asked whether English physicians enjoyed the same status in France, and replied that in France they did not find themselves treated as gentlemen.

'What opinion do the foreign physicians entertain of English physicians?—They say they always speak *comme s'ils avaient inventé la science.'*

In 1847 another president of the College of Physicians, Dr John Ayrton Paris, had to admit to a Select Committee that his College was unable to execute the duties for which it was created. Nevertheless he was opposed to a Bill sponsored by Wakley and Henry Warburton which would have deprived the College of its empty powers. Asked how the College disciplined its own licentiates, he said there was power to summon, censure or fine. It emerged that a licentiate in London had been selling 'Water from the Pool of Bethseda' which had to be drunk when it turned turbid (and only the five-guinea jar could be relied upon to turn turbid). This offender had been punished by having his name omitted from the list of licentiates. Like many before him, Dr Paris could give no good reason why a higher standard of skill should be expected from London practitioners, save that 'it has preserved very much the dignity of the profession.' In the popular view, the object of preserving a higher standard in London was so that the rich pickings of the city should not have to be too widely shared. At this date there were 160 fellows and 276 licentiates in London and 255 licentiates in the country.

In the general clamour for medical reform, the doctors' passion for prescribing in Latin and for having Latin names on their gallipots did not pass uncriticised. This custom, it was argued, was perpetuated merely so that the public should be kept ignorant of the trash bottled for it. Dr Paris in his *Pharmacologia* (1843) pointed out that Latin was employed because 'an invalid travelling through many parts of Europe might die before a prescription written in English could be interpreted.' He heartily deplored the fact that the College of Physicians in Edinburgh had seen fit to print a pharmacopoeia in English.

The fruits of this half-century of agitation did not come until 1858, with the passing of the Medical Registration Act (Chapter 20).

XVI

MIDDLEMARCH AND BARCHESTER

APPROPRIATELY, in the year that Thomas Wakley founded *The Lancet* the reign of the gold-headed cane came to an end.

The most celebrated cane in the profession had belonged to Dr Radcliffe, was bequeathed by him to Dr Mead and finally came into the possession of Dr Matthew Baillie. Now, on Baillie's death, it was handed, ceremoniously, to his widow. In a tribute to her late husband, Sir Henry Halford said that before Dr Baillie's time:

'... it was not usual for a physician to do much more than prescribe remedies for the malady and to encourage the patient by such arguments and consolations as might present themselves to humane and cultivated minds. But as the assured gravity and outward signs of the profession were now considered obsolete customs and were by general consent laid aside by the physicians, and as a more curious anxiety began to be observed on the part of the patient to learn everything connected with his complaint, arising naturally from the improved state of general knowledge, a different custom became necessary in the sick room.'*

In other words, it was becoming harder to bluff the intelligent patient. This did not mean, however, that the doctor could afford to dispense with a dignified presence, or that there was no professional value in a confident and reassuring bedside manner.

There were patients who fancied they knew all the pros and cons of 'the strengthening treatment' and 'the lowering treatment' and exercised free choice of doctor accordingly. But the great mass of patients had no views on such subjects. They chose the doctor who seemed to get the best results, and whose fees they knew they could pay, putting a largely uncritical faith in him, and remaining cheerfully ignorant of the fact that of all the

* W. MacMichael: *The Gold-Headed Cane.*

163

mysteriously labelled substances in the gallipots there were perhaps fewer than a dozen with any real curative value.

It was only in the big towns that the professional and social distinctions between physicians, surgeons and apothecaries could be effectively preserved. In thinly populated areas the differences were blurred or lost. A rural doctor had to be able to tackle anything and his versatility made him the more readily acceptable in all walks of life. If he called at the big house to attend a servant he might have to use the tradesman's entrance, but if he was attending a member of the family it would be in order for him to present himself at the front door. Increasingly, the backgrounds of practitioners were becoming mixed. Youngsters from lower middle-class homes performed the drudgery of the apothecary's apprentice, bottling leeches and pounding pills, then broke away and became fashionable physicians or surgeons in London. As against this, young gentlemen who had seemed set for a prosperous medical career in London, having met all the right people during their sojourn at Oxford or Cambridge, would be driven out of the capital through lack of practice and forced to set up as rural practitioners, swallowing their pride as best they could.

In the circles in which Jane Austen moved, apothecaries were well esteemed and one at least was a favourite guest. In the late stages of her last illness Jane wrote: 'Instead of going to town to put myself in the hands of some physician, as I should otherwise have done, I am going to Winchester instead for some weeks, to see what Mr Lyford can do towards re-establishing me in tolerable health.' Mr Lyford, though recognising that there was no future for her, gave her hope. In jest, she wrote, 'Mr Lyford says he will cure me, and if he fails I shall draw up a memorial and lay it before the Dean and Chapter, and have no doubt of redress from that pious, learned and disinterested body.'*

It is clear that already, in late Georgian days, the general practitioners were beginning to assume the status of family friend and counsellor which they consolidated in the Victorian period. They knew the domestic background of their patients and could gauge how much of a man's troubles were due to a shrewish wife or to financial stress. Unlike many physicians, they did not live withdrawn from the vulgar world, intimate only with a few prosperous families.

Many apothecaries now maintained shops only long enough to

* Elizabeth Jenkins: *Jane Austen.*

enable them to find their feet in practice. They would then leave the indignity of counter trade to the new race of chemists and druggists. Thackeray introduces his Dr Pendennis as a humble surgeon-apothecary-midwife operating from a shop in Bath. Then Fortune befriends him; Lady Ribstone is passing in a chair under the charge of a drunken Irishman, who drives the chair-pole 'through the handsomest pink bottle in the surgeon's window.' Pendennis revives the hysterical lady with cinnamon and sal volatile and is soon introduced to fashionable practice. His shop becomes a smart place at which to call, but he has no wish to be known as a shopkeeper. First, he stops selling tooth-brushes and soap, then he closes down the shop altogether, con-tenting himself with a surgery run by a genteel young man. Next he hires a gig with a man to drive him, then a one-horse carriage bearing his family arms. By now he is well on his way to achieving the coveted status of gentleman; but still, when called in by wealthy patronesses, he must wait like any tradesman until they ring for him.

If the light-hearted *Adventures of Mr Ledbury*, by Albert Smith, is any guide, all that distinguished the shop of an apothe-cary from that of a druggist was the framed certificate of the Apothecaries' Society in the window. The stuffed crocodiles and flying fishes of a less sophisticated day were no longer fashionable. Much preferred were elegant arabesques of teeth set out on black velvet tablets, mysterious instruments and chemical apparatus, packets of soda-powders, ready-made pitch plasters, and a white plaster of paris horse in the centre of the window. There would be notices intimating a willingness to bleed, and advertisements of patent medicines. If the practitioner was really impecunious, he might extend his range of goods to include windsor soap, ju-jubes, snuff and even lucifers and lamp-oil. A much dispensed drug, according to Ledbury, was *Pil. Hum.* or *Pilula Humbu-giensis,* being a mixture of yellow soap and liquorice powder.

Between some apothecaries and physicians there was still an unwritten conspiracy to 'soak the patient.' When Henry Acland was in practice in the 1840s in Oxford, he was called in by a country practitioner who afterwards complained: 'When we send for a physician from Oxford we expect the prescription to come to at least a guinea. This comes to eighteen pence.' Acland did his best to break the system.

A brisk traffic in practices had grown up. *The Lancet* in its early issues contained advertisements like these :

'To be disposed of in the vicinity of Hackney, an ELIGIBLE CONCERN with good retail. Rent and Taxes low. This is worth the attention of any Gentleman about to commence practice.'

'A GENTEEL practice producing above £300 per annum—cheap lease to a house—the whole of the good modern furniture—surgery, drugs, etc., to be disposed of for £1,000.'

'To be disposed of A VERY SNUG PRACTICE, average for the last five years of money received, more than £200 a year. No practitioner within nine miles. Eligible for a medical gentleman on half-pay or who has some property. Terms are 100 guineas and premium and surgery, etc., at a valuation.'

'To be disposed of, the PRACTICE of a SURGEON and APOTHECARY situated within three miles south of the Bridges and averaging £400 a year. Premium, including costly modern household furniture, drugs, fixtures, etc., 500 guineas.'

The emphasis in these announcements seems to have been on snugness and gentility, rather than on opportunity and service. There was, however, an appeal to self-sacrifice in the following :

'To Surgeons : The directors of a public institution under the highest patronage are about to APPOINT several MEDICAL VISITERS whose emolument will be but trifling but it is presumed that the appointment will greatly increase the popularity and practice of young Practitioners of talent.'

Shady traffic in practices is hinted at in *The Adventures of Mr Ledbury* :

'A great many "eligible opportunities" presented themselves; but the majority were from individuals whose only property was a brass plate with their name thereon; and with this they migrated about, screwing it upon their doors, until they enticed somebody to buy a practice "capable of great improvement"; when they moved somewhere else and established another with the same view.'

The usual excuse for giving up a practice was 'his health would not allow him to practise any longer.'

The same source sheds satirical light on the practice of canvassing, which was the subject of Wakley's censure. Two practitioners decide to compete for the post of doctor at the local dispensary. At a cost of ten shillings each they insert in the local

A Fashionable Physician, 1841

newspaper grovelling addresses to the governors, promising their devoted offices if they can but have the honour of being selected. One of them hires a gig in order to canvass the governors. Among those to be visited is the landlady of a public-house, who is a wielder of patronage because she has a contract to supply porter to the convalescents. The other aspirant sends small legs of mutton to a number of doubtful voters, describing them as 'part of a small present he had just received from Wales of Llangollen mutton.'

For a shrewd, ironical picture of the medical profession and its pretensions and jealousies, in the days of Wakley's thunder, there is no equal to George Eliot's novel *Middlemarch*. She describes the period—the 1830s—thus:

'The heroic times of copious bleeding and blistering had not yet departed, still less the times of thorough-going theory, when disease in general was called by some bad name, and treated accordingly, without shilly-shally . . . It must be remembered that this was a dark period; and in spite of venerable colleges which used great efforts to secure purity of knowledge by making it scarce, and to exclude error by a rigid exclusiveness in relation to fees and appointments, it happened that very ignorant young gentlemen were promoted in town, and many more got a legal right to practise over large areas in the country.'

Dr Lydgate, the doctor of *Middlemarch*, was the son of a military man, well connected. 'It seemed easier to his guardians to grant his request (to study medicine) by apprenticing him to a country practitioner than to make any objections on the score of family dignity.' His social status disconcerted Lady Chettam, who said : 'One does not expect it in a practitioner of that kind. For my own part, I like a medical man more on a footing with the servants, they are often all the cleverer. I assure you I found poor Hicks's judgments unfailing; I never knew him wrong. He was coarse and butcher-like but he knew my constitution. It was a loss to me, his going off so suddenly.'

Dr Lydgate's ambition was to hold himself free from London intrigue and jealousy. He determined 'to act stoutly on the strength of a recent legal decision and simply prescribe, without dispensing drugs or taking percentage from druggists.' This antagonised his professional brethren, not least because his action tended 'to obscure the limit between his own rank as a general practitioner and that of the physicians,' who were naturally jealous of 'a man who had not been to either of the English universities and enjoyed the absence of anatomical and bedside study there, but came with a libellous pretension to experience in Edinburgh and Paris, where observation might be abundant indeed, but hardly sound.'

One of Dr Lydgate's rivals was Dr Sprague, a latter-day John of Gaddesden, in so far as his study was 'but litel on the Bible.' The town of Middlemarch preferred a strong scepticism in its medical men :

'It is probable that his professional weight was the more believed in, the old-world association of cleverness with the evil principle being still potent in the minds even of lady patients who had the strictest ideas of frilling and sentiment. It was perhaps this negation in the doctor which made his neighbours call him hardheaded and dry-witted ... at all events it is certain that if any medical man had come to Middlemarch with the reputation of having very definite religious views, of being given to prayer, and of otherwise showing an active piety, there would have been a general presumption against his medical skill.'

It is interesting to compare the professional relationships in *Middlemarch* with those in Anthony Trollope's *Dr Thorne,* the period of which is some 20 years later. Unlike Dr Lydgate, Dr Thorne did his own dispensing, as all country practitioners ought to do (according to Trollope) 'if they consulted their own dignity a little less and the comforts of their customers somewhat more.' But in doing so he was much reviled, not only by his public, who felt that he could hardly be a proper doctor, but by his fellow practitioners. It was undignified, they said, that he allowed himself to be seen pounding pills in his shop, instead of 'making experiments philosophically in *materia medica* for the benefit of coming ages.'

Dr Thorne made himself further unpopular with his colleagues by letting it be known that his fee was to be seven shillings and sixpence within a circuit of seven miles, with higher charges for longer distances. The Barchester physicians found this sordid proclamation to be low, mean, unprofessional and democratic. It showed he was always thinking of money, like the apothecary he was ... 'whereas it would have behoved him, as a physician, had he had the feelings of a physician under his hat, to have regarded his own pursuits in a purely philosophical spirit, and to have taken any gain which might have accrued as an accidental adjunct to his station in life. A physician should take his fee without letting his left hand know what his right hand was doing; it should be taken without a thought, without a look, without a move of the facial muscles; the true physician should hardly be aware that the last friendly grasp of the hand had been made more precious by the touch of gold. Whereas that fellow Thorne would lug out half-a-crown from his breeches pocket and give it in change for a ten-shilling piece.'

Dr Thorne's harshest critic was Dr Fillgrave (a name which has done duty for more than one fictional doctor), who was accustomed to meet the great medical baronets in consultation at the houses of the nobility. It was gall to Fillgrave that the old squire of Greshamsbury was willing to treat Thorne as a social equal. One of his most unpleasant moments was to be kept waiting in the house of a *nouveau riche,* 'as though he were some apothecary with a box of leeches in his pocket.'

An initial handicap of Dr Thorne was that he was a bachelor. Explains Trollope : 'Ladies think, and I, for one, think that ladies are quite right in so thinking, that doctors should be married men. All the world feels that a doctor when married acquires some of the attributes of an old woman—he becomes, to a certain extent, a motherly sort of being; he acquires a conversance with women's ways and wants, and loses the wilder and offensive sparks of his virility.'

Dickens, though prolific in passages about medical students, midwives and resurrectionists, has not a great deal of interest to contribute about doctors. But he makes a useful point in *Martin Chuzzlewit,* when he describes the tactful way in which doctor and undertaker, at funerals, ignore each other's existence, however often their professional paths may have crossed.

For the doctor who did not relish private practice, or the exactions of the hospital wards, there were other opportunities. In 1819 John Keats, by now a Licentiate of the Society of Apothecaries, toyed with the idea of becoming surgeon on an East Indiaman, a post which he thought might help to concentrate the mind on its own resources. He doubted whether he could make a conventional doctor. 'I am sure I could not take fees—and yet I should like to do so; it's not worse than writing poems and hanging them up to be fly-blown on the Review shambles.'

Another opening for a doctor was to accompany a person of high estate on his travels. This was rarely the road to wealth, unless the doctor was fortunate enough to make the right contacts at Continental spas. One of the best-known travelling physicians of the post-Waterloo years was Dr Charles Badham, who spent half his professional life on the road, much of it in places where he was more likely to find fleas than fun.

Sir George Lefèvre, who was a travelling physician for 20 years, was advised as a young man to go abroad for his health. In 1819 he was able to attach himself to a consumptive nobleman, haggard but affable. On the journey to Paris, which took six days, Lefèvre was somewhat surprised to find himself sharing a calash with the *femme de chambre.* Hardly had they reached the southern spas when the nobleman died, leaving his physician with nothing to do but reflect on the foolishness of the English who took their phthisis to Montpellier and Pau, when the prudent folk of those towns, if their lungs were affected, were quick to move elsewhere. There is little doubt that many wealthy consumptives were induced to set off on long uncomfortable journeys for the supposed good of their health, when they might just as beneficially have stayed at home and opened their windows.

Sir George found himself another master in a Polish aristocrat, with whom he travelled Europe for some years, then practised in St Petersburg. His knighthood was a reward for services to the British Embassy, where he doubtless discharged his duties more conscientiously than did Charles Lever, the novelist, in his self-appointed post of physician to the British Embassy in Brussels. In Germany Sir George did not fail to note the sharp practices indulged in by some of his colleagues who established themselves for the season beside alien springs. At one spa patients were induced to bathe in champagne. Sir George tried the experiment for himself—'a luxury of the first order . . . delicious to lie still and feel the bubbling as the carbonic acid gas escaped all round.' He does not say whether it was a vintage wine.*

At about the same time that Lefèvre set off with his ill-starred nobleman, a former naval surgeon called James Clark was conducting a consumptive patient to the South of France and Switzerland. Dr Clark had an obsession about the effects of climate on disease. Wherever he stopped he noted down statistics of temperature, humidity and wind and wove them into elaborate theories. He is remembered, alas, not for his climatic researches but for the scandal he precipitated in the English Court in 1839. At a German spa he met Prince Leopold, future King of the Belgians, who secured him an appointment to the Duchess of Kent. It was a notable elevation for a naval surgeon, but perhaps Sir James—as he now became—fortified himself by the knowledge that a one-time Portsmouth assistant surgeon and man-midwife (Sir William Knighton) had become Keeper of the Privy Purse to the previous sovereign. All went well at Court until the changing contours of Lady Flora Hastings, Lady of the Bedchamber to the Duchess, led the Court gossipers to whisper that she was pregnant. Lady Flora was already Sir James' patient; yet he was induced to ask her whether she was secretly married, and to conduct a superficial examination of her person.

* *The Life of a Travelling Physician.*

Indignantly, she denied the charge and gave Sir James only the most limited facilities for investigation. To the Court inquisitors he admitted that there seemed at least a *prima facie* case for supposing Lady Flora to be with child. The circle of gossip widened and eventually Lord Melbourne, who should have known better, directed Clark and a colleague to conduct a full examination of Lady Flora. This showed that the alarm was a false one.

Then the storm broke. Lady Flora was vindicated and it was her physician who was in disgrace. The politest thing said about Sir James was that, as a sailor, he was somewhat out of his depth. His mistake, according to the ethics of his profession, was in not reserving his loyalty to his patient, but divulging secrets to those who, no matter what their social position, had no right to the information. Lady Flora died soon afterwards of an abdominal disease, supposedly accelerated by humiliation. Sir James's private practice suffered, but not his position at Court.

The controversy over whether men should act as midwives still broke out sporadically. In 1827, after numerous instances had come to light of mothers dying at the hands of self-taught *accoucheurs,* there was talk of making all man-midwives sit examinations. The Royal Colleges, however, were still unwilling to take official notice of man-midwifery. As *The Lancet* tartly observed, physicians condescended to prescribe for colic and surgeons to examine cut fingers, but both considered childbirth to be below their notice. Sir Anthony Carlisle, a member of the council of the Royal College of Surgeons, wrote to *The Times* in 1827 in an effort to induce Sir Robert Peel to put an end, once and for all, to the practice of man-midwifery, which was kept going, he said, only to satisfy 'the prevalent vice of avarice' in the profession. 'Why are we to licence adventurers who may seek notoriety by desperate acts, often involving manslaughter— operative acts the moral propriety of which is very doubtful and the time and the methods for performing them still subjects for rancorous disputes?' Country surgeons and apothecaries were now being driven to adopt this 'humiliating office'; the number of women practitioners had been so reduced that paupers in many places were being delivered by apprentice boys under 16. Happily, however, 'no London physician educated at Oxford or

Cambridge has yet condescended to be a man-midwife.' For what it was worth, Sir Anthony passed on a rumour that 'our changeable neighbours' in Paris were already tiring of 'their fashionable freak.' He believed that only one woman in a thousand needed help other than that which any moderately experienced woman could safely give. 'Even so late as the time of the illustrious mother of his present Majesty, that exemplary Queen was personally attended by good Mrs Draper without misadventures; whereas the contrary result under male management in the fatal affair of Princess Charlotte will be long remembered.'

This was a reference to the death in 1817 of the Princess and her child after she had been allowed to exhaust herself in an unusually long, unassisted labour. Sir Richard Croft, her obstetrician, had an aversion to using instruments. Soon after the tragedy, which caused a public outcry, he shot himself.

Even when Queen Victoria's reign was well advanced, man-midwives were still being attacked. Dr John Stevens published in 1862 his *Man-Midwifery Exposed*, dedicated hopefully to the Society for the Suppression of Vice. 'Husbands, beware the man-midwife. Regard him as the most subtle and venomous reptile that crawls upon this earth,' warned Dr Stevens. He did his best to convince husbands that they were being cuckolded by the fiend with the forceps. Why had they not the moral courage to stand out against a practice which was 'a fruitful source of seduction, adultery and prostitution?' He published a round-up of quotations from like-minded moralists, one of them being Count Buffon, who considered that 'every situation which produces an internal blush is real prostitution.' According to a work called *Hints to Husbands*, male-midwifery was a upas tree which 'treacherously, mysteriously and silently distils the poison of its presence deep into the sanctuaries of human life.' Poets too had been suborned to attack the man-midwife:

'Not even the Nubian by the harem door
Dare show his face until the birth is o'er.
Talk of the sanctity of married life—
Nation of fools! to thus degrade the wife!
A natural process for the nonce becomes
An "operation" costing goodly sums;

> While all is managed with parade and fuss,
> And drugs enough to drench an omnibus.'

Dr Stevens was particularly scandalised by the illustrations to a manual of midwifery, one of those works which, in the memorable words of Richard Gordon, show 'nonchalant babies being rescued from disquieting predicaments.'* The operators depicted in these illustrations were male. 'If such plates are necessary,' said Dr Stevens, 'why not introduce women instead of men?'

* *Doctor in the House.*

XVII

AGAINST THE STOPWATCH

THE surgeons were passing through a frustrating phase. In spite of the limitless orgies of dissection in which they were supposed to have been indulging, many of them had inadequate knowledge of the human frame. John Bell in his *Principles of Surgery* (1826), has an alarming picture of the novice surgeon at work, 'faltering and disconcerted, hesitating at every step . . . agitated, miserable and trembling.' He continues :

'We see untaught men operating upon their fellow creatures in cases of life and death, in aneurism, lithotomy, hernia, trepan, without the slightest knowledge of the anatomy of the parts . . . feeling in the wound for things they do not understand, holding consultations amid the cries of the patient, or even retiring to consult about his case, while he lies bleeding in great pain and awful expectation; and thus, while they are making ungenerous struggles to gain a false reputation, they are incurring reproaches which attend them through life.'

Bell deprecated the passion for operations which had characterised some of the surgeons of an earlier day—'as the cutting off of limbs, the searing of arteries, the sewing of bowels, the trepanning of skulls round and round, and all the excesses and horrors of surgery.' He deplored too, the vogue for 'mere whiffling agility' and the emphasis on speed 'merely to gratify the fools who estimate dexterity by no other criterion than the stopwatch.' A surgeon, he said, should cut swiftly when all is safe, slowly and cautiously when there is danger, 'yet we every day see surgeons cutting out harmless tumours with affected and cruel deliberation, and in the same hour plunging a gorget among the viscera with unrelenting rashness.'

No doubt there was a certain amount of exhibitionism in the operating theatre. Yet a surgeon aware of the torture he was inflicting on an unanaesthetised patient could hardly be blamed for working with utmost speed and taking pride in saying to his audience, like Robert Liston, 'Now, gentlemen, time me.' Liston, who was said to have had a wrist strong enough to screw off a man's head, could amputate a leg at the thigh, single-handed, compressing the artery with his left hand, 'in as few seconds as a first-class sprinter takes to run a hundred yards.' Another surgeon was reputed to have taken off an arm at the shoulder while his colleague turned for a pinch of snuff.

This rapidity of action makes it slightly, but only very slightly, easier to comprehend the stoicism of those whose limbs were removed while they were fully conscious. Very occasionally, an impressionable patient might be put into a trance, in the fashion popularised by Mesmer, before undergoing a minor operation, but for the majority there was no such release. Flesh might be numbed by tourniquets, or by chilling, but neither rum nor opiate sufficed wholly to still the imagination of the victim, especially if he listened to the surgeon telling his audience what he proposed to do. Soldiers and sailors, born to hardship, could face the ordeal of amputation more stolidly than the delicately nurtured, allowing their limbs to be lopped with little more than a grimace. At Corunna Sir David Baird was injured in his left arm near the shoulder, in such a way that the ordinary method of amputation was impossible and it was necessary to remove the arm from the socket. Baird sat at a table, on which he rested his right arm. Only when the left arm was finally severed from the body did he make a single exclamation of pain. Lord Raglan's cry to the surgeon at Waterloo has become a legend—'Here, don't take that arm away until I have taken the ring off the finger!' General Sir Harry Smith hobbled round with a ball embedded under the Achilles tendon of his foot. When the time for operating came he cocked his leg on the table and said to the surgeons, 'There it is, slash away.' The ball was jagged and the fibres had partly grown into it. Thus, the five-minute operation involved both extraction and dissection. A pair of forceps was broken in the process. There were examples of equal courage among the lower ranks, but there was rarely a chronicler standing by. To keep the whole business in perspective, it is worth remembering, as one chronicler has pointed out, that the pain from the initial incision from lithotomy was probably no greater than that sustained from one blow of the lash—and an errant soldier might be ordered to receive 500.

So much for soldiers. But women, too, showed a daunting fortitude under the knife. A not infrequent operation was amputation, or partial amputation, of the breast, a task which was made no easier for the surgeon before Sir Astley Cooper's day because modesty allowed only the minimum area of the bosom to be exposed. There is a description of such an operation in that best-selling tale, *Rab And His Friends,* by Dr John Brown, of Biggar. The patient was an elderly Scotswoman identified only as Ailie. Young Brown, then a clerk at Minto House Hospital, Edinburgh, himself put up the notice, 'An Operation Today,' which served to pack the theatre with eager, noisy students. As Ailie walked in with her husband *and dog* one glance at her simple dignity was enough to reduce the audience to silence. The husband withdrew to a corner of the room and held the dog's head between his knees. Stretched on the table, Ailie took a quick look at her husband, closed her eyes and held young Brown's hand. During the operation the dog sensed that his mistress was suffering cruelly and gave an occasional angry yelp. His master had to hold him firmly under restraint. Ailie's face showed what she was suffering but she remained still and silent. When it was over and the wound was dressed she stepped down from the table, turned to the surgeon and students, then curtseyed, begging their pardon if she had behaved ill. The students wept like children. Ailie died shortly afterwards; she had waited too long for the surgeon to have a fair chance of saving her.

Another description of a breast operation, though the word breast is never mentioned, appears in Samuel Warren's *Diary of a Late Physician* (1832), one of the first popular works purporting to give glimpses from a doctor's private records. In Warren's account, the patient, a naval officer's wife, awaits the surgeon in her home, sitting in a chair in a white muslin dressing gown with an Indian shawl over her shoulders. She has sent the servants out of the house. The medical attendants pour her a glass of port, but she barely touches the glass with her lips. One of the attendants removes the shawl, and the patient then displaces as much of the dress as is necessary. She looks fixedly over her shoulder at a letter from her husband, which is held there for the purpose. At the first incision she gives a convulsive shudder, and seems likely to faint, but after that she barely moves a limb or sighs. When it is over she proposes to walk to her bedroom, but is told she must be carried. Only when she is in bed does she swoon.

Warren's style is melodramatic and often nauseous, and his book did not please the medical profession; but there is no doubt that the operation he describes was commonly carried out in very much that fashion. It was after watching the agony of a Highland woman undergoing a breast amputation that young James Simpson left the classroom in horror and went straight to Parliament House, Edinburgh, to seek work as a writer's clerk. Then he changed his mind and returned, saying, 'Can nothing be done to make operations less painful?'

The surgeon who dominated the early decades of the nineteenth century was handsome Sir Astley Cooper, whose audacities in the realm of anatomy have already been described. He had probably the largest practice any surgeon had yet enjoyed, and it was his boast that he had educated 800 English surgeons. Over and above, he inherited John Hunter's passion for dissecting unusual mammals. Once he acquired a dead elephant and had it carted to his house at St Mary Axe, where he was unable to get it in an outhouse. A big crowd watched him dissect it in the open air, with the aid of his eager students.

Sir Astley's baronetcy was the prize for removing, at short notice, a small tumour from the head of George IV. It seems a trivial service to have been rewarded by a hereditary honour, but the risk of fatal complications was high. 'I was thunderstruck and felt giddy at the idea of my fate hanging upon such an event,' said Sir Astley, who would have been far happier removing a trunk from an elephant. The patient was fit enough afterwards to make a bad pun, for on enquiring the name of the tumour and being told 'a steatome,' he expressed the hope that it would stay at home in future and not bother him.

In his first year of practice Sir Astley earned five guineas. In his most successful year, he is said to have touched £21,000, his average being nearer £10,000. One of his biggest single fees was received from a West Indian merchant whom he relieved of a kidney stone. After handing his physicians 300 guineas each, the patient threw his nightcap at Sir Astley, saying, 'There, young man, put that in your pocket.' Sir Astley, with a joke about pocketing the insult, extracted a draft for 1,000 guineas and returned the nightcap, saying he would not like to rob the patient of so useful an article.

A day in the life of Sir Astley Cooper was fully as exacting as a day in the life of John Hunter. According to Bransby Cooper, he rose at six, even in winter, dissected until half-past seven or eight, when he had his hair dressed (he wore it powdered with a queue). Then at half-past eight he began to interview his free patients. His breakfast consisted of two rolls, followed by a quick glance at the newspaper. After that he received patients in his consulting room until one. (His servant Charles gave gentlemen preference over ladies, whose time he rated as of little importance; but he could be bribed.) At one o'clock Sir Astley left in his coach, sometimes going out of the house by the back door in order not to run the gaunlet of the disappointed and irate patients still waiting to see him. A very different atmosphere awaited him at Guy's. The steps would be thronged with as many as 100 persons—apprentices, students, hospital staff—who would greet him with great animation and jostle for his recognition. The cavalcade would then tour the wards, Sir Astley courteously explaining any interesting cases. Next he would go to the operating theatre to lecture for perhaps an hour, then out by way of the dissecting room to tour his professional circuit until half-past five or later. After dinner he might fall asleep for ten minutes, but often he would set off again to the hospital to deliver another lecture or to address a medical society. He would be home again by midnight. It was a great day for a great man, who did not conceal that he enjoyed his popularity.

The way in which Sir Astley Cooper was presented with his 1,000 guineas fee might or might not have commended itself to John Abernethy, whose crustiness inspired as many stories as did that of Radcliffe. According to Clement Carlyon, 'the delicate contrivances of his patients to put a fee into his hands used greatly to annoy him, as if they might not as well, he said, have set the guinea openly on the table, instead of appearing to be engaged in a clandestine transaction of which they were ashamed and which they thus rendered embarrassing to both parties.'*

Babbling women were the bane of Abernethy's life. He would interrupt them by ordering them to open their mouths, then tell them 'Now shut your mouth and keep it shut.' One tale is of a lady who called on him with a cut finger. The dialogue went:

First day: ABERNETHY : Cut?
                PATIENT : Bite.
                ABERNETHY : Dog?
                PATIENT : Parrot.

* *Early Years and Late Reflections.*

ABERNETHY : Go home and poultice it.

Second day: ABERNETHY : Better?

PATIENT : Worse.

ABERNETHY : Go home and poultice it again.

Third day: ABERNETHY : Better?

PATIENT : Well.

ABERNETHY : You are the most sensible woman I ever met. Good-bye. Get out.*

Another woman patient brought Abernethy her daughter, who found it difficult to breathe when taking exercise and after meals. Picking up a pair of scissors, Abernethy slashed her stays from top to bottom, then told her to walk about for ten minutes. After ten minutes she was 'better'; after ten more minutes, 'quite well.'†

Occasionally he over-reached himself. One woman told him, 'I had heard of your rudeness before I came here, sir, but I did not expect this.' When he tossed her a prescription she said, 'What am I to do with this?' The reply was 'Anything you like. Put it in the fire if you please.' She took him at his word and burned the paper, laid her fee on the table and swept out. Abernethy pursued her, asking her to take her fee back or to accept another prescription, but she refused. Another time, when consulted by a young baronet, Sir David Scott, he scoffed : 'I suppose you are an idle man-about-town, perhaps an officer in the Guards.' After asking a few questions he gave a prescription and told the patient to buy his book. Sir David laid down the fee, then picked up the prescription, crumpled it and tossed it away. When Abernethy demanded the reason, he said, 'Because you have not gone into my case.' Calling him back, Abernethy carried out a careful examination, saying, 'I cannot tell you with what nonsense I have to bear from the fools who come here after my advice.'‡

At least Abernethy was no respecter of rank. 'I suppose you know who I am?' inquired the Duke of York when the surgeon greeted him with hands in pockets. 'I suppose I do. What of it?' was the reply. His advice to the Royal patient was : 'Cut off the supplies, as the Duke of Wellington did in his campaigns, and the enemy will leave the citadel.'§

Abernethy was sometimes criticised because he sent patients away to buy one of his books, specifying the page to be studied.

* John Timbs: *Doctor and Patient.*   † *Ibid.*
‡ T. Gordon Hake: *Memoirs of 80 Years.*
§ Sir D'Arcy Power: *Selected Writings.*

His loyal biographer, George MacIlwain, thinks this was an
excellent idea, and suggests that a doctor should issue to his
patients brief printed digests describing the characteristics of the
better-known diseases. Surgeon and patient should understand
each other perfectly on general principles, says MacIlwain, and
quotes his master as saying : 'If a medical man thought he had
done his duty when he had written a prescription and a patient
regarded his as fulfilled when he had swallowed it, they were both
deceived.'

For all his cantankerousness, Abernethy was sound at heart.
Often he declined fees when in doubt about the patient's means.
After a lengthy treatment of a half-pay lieutenant who had
cracked his skull, he told the patient to come back and talk about
the fee when he became a general. His frailties, says Clement
Carlyon, 'had nothing to do with the real colour of his heart.'
Unlike some of his contemporaries he refused to perform any
operation which he would not have been willing to undergo himself.

Another memoirist recalls that Abernethy had a great scorn
for the way in which the Church endowed its livings. 'Imagine
the great profession of physic endowed, and its baronets, arch-
doctors of Canterbury and York, giving away livings to their
nephews and nieces : the doctor of St James, £1,000 per annum;
the doctor of St Giles, £150.'* Physic was not without its lucky
nephews, as Thomas Wakley never tired of pointing out; but
Abernethy's jibe was a legitimate one.

Among lesser lights of the profession a roughness of manner
was still being cultivated. It served to earn surgeons a reputation
for hard-heartedness, but their scorn of gentleness and their foulness of tongue were to some extent an affectation and an expres-
sion of contempt for the prissy ways of physicians. The historian
of Guy's, H. C. Cameron, relates that in the 1840s, whereas the
physicians in that hospital moved gravely about the wards, the
surgeons would stamp noisily up to the beds, still with their hats
on.* The rudeness was not all affectation, for many surgeons
were by nature and upbringing uncouth.

This type of surgeon would pass away only when the torture
and the stench of gangrene passed from the hospitals. For, despite
all the new physiological knowledge, surgery was inhibited by

* T. Gordon Hake: *Memoirs of 80 Years.*
* *Mr Guy's Hospital.*

lack of two prerequisites : anaesthesia and asepsis. Not till 1846 was the first operation under ether conducted in Britain—by Robert Liston. ('This Yankee dodge, gentlemen, beats mesmerism hollow.') Then came Sir James Simpson's experiments with chloroform. The victory over pain allowed surgeons to cut more adventurously and more slowly, but the net, and notorious, result was that more patients died from the seemingly inevitable gangrene.

When Sir James Simpson began to use chloroform to ease the pangs of childbirth (the first child to be born in this fashion was christened Anaesthesia) he stirred the pools of religious bigotry to their ugliest deeps. The outcry created was almost comparable to that which greeted the first man-midwives. Chloroform was the devil's decoy. With its aid, doctors were frustrating the will of God, who had ordained of woman : 'In sorrow thou shalt bring forth children.' Happily, Sir James was a man who could bandy texts with the best of them. He reminded his critics that God, before conjuring Eve from Adam's rib, had put Adam into a deep sleep.

Many doctors were unhappy about the use of chloroform. One of them, quoted by Simpson's biographer, said that the profession was taking a profound risk in seeking to induce patients 'to pass into a state of existence the *secrets* of which we know so little at present. I say *secrets* because from the dark chambers of that existence we have as yet had presented to us but fitful and indistinct gleams, and these so little to encourage the gaze of a thoughtful and modest eye, that I should be sorry to expose any human being unnecessarily.' What right (argued this doctor) had the profession to urge their patients to let go of that capacity for thought and reason that God had given them and become trembling cowards?*

Other objections to the use of chloroform were that it would facilitate the committing of crime and of offences against women, and would increase the risk of persons being buried alive. Opposition continued strongly until 1853, when Queen Victoria allowed herself to be anaesthetised in labour. No one cared to accuse the Queen of being in league with Satan. *The Lancet,* however claimed to have inside knowledge that the report was untrue and said that no responsible medical adviser would have dreamed of jeopardising the Queen's life in this wanton manner. It was an

* J. Duns: *Memoirs of Sir James Simpson.*

ingenious way of criticising what could not otherwise have been criticised.

By mid-century the passion for bleeding had largely subsided. James Syme as a young surgeon in Edinburgh Royal Infirmary during the 1820s was once ordered to bleed 65 ounces from a patient in a day, followed by 35 ounces the next day; a further 20 ounces on a later occasion finished the patient. Syme's prescription of porter and beef steak for another patient was angrily countermanded by a senior who ordered bleeding instead. This patient also died.* As a treatment for shock, bleeding was slow to be abandoned. At the draw in the last State lottery, in 1826, impecunious surgeons haunted the Guildhall, ready to lance those members of the public who might be overwhelmed on hearing their numbers called.

Apprentices to surgeon-apothecaries were expected to maintain a jar of leeches in good fettle, ready for emergencies. The creatures were kept in a glass jar topped with porous cloth. Periodically, the apprentice rubbed them between his palms, half a dozen at a time, in order to remove the slime. If, before application, they were briskly towelled they were supposed to suck with more avidity. They spent long periods of extreme hunger and sometimes, despairing of pasturing on a poet's brow or a bishop's ankle, they would resort to cannibalism. A healthy leech was expected to be able to take in half an ounce of blood before being gorged. The charge to the patient was usually sixpence a leech.

* Robert Paterson: *Memorials of the Life of James Syme.*

XVIII

OUT OF STEP

WHILE medicine and surgery were beating at half-open doors, the quacks flourished exceedingly, thanks in great measure to the growing number of newspapers, hungry for advertisements.

One of the most audacious and, for a while, successful operators was John St John Long, a young Irishman of undistinguished antecedents, who brought notoriety to Harley Street in a day when that thoroughfare could boast fewer than half a dozen brass plates of physicians. There are some who will say that the aura of quackery has never quite lifted from Harley Street; but it is certain that no latter-day consultant has ever looked out on such a jostling of carriage trade at his door.

Long claimed a special talent for the cure of tuberculosis, either by the application of corrosive ointments or by the breathing of medicated vapours. In one room he had two huge inhalers from which radiated a number of flexible tubes with mouthpieces. These were snatched from each other by excited women anxious to draw in the healing airs. As a high-class germ exchange, this room probably had no rival. In another room the quack was busy at the congenial task of rubbing the bosoms of his female patients. Sometimes, after his ministrations, their flesh looked as if he had lit a fire on it. One day in 1830 Long regretfully bade good-bye to his clientèle and journeyed, in some state, to the Old Bailey, there to be tried on a charge of causing a patient's death. Scores of his fashionable followers crowded the court and made no secret of their desire to see him acquitted. He was fined 'only £250' (as the *Annual Register* said), no great setback to a man reputedly earning £10,000 a year, and was driven away by Lord Sligo. His subsequent increased success went to bear out Smollett's dictum that there is nothing like a whiff of malpractice to bring prosperity to a practitioner. Long was brought to trial again on a

James Morison, The Hygeist. He died reaching for his Universal Pill

charge of 'feloniously assaulting the person' of a naval captain's wife, who also died after he had treated her, but this time he was acquitted, and elegant ladies shook his hand. In 1834 Long succumbed to the disease he had professed to cure, declining to adopt his own treatment, but deeming the secret worth leaving as a legacy to his brother. Grateful patients built him a worthy monument at Kensal Green. His career is a reminder that a love of quackery is not an exclusive addiction of the poor and ignorant.

The fame of Sir Astley Cooper encouraged many adventurers to trade on his name, or on approximations of it. Bransby Cooper tells of the activities of the 'Ashley Cooper set' who fleeced the unwary in their headquarters in Charlotte Street, Blackfriars. A negro servant would lead the caller into an imposing room in which sat three, four or five grave-looking, robed gentlemen whose wigs served to disguise as well as to impress. One of them, enthroned above the others, was presumed to be Dr Ashley Cooper. He asked the questions and the others took notes, then all held a consultation. By now the patient had begun to suspect that he would not receive the benefit of five men's advice for a single fee, and he was right. One aggrieved victim picketed the premises, warning off all callers, until he was given his money back. The Ashley Cooper set thrived despite exposures, just as the plagiarist-in-chief of Dickens thrived on his *Oliver Twist* and *Martin Guzzlewit*.

Among advertising quacks, a pre-eminent performer was James Morison, the Scot who originated the Universal Pill. He called himself 'The Hygeist' and had an imposing headquarters called 'The British College of Health.' His pill was harmless compared with some of those of an earlier generation. Morison was a great derider of doctors and performed some useful service in condemning the practice of bleeding. If a patient died there could be only two reasons : he had not taken Morison's pills, or alternatively had not taken enough of them. In ten years he paid a grateful Government £60,000 in stamp duties. Unlike John St John Long he had courage to take his own medicine and is said to have been reaching for another bottle when he expired.

Bitterly condemned by the orthodox of the profession were those new systems of treatment which masqueraded as science. The vogue for hydropathy, or water cure, had been growing steadily, in spite of much mockery, since the end of the eighteenth century. Writing in 1827 William Wadd said : 'At this present time at Strathpeffer, a sort of Scotch Harrogate, the fashionables inhabit small cabins and for the sake of the wonder-working "mineral" the pigs and the patients are found in the same hotel.'* A century before, he recalled, ladies and gentlemen had shared hovels at Buxton.

Luxury was only just round the corner. In the 'fifties and 'sixties, the country began to be studded by new temples of health called hydropathics, at the gates of which the *beau monde* clamoured for admission. Within, they were subjected to cold affusions, water douches, sweating baths, shower baths and plunge baths, and were put on a diet of water or milk, and bread. These rigours were not enough for Sir Francis Burdett, a robust believer in the new science, who used to ride out on horseback enveloped in cold, wet towels, a form of exercise which, in the view of his family and of posterity, accelerated his death.

An anonymous doctor who published a pamphlet *Quacks and Quackery* in 1844 deplored that his more simple-minded colleagues were becoming addicted to this ridiculous cult initiated by a rude Silesian peasant, with all its retinue of 'foreign shampooers, tooth-scrapers and toe-trimmers.' How exquisitely degrading, he said, for a man of liberal education to advertise himself as superintendent of a wash-house, to boast that he had *studied* under Vincenz Priessnitz, to waste his talents in learning how to scrub! One physician who succumbed unreservedly to the cult of hydropathy was Dr James Manby Gully, who has some claim to be called the father of modern Malvern. He ended his career in disgrace, his name having been linked ineluctably with the wife of that mysteriously murdered barrister, Charles Bravo.

Not a few businessmen burned their fingers in the erection of hydropathics, for the cult went the way of all cults. Many of the eyesores they erected degenerated into luxury hotels, in which water was merely a convenient substance for the dilution of whisky. Luxury had corrupted Sparta.

The profession's most powerful scorn, perhaps, was reserved for the practisers of homoeopathy, an upstart system of medicine based on the ancient theory of 'a hair of the dog that bit you.' This science, too, was developed by a messianic practitioner from Central Europe, Dr Samuel Hahnemann. His basic principle was that a disease should be treated by drugs that can produce in a healthy person symptoms similar to that of the disease. It was the

* *Mems, Maxims and Memoirs.*

homoeopaths' faith in the infinite dilutability of their medicines that roused such sardonic derision among the doctors, and bitter resentment among struggling druggists. The anonymous pamphleteer mentioned above said that administering a homoeopathic medicine was like seeking to put out a raging fire in a house 'by slily injecting at one of its windows, once in every few minutes, a spoonful of water containing a globule (tenth dilution) of a solution of a grain of some suffocative chemical substance.' Witty doctors vied with each other to supply analogies of this kind. One thought that the homoeopathic treatment was akin to putting a cupful of medicine in the Thames at Windsor and taking out a spoonful at Southend. Sir James Simpson said that if the entire population of the world (say, 900,000,000) lived 6,000 years and each swallowed a decillionth of a grain every month they would still not have finished a single grain. Dr John Paris showed that a dose which an English practitioner would have given to a suckling would, in the hands of a disciple of Hahnemann, be sufficient to cure the inhabitants of a whole solar system. It was not medicine, he said, but mysticism. According to Oliver Wendell Holmes, homoeopathy was 'a mingled mass of perverse ingenuity, of tinsel erudition, of imbecile credulity and of artful misrepresentation'; but it had become encysted on the body medical and was carried 'as quietly as an old wen.'*

Hahnemann, who had been hounded out of Leipzig by the apothecaries, made his teaching no more acceptable by claiming that all other systems of medicine were fraudulent, and by describing all doctors who did not subscribe to his theories as 'allopaths.' The controversy rattled the easily rattled medical world as the Brunonian doctrines had done, and professional bodies were greatly exercised to decide whether an orthodox practitioner should, or should not, speak to a homoeopath. As an example, in 1851 the Medical Society of London decided that its members could not 'honourably hold any professional communion with homoeopathists.' Two Scots universities refused degrees to students who would not pledge themselves to abjure this heresy. Most of the profession needed no warning; they were solidly against 'globulism.' It was unusual to find a medical writer like J. G. Millingen admitting that 'while we reject his (Hahnemann's) errors, great and important truths beam from the chaotic clouds that shroud his wanderings.'† It has become customary to say

* *Medical Essays*.   † *Curiosities of Medical Experience*.

that, whatever one thinks about homoeopathy, its advent did much to wean mankind from the excessive dosage of physic to which it had been so long addicted. A very long time was to elapse before homoeopaths and 'allopaths' were able to dwell in something like comity, tolerating if not respecting each other's beliefs.

The other highly controversial practice of the period was mesmerism, with its sub-cult of mesmero-phrenology. Anton Mesmer, who died in the year of Waterloo, claimed to have discovered a new natural force, animal magnetism, with the aid of which susceptible patients could be cured of various *malaises*. Millingen described it, rather unsympathetically, as a system of titillating 'nervous and enthusiastic females, who seek for some saving clauses in a pact between vice and virtue, depravity and religion.' Interest in Mesmer's methods was periodically revived and London was much entertained by quacks who demonstrated their various forms of mesmerism and somnambulism. In mesmero-phrenology the demonstrator threw his dupe, or accomplice, into a trance and then transmitted from his fingers a 'magnetic fluid' into the other's brain. He was then ready to excite any phrenological 'bump' the audience cared to nominate. The dupe called on to demonstrate veneration would genuflect, roll his eyes upwards and recite the Lord's Prayer, if he knew it; to illustrate combativeness, he would assume a prize-fighting attitude; to show acquisitiveness he would make a clumsy attempt at theft; and to display benevolence he would make someone a loan of a shilling, reclaiming it as soon as he was in his right mind.

The doctors could afford to smile at such naïve entertainments but they were not amused when they heard of the mesmeric experiments being conducted on patients in University College Hospital, London, at the instigation of the senior physician, Dr John Elliotson, who had brought over Baron Dupotet from Paris to help him. Elliotson's most-publicised experiments were conducted with the aid of two impressionable, and perhaps deceitful, young women, Elizabeth and Jane O'Key, whom he threw into a state of somnambulism and then led round the room apparently with a metal magnet. Elizabeth was credited with being able to sense the presence of a dying person in the wards, a power which seems unlikely to have endeared her to the patients at large. A demonstration with the O'Keys was held in the house of Thomas Wakley, who was decidedly not impressed. Dr J. F. Clarke.

describing the 'bewildering episode' of 1837–8 at University College Hospital, says that clinical clerks nearly wore themselves out pawing the patients, and learned doctors took part in experiments to ascertain whether persons could be suborned by the reflection of mesmeric rays in a hand-mirror at 60 yards or more.* Eventually pressure was put on Professor Elliotson to resign from the hospital, which he had rendered too notorious. Later he opened a mesmeric hospital of his own.

It was, as Dr Clarke says, a bewildering episode; but Elliotson's fate did not deter other investigators. James Braid, surgeon to the Earl of Hopetoun's miners in Lanark, wrote and lectured much on the subject, stripping it of many of its fallacies and showing that the state of trance could be self-induced. Experiments went on in many countries. In the 'eighties Dr Josef Breuer of Vienna hypnotised a hysterical female patient who was able to recall long-distant incidents apparently associated with her disordered state. One of the colleagues whom Breuer told of this development was Dr Sigmund Freud, who, forsaking hypnotism, encouraged his patients to dredge up old memories by the method of 'free association.' The resulting cult of psycho-analysis, with its powerful emphasis on sex, was to stir the *odium medicum* as never before.

* *Autobiographical Recollections.*

XIX

ENTER THE M.O.H.

In the year that Queen Victoria assumed the throne, a newly-fledged practitioner, Dr George Walker, set up his surgery in Drury Lane, London. It was, as he soon found out, one of the least salubrious spots in Britain. On all sides he was surrounded by neglected churchyards and ramshackle crypts, all stuffed to overflowing with the rotting and unregarded dead—the dead for whom his fellow citizens professed such reverence when the surgeons proposed to cut them up.

Dr Walker rebelled at the stench. He also rebelled at the attitude of those who dismissed him as just another ambitious doctor trying to draw publicity to himself. Unabashed, he wrote a book called *Gatherings from Graveyards* (1839) as full of charnel-house horrors as any of the penny dreadfuls of the day. This, and his later writings, earned him the nickname of 'Grave-yard' Walker, but it was one he was proud to bear. He remained unshaken in his belief that the dead ought not to be allowed to poison the living.

The healthy imagination shies at its fences when it tries to take in Dr Walker's London in those days of intra-mural burial. Basically, the problem was that an ever-expanding population was trying to bury its dead in a limited number of churchyards, cellars and death-pits which were already stacked deep with corruption. Urged on by rapacious owners, grave-diggers in a state of chronic drunkenness turned over the churchyards like dung heaps, clearing away partly decomposed corpses to make room for the newly dead, and the unwanted bones and skulls were either consigned to pits or sent to the northern towns to be pounded up for fertiliser. Iron coffins were unpopular because they delayed the rate of turnover : what right had a man to a permanent plot when the dead were queueing ? The stench which

overhung these operations was only a concentrated version of
that which already filled the city's churches, sitting as they did on
reeking vaults.

In St Clement's Lane were four burial grounds within 200
yards, plus numerous slaughter-houses. Under St Clement's
Church was the 'Rector's vault,' in which candles stayed lit no
longer than a few seconds. No one dared enter it until the stench
had been allowed to dilute itself over the neighbourhood for two
or three days. St Clement's, however, was a temple of fragrance
compared with the Enon Chapel, a Baptist conventicle in St
Clement's Lane. Its congregation were separated only by shrunken
boards from a cellar 59 feet by 28, with a capacity, by Dr
Walker's reckoning, of 1,200 bodies at most. In 16 years between
10,000 and 12,000 bodies went into this 'dust hole,' as the under-
takers' men jokingly described it. Most of them passed out again,
it was suspected, by way of a sewer which, by happy accident,
ran through the centre of the cellar. The stove of 'the reverend
proprietor' was kept going on coffin wood. Children who attended
Sunday school in the chapel were covered with black flies from
the burst coffins, but the proprietor continued to circularise parents
in the area in an attempt to increase the size of his classes.
Originally, this not unlucrative Golgotha had been founded in an
attempt to preserve the dead from the resurrectionists. Eight years
after Dr Walker drew public attention to it, it was still there,
rotting vigorously; but at this point 'Graveyard' Walker obtained
possession of the cellar and, at his own expense, shifted its stacks
of cadavers to the cemetery at Norwood.

'Graveyard' Walker fought more than apathy. He was attacked
by those who said he was interfering with a pious practice long
hallowed by Christian usage. What heartless wickedness, to try to
prevent a man being buried with his forefathers! Anyway, how
could our Gran (God rest her soul!) give anybody cholera?

The doctor did not fight alone. He had the support of that
hard-hitting reformer Edwin Chadwick, whose *Report on Intra-
Mural Interments* was the most emetic publication of 1843.
Reform was staved off by the usual clash of interests, but at
length, in 1850, was passed an Act which strictly limited the
practice of intra-mural burial. This did not mean that the
churches of London became sweet-smelling overnight. In 1859,
when the surgeon-zoologist Frank Buckland began his search for
the body of John Hunter in the vaults of St Martin-in-the-Fields,

he spent 16 days in mephitic gloom inspecting some 3,060 coffins. Hunter's casket was at the bottom of the last tier but one. Buckland contracted severe fever but recovered in time for Hunter's reinterment in Westminster Abbey.

There were many fellow practitioners of Dr Walker who did not earn so much as a nickname in their agitation for a clean-up of early Victorian England. A surgeon of Sunderland, Reginald Orton, should have been known as 'Window' Orton for the persistence with which he badgered the Chancellor of the Exchequer to end the imbecility of the window tax, which was abolished in 1851. Agitators, whether medical or radical, were unpopular with manufacturers and landlords. Only a sharp visitation of cholera, like that of 1831–2, could provide a temporary impetus towards reform. When the cholera died, so did the urge to spring-clean. Cholera frightened only because it was not constantly present; typhus and typhoid were always there and slew by the ten thousand, but these deaths were accepted as a normal wastage, as traffic accidents are today.

Happily, the 1832 epidemic of cholera served as a springboard for Chadwick, the lawyer with the 'sanitary idea' which in due course bored his fellow citizens silly. He was a single-minded, browbeating fellow who made it clear that he would not rest until he had cleaned up England; and England made it clear that, while it did not actively resent being cleaned up, it did not want to be cleaned up by Chadwick. Though a number of doctors gave him unstinted aid, Chadwick was no flatterer of the medical profession. Most of them, in his view, were parasites with a financial interest in perpetuating disease. It was engineers alone who had the key to health, not the doctors. As a result, Chadwick found himself antagonising the College of Physicians at one extreme and Thomas Wakley at the other.

Remorselessly, Chadwick bludgeoned the country with the statistics of its infamy. He showed that the annual hecatomb from typhus in England and Wales was double the Allies' losses at Waterloo; that more than half the children of the poor died, as against one-fifth of the children of the gentry; and that there were parts of Manchester with one privy to 215 people.

Every town had its individual horrors. Edinburgh, the modern Athens, was in a state of filth no ancient Athenian would have tolerated. Dogs and horses shared dwelling-houses and chickens roosted on bed-posts. It was said that the Infirmary officers could

G

recognise from the symptoms of a fever patient whether he came from the West Port, St Mary's Wynd or Meat Market Close. In many industrial towns every other back court was a dung-hill, a lethal compost heap which rose foot by foot as evilly and inexorably as did the burial grounds. There were houses set so close together that a person could step from the bedroom window of one into the bedroom window of another.

London remained the Augean Stables. In 1850, in Bayswater and Notting Hill, lay an area called the Potteries—described as 'seven or eight acres of hovels where colonies of pigs and ducks were guarded by dogs.'* Here, a glass of clear water would have been regarded as a splendid novelty. The polluted air was further fouled by fat-boiling. Walls were fetid and the windows dark from the fumes of sulphuretted hydrogen. All over the city ill-kept stables and underground cowsheds reeked. Through it all wound that mighty sewer the Thames, its stench driving the legislators at Westminster from their committee rooms. Yet the public, or a large part of it, preferred the stink to the inspector who came round sniffing it.

Because of Chadwick's prejudices, the first General Board of Health, formed in 1846, had at first no medical member; then the faithful Dr Southwood Smith was appointed. But Chadwick offered work in plenty for those doctors who were prepared to labour to prevent disease, for local boards were now empowered to appoint medical officers of health. The first State doctor, if Dr Southwood Smith is excepted, was Dr William Duncan, who became Medical Officer of Health for Liverpool in 1847. Loyally backed, he set about cleaning up the vile courts of that city and the 7,800 cellars in which 45,000 persons lived. In 1848 London appointed Dr (later Sir) John Simon in a similar capacity. Of some 200 boards, fewer than 40 could bring themselves to appoint a medical officer, and many of these afterwards regretted their extravagance.

Not every doctor had the knowledge, the vision or the energy to tackle the exacting duties of the post. But the dedicated few set out valiantly to clean up the ulcers of the industrial revolution. They called for sick returns, for death rolls. They worked for the abolition of cesspools, of open drains, of immovable dustbins. They clamoured, above everything else, for new houses. They condemned filthy dairies, reeking slaughter-houses and tainted

* *Household Words*, Oct. 21, 1854.

Splendid Opening for a Young Medical Man

Chairman: Well, young man. So you wish to be engaged as Parish Doctor?

Doctor: Yes, gentlemen, I am desirous——

Chairman: Ah! Exactly. Well—it's understood that your wages—salary I should say—is to be twenty pounds per annum; and you find your own tea and sugar—medicines I mean—and, in fact, make yourself generally useful. If you do your duty, and conduct yourself properly, why—ah—you —ah——

(*Punch:* Will probably be bowled out of your situation by some humbug, who will fill it for less money.) (1848)

oyster beds. They penetrated into basement sweat-shops and school lavatories. They exposed the adulteration of food and the sophistication of drugs. They protested at the free sale of poisons and opiates (at a Carnarvon inquest a druggist said that he usually dispensed laudanum to 60 servant girls on a Saturday night for the purpose of stupefying their charges, so that the girls might enjoy their pleasures undisturbed).

In these activities the medical officer of health could by no means count on the whole-hearted support of the ratepayers, and of the propertied classes. The justices to whom he had power to appeal might well have a financial stake in smoke and filth. A medical officer who was employed on a part-time basis at perhaps £15 a year—and some had retainers of as little as £2—would think twice before antagonising too many of the townsfolk among whom his practice lay. The perfect medical officer of health had to be a lonely, single-minded, incorruptible being, yet not too aloof to antagonise those whom it was necessary to convert to his way of thinking. He had to be more than a sanitary inspector, less than a politician. He had to know how to shock respectability without disgusting it. If he could get others to dramatise his facts and figures, so much the better. There would always be somebody to call him a petty Chadwick, a doctrinist, a self-advertiser and a crank, or to dispute his statistics, to accuse him of partiality, over-emphasis and harming the town's good name. It is true that medical officers of health have ridden some curious hobby horses in their time, but their occasional eccentricities are a trivial price to pay for a cleaner world.

If the lot of the medical officer of health was disagreeable, what of the life of the general practitioner—usually a doctor holding a poor law appointment—in those overcrowded miasmic streets? He might be called on to deliver a child into the same room as a corpse which the family were saving up to bury. If the family belonged to a burial club, he would think twice before signing a death certificate, not wishing to be an accessory to murder. In the simplest of his ministrations he would be baulked by the absence of clean water and clean bedding. He could not order isolation when families lived eight or ten in a room. There was little he could do except mitigate the more acute misery and leave as soon as he decently could.

Despair and defeatism rivalled ignorance and fecklessness as the doctor's worst enemies. This was noticeable not only in the home life of the poor but in their attitude to the lethal trades in which so many were employed. Frederick Engels describes the efforts of a Dr Knight to warn the Sheffield grinders of the perils of 'grinders' asthma.' It was of no avail—'he who is once a grinder falls into despair as though he had sold himself to the devil.' Always they went back to work, and even destroyed the devices erected for their protection, lest more workers might be attracted into the trade.* Other doctors who gave evidence in factory enquiries testified to the prevalence of suicidal apathy of this kind.

The rest of the community was quite willing to leave the doctor to get on with the good work. Was it not the ancient privilege of the medical man to look after the poor with no thought of reward? Was he not fortunate to be able to pay such a premium in this world in order to ensure his reward in the next? Was it not equally his good fortune to have the poor on whom to sharpen his skill, and gain that experience which would qualify him to attend superior tradesmen? The writer (apparently a doctor) who discoursed on this theme in *Household Words* in 1854 protested that the members of no other profession were expected to carry the burden of the poor at their own expense and to provide themselves with an assistant and a horse in order the more comfortably to lose money. And what reward other than financial did the doctor receive for his sacrifice? There were boards of guardians who behaved towards him 'with autocratic condescension or with inflated incivility, as if surgeons were slaves and they assemblies of three-tailed bashaws.' Not every practitioner, he said, was prepared to fob off paupers with pump water, Epsom salts and gentian; many were conscientious enough to prescribe quinine and sarsaparilla, at their own expense.

Nor did the doctor necessarily receive the gratitude of the poor he treated. They resented the speed with which he handled them at his surgery. If he was bad-tempered, they assumed it was because he resented having to work for nothing, whereas he was probably impatient at their fecklessness. He knew that though they did not pay him for his drugs they contrived to buy quack remedies which might have no relevance to their illness.

When panic struck, the competition for the doctor's services

* *The Conditions of the Working Classes in England.*

could be a perilous embarrassment. Dr John Brown, the author of *Rab and His Friends*, was a young practitioner at Chatham when the pestilence broke out in 1832. One morning a sailor arrived to report a furious outbreak in a village down-river, and off they rowed, past the convict hulks, to a landing-stage where men and women were all shouting frantically for his services. Before the boat could reach shore a big, bald, elderly man waded out, picked up the doctor from the boat and splashed back, 'carrying me high up in his left arm and with his right levelling every man or woman who stood in his way.' This was Big Joe, bringing help to his godson, Little Joe. He challenged the doctor to leave him until Little Joe was better. In fact, Little Joe recovered, but Big Joe died that same night; he had the disease on him when he carried the doctor ashore.*

Many a parish doctor was hauled over the coals by miserly boards of guardians and accused of over-spending on drugs, of debauching able-bodied labourers by prescribing food and drink for them. This might be the doctor's opportunity to flourish in the guardians' faces receipts for provisions which he had bought out of his own pocket for paupers. It was not easy, however, to make a board of guardians blush. They were convinced that in appointing a parish doctor they were giving him valuable experience and introductions; but the introductions forthcoming were not to bankers and bishops. If the practitioner demurred at the rates of payment or at the size of the area he was supposed to cover he would be told that there were plenty of ambitious young doctors streaming from the medical schools who would be willing to take the post for even less remuneration; and the practitioner, having no illusions about professional loyalties, would know when he was beaten. Bottling his indignation for the day when he could afford to throw back the job in the guardians' face, he would accede to a system which might mean treating a patient for several months at a maximum fee of half-a-crown. Or, bottling his conscience as well as his indignation, he might take on a plurality of parish posts, which meant that his patients would receive even more cursory treatment.

When a Select Committee held an inquiry into the workings of the Poor Law in 1844, Charles Jennery, vice-chairman of the Bethnal Green Union, said three doctors were responsible for 74,000 persons in that fever-prone district. One of them con-

* John Brown: *Horae Subsecivae.*

centrated on the workhouse, which held 1,000. 'We have never had any complaints,' said Mr Jennery. One of his surgeons, Charles Goodwin, who was paid £70 a year, protested : 'I cannot get wine and porter *ad libitum* or animal food to the extent they ought to have.' The guardians cut down the quantities he prescribed and substituted raisin wine for port. (The extent to which port and porter were prescribed as strengtheners for the poor is one of the oddest facets of medical practice at this time.)

Asked why he slaved in Poplar for £75 a year, Horatio Bloomfield explained : 'As a young man it is by no means an unimportant situation for me to hold; in the first place I cannot be too much occupied, and I cannot be too much seen, nor can I be too much talked of so long as I discharge my duties faithfully.' One or two doctors told of their efforts to put down nuisances. Adolphus Barnett, who practised in Stepney, said that his father, a member of the board of guardians, assured him that if he remonstrated against nuisances he would be removed at the next election.

'You think few medical officers would dare to make representations unless they were independent?—I am sure they would not.'

A consulting surgeon in North Wales said that he had made 'a great deal of noise' in order to persuade a quarry owner to build a house for his numerous accident victims.

One of the reasons why Poor Law doctors did not remonstrate about their salaries, it emerged, was that they did not like to see their posts being continually advertised. The inference drawn by the public was that they were not doing their job. Similarly, dismissal on whatever grounds was liable to be interpreted as a slur.

It was not necessarily the urban doctors who saw the worst poverty, or were treated the most scurvily. Dr John Fox, a joint union medical officer at Cerne, Dorset, was paid £70 a year for looking after 4,283 persons in 12 parishes (an assistant attended to four parishes). In a typhus epidemic Dr Fox paid 705 visits to the workhouse in a year, sometimes five times within 24 hours, always on foot. Hearing that his reward for walking between 300 and 400 miles was only £4, some of the guardians could not quite suppress the springs of generosity, and suggested that Dr Fox be paid a gratuity. The rest were made of sterner stuff; they voted down the proposal on the grounds that 'having accepted a certain sum he must abide by the consequences.' Dr Fox's horse cost him a minimum of £25 a year and like many other doctors he had to pay about £3 a year at turnpikes. 'I am quite sure,' he said, 'that for the past year I have not risen above £10 or £12 for 857 cases.'

He was one of many who told of the reluctance with which the guardians granted midwifery orders, which committed them to paying the doctor a fee of ten shillings. Had the midwives been more skilled this would have mattered less. Dr Fox said that once he was called to a confinement and found the child's hand protruding from the womb. It was bruised because the midwife had been pulling it. Ambroise Paré had taught podalic version in the sixteenth century but the art had not reached the midwives of Dorset. Dr Fox turned the child and it was successfully delivered. Many a rural practitioner faced similar emergencies.

In 1846 a census held in Scotland showed that out of 253 doctors, 208 had not only treated patients free but, on occasions, had given them food, wine and clothing. One doctor had received 'three shillings for 12 years' attendance on 70 constant and 13 occasional paupers'; another attended 400 paupers for eight years and was never paid a farthing, even for drugs; another visited 350 paupers, some of them living at 30 miles distance, at an estimated cost to himself of £75 a year. Dr John Brown comments: 'Such active charity, such an amount of public good, is not likely to have been achieved by men whose lives were little else than the development of a juvenile mania for hanging sparrows and cats.'* By his estimate the doctors of Scotland performed one-third of their work for nothing. Often the beneficiaries were persons who would be too proud to leave their shoes or their chair seats unrepaired.

A few of these country doctors had their expenses partly met by local philanthropists, but they were the fortunate ones. The others did not greatly grumble. They had inherited a system in which it was customary to overcharge the wealthier for the benefit of the poor; in other words, they operated in the best traditions of Robin Hood. The notion that they should become servants of the State at a fixed salary would probably have horrified them as much as it horrified their successors.

Contract practice, in which a doctor treated the members of a friendly society for an agreed annual sum, or formed his own penny-a-week club among his flock, was already in existence in

* *Horae Subsecivae.*

the early Victorian years. To physicians of the old school this
form of practice was anathema. It was undignified. It was mere
trading. It was a prostitution of the doctor-patient relationship.
It was making the doctor a hireling of Buffaloes and Foresters
and secret societies. The controversy within the profession on this
issue became steadily more acute as the century progressed.

XX

AT LAST, A REGISTER

By mid-nineteenth century Medicine, in one respect, no longer trailed behind the Church and the Law. On January 25, 1856, *The Times* wrote:

'Of the three learned professions, the medical has attained the highest character for disinterestedness. Hard things are said of the cupidity of the clergy, the wealth of certain benefices affording a strange contrast to the poverty of the primitive Church; still harder things are said of the lawyers, who are supposed to eat the contested oyster while the plaintiff gets one shell and the defendant the other; but there is probably no class of the community generally so free from mercenary motives as the members of the medical and surgical profession.'

These were welcome words, but they did not mean that *The Times* thought highly of Medicine as a science. On April 3 of that year, criticising a medical reform Bill, it expressed little faith in examinations for medical men, since there was so much guess-work involved in their profession. 'The President of the College of Physicians is so nearly on a level with the meanest herbalist,' it said. 'The result of the longest, most varied and most profound medical experience is so often a discussion of the worthlessness of medicine.' And it quoted a celebrated physician as saying, 'When I began to practise I had a dozen cures for every disease. Now I have one remedy for a dozen diseases.' (This saying, or something like it, is usually attributed to Radcliffe.)

The Times was not being unfair to medical science. Although there had been big improvements in diagnostic methods—percussion and the stethoscope were in general use, though not yet the thermometer—the number of certain cures still remained very small indeed. In 1867 the president of the Royal College of Physicians, Sir Thomas Watson, said: 'Certainly the greatest gap in the science of medicine is to be found in its final and supreme stage, the stage of therapeutics . . . we know tolerably well *what* it is we have to deal with, but we do not know so well, nor anything like so well, *how* to deal with it . . . We want to know distinctly what is the action of drugs and of other outward influences upon the bodily organs and functions.'

Sir Henry Dale has said that in mid-nineteenth century 'medical treatment was hardly ever given with any idea that it could suppress or remove the cause of a disease.' It was the physician's duty to maintain the patient's strength and keep him comfortable and confident and thus give Nature a free hand. 'We cannot on the other hand ignore the wide opening which a medical treatment with no other objective than this offered to self-delusion, oracular posturing and benevolent humbug.'*

The Bill which had elicited those comments by *The Times* was one of an unsuccessful series inspired by Thomas Wakley's long campaign for medical reform and by the efforts of the British Medical Association.

In 1858, however, grudging compromise in high places allowed a Medical Registration Act to reach the Statute Book. This was one of the big landmarks in medical history. It set up a General Register of the profession along with a General Medical Council responsible for determining the minimum qualifications for admission to that Register.

When the Act was passed it was estimated that only one in three of the practitioners in the British Isles had taken the trouble to obtain formal qualifications of any kind. Establishment of a General Register did not mean that the unqualified and the quacks were out of business; but they could be prosecuted for claiming to be registered practitioners. They were debarred from signing death certificates (and were quick to point out the dangers of allowing an orthodox practitioner to sign his own death certificates).

The General Medical Council was a body composed of representatives of the profession, the medical corporations, the universities and the Crown. Today the layman knows it as a severe, high-minded body which sits in judgment on doctors who stand accused of infamous conduct.

The Act left much still to be done. Thanks to difficulties raised

* Festival of Britain Lecture, June 20, 1951.

by the Royal Colleges, it was still possible for a man to qualify in medicine and then practise as a surgeon, or to qualify as a surgeon and practise in medicine. Not until 1886 was this anomaly removed and a triple standard of qualification—in medicine, surgery and midwifery—made compulsory.

Gradually, after the passing of the 1858 Act, the Royal Colleges began to accept the facts of progress, to strike off some of their more reactionary by-laws and to take an interest in the methods of educating the profession. They were only too well aware that the Crown had its eye on them. As they opened the way to brains instead of to privilege and social status, so they gained in public respect. It may be that in the foregoing pages the shortcomings of the Royal Colleges have been overstressed. Great men had served them; great men had lectured in their halls; but too often the great men, as they grew old, had grouped themselves into privilege-preservation societies. Henceforth the higher awards of the Colleges were to become the goal of those ambitious practitioners who wished to set up as consultants and specialists, or to reach the top posts in the teaching hospitals. The word physician, as denoting a socially privileged class of practitioners, began gradually to go out of popular use.

The system of apprenticeship was not yet at an end. The drudgery of the shop, the keeping of ledgers, the bottling of medicines, the care of leeches—all this fell to the lot of those who could not afford to enter the profession by going straight to Oxford or Cambridge, or to one of the new medical schools now being run by junior universities. There was much controversy on this issue. Many argued that it was better for a practitioner to have a grounding in the practical routine of medicine, rather than to spend his time learning the answers to questions like: 'Upon what grounds has it been maintained that all demonstrative science is hypothetical?' and 'What is meant by the doctrine that time and space are forms of thought?' These questions stumped Sir Charles Brown, an apprentice at 14, when he went up to London University to sit his MD examination in 1863.* Medicine, the traditionalists said, was a science of observation, and the clinician's mind was no better off for being stuffed with the *minutiae* of scientific knowledge. The apprentice learned first-hand from patients, not second-hand from lecturers.

It was still, in many ways, a strife-torn profession. Con-

* *Sixty-Four Years a Doctor.*

sciensiously, the British Medical Association, with the aid of its *British Medical Journal*, set about organising harmony and solidarity. In 1859 an unpleasant squall blew up when Dr Thomas Smethurst, a devotee of hydropathy, was convicted of murdering a woman by administering poison. The medical evidence against him was profoundly unsatisfactory. Dr Alfred Taylor, who held an appointment at Guy's, admitted that arsenic which he found in the body had come from apparatus used in his tests. Thanks to this revelation, and to other baffling inconsistencies from the lips of experts, Dr Smethurst was granted a free pardon, then tried and jailed for bigamy. Public respect for medical evidence had never been very high; now it slumped badly.

Worse was to come. Several times, in the 'sixties, the *British Medical Journal* wrote in sorrow and anger about the apparently irresponsible way in which doctors contradicted each other in court. On May 2, 1863, it said:

'Medical evidence delivered in our courts of law has of late become a public scandal and a professional dishonour. The Bar delights to sneer at and ridicule it; the judge on the bench solemnly rebukes it; the public stand by in amazement; and honourably minded members of our profession are ashamed of it . . . What is the public to think when, for example, they see three doctors on one side swearing on behalf of a railway company that the plaintiff is not suffering from any injury at all; and three on the other side swearing that he is not only suffering from an injury but is seriously damaged and probably for life?'

Similarly, the *Journal* said, there were doctors prepared to swear that a certain professional practice was proper, while others were equally ready to swear that it was improper. Even worse, in its opinion, was the type of case which involved 'most unseemly prosecution of medical men by medical men.' It deplored 'celebrities who go into a court of justice to assist on the strength of a mere opinion' in 'blasting a brother practitioner's fair fame.' These remarks were drawn by the medical evidence in an unsuccessful prosecution of a doctor who was said by a hysterical female patient to have seduced her while she was unconscious. The *Journal* asserted it had no wish to protect discreditable practice or pervert the ends of justice, but 'something stronger than conscience is required to force certain members of our profession to act justly towards their brethren.' The *Journal* promised that the British Medical Association would formulate a code of rules to guide doctors in the witness box.

Sir Robert Christison in his *Autobiography* says that much mischief was done to professional reputations in the Scottish courts, at a rather earlier period, by 'a small section of men belonging to the Extra-Academical School of Medicine who could scarcely ever meet a university man on a public occasion without setting up their backs and spitting at him. It was quite enough that a professor was a professional witness in a court of law for one of this brotherhood to appear on the other side; nor did they ever seem taken aback by the sorry figure they were made to cut on divers occasions.'

The task of the Bar was made easier, in that it was always possible to find a doctor to support the unlikeliest case. Christison quotes Henry Cockburn, then a barrister, as telling a litigant : 'Go to Dr ——, he will say anything you like.' Of doctors employed by railways, Christison writes : 'I am sorry for these brethren of mine who seem to consider it a matter of duty and necessity that they must always be on the railway side of a question.'

In an attempt to preserve doctors from legal and professional pitfalls, the *Medical Register* began to publish a good deal of cautionary material in its annual volumes. A warning was issued on the acceptance of gifts from patients. The courts, it was explained, watched such matters with great jealousy and if they thought that undue influence had been exerted on the part of the doctor a gift would be set aside. The burden of proving that the transaction was in order fell on the recipient, who must show that the donor knew what he was doing and how his 'intention was produced.'

One of the more curious offices for which a doctor was liable, the *Medical Register* pointed out, was that of sitting with a jury of matrons empanelled to try whether a female prisoner was quick with child. The law said that a pregnant mother convicted of a capital offence was not to be executed while in that condition.

Periodically, the high fees charged by leading physicians came in for criticism. In 1862 a Dr Vose, of Liverpool, was called by telegraph to Aberdeen to attend one of his patients, whom he escorted back to Liverpool. After the patient's death the executors disputed Dr Vose's bill for 205 guineas, of which 186 guineas represented travelling expenses to Aberdeen and back, a round trip of 372 miles. One of the executors said he understood that doctors in Edinburgh charged a flat sum of £25 a day for an out-of-town call, or £30 if a night's stay was included; therefore, as Dr Vose had been absent two days and two nights, a fee of £60 would be adequate. To this Dr Vose replied that the leading fellows of the Royal College of Physicians were entitled to charge at the rate of not less than two-thirds of a guinea per mile for a rail journey, and at the rate of a guinea a mile on post roads. Since the patient had been an old friend he had charged him only half a guinea a mile. The executors still thought that 205 guineas was 'very heavy' for 'a country practitioner.' Loftily, Dr Vose replied that, as a fellow of the Royal College, he made no demand for the money; 'the fees are merely a debt of honour.' *The Lancet* heartily supported Dr Vose, saying 'it is the bounden duty of the affluent class to reward their medical attendants not only justly but liberally.' Only thus could doctors be compensated for the many services they performed free for the poor. James Syme, the surgeon, entered the controversy, saying that he had never heard of any £25-a-day arrangement in Edinburgh. He was opposed to fixed charges, the ideal course being to 'place the liberality of the rich to the credit of the poor.'

Not all physicians had been in favour of cutting the rate for rail travel to two-thirds of a guinea a mile; such travel, they thought, was dirty and dangerous. They found it difficult to convince the public that by leaving their practices for only a day or two they lost a great deal of money and irritated many regular patients. To the sore-bellied but hard-headed patient in Stockport or Doncaster this argument was of little weight; his imagination would be obsessed by the thought of a sleek opportunist being paid at an exorbitant rate to sit in a first-class seat, smoke a cigar and admire the scenery.

Although fellows of the Royal College did not sue for fees, lesser men could and did. Often, however, they received little sympathy in the courts, for the law liked to show its superiority by whittling down the fees of other professional men. In 1869 a general practitioner sued the guardians of two girls for £310 5s. 6d. He had treated the elder one for a minor complaint and the younger one for measles and 'other ailments of a dangerous kind which required his continuous care for many weeks.' In all, he paid the girls 125 visits, mostly at their school at St John's Wood, but on three occasions he went to see them at

Brighton and twice to Worthing. He had charged at the rate of a guinea a visit, but only half a guinea per patient when he examined them both. His bill included six guineas for a consultation with Sir William Jenner and 40 guineas for correspondence and consultation with solicitors 'etc.' The guardians of the girls offered 100 guineas, which the doctor refused. The Master of the Rolls decided that the guardians had erred on the side of generosity and awarded £82 13s. *Punch* was quick to point out that if a similarly severe tariff were to be fixed by the Master of the Rolls for his own profession there would soon be a flight from the Bar. The doctor in the case was able to console himself, perhaps, by reading a report in the *Examiner* which said that poor law doctors in London were receiving an average of threepence per case.

The anonymous author of *My Doctors, by a Patient,* writing in 1891, complained that the charge of a guinea a mile was still exacted within 12 miles of London. 'A fee of 35 guineas is sometimes charged on going from London to Brighton, but 25 is in all conscience enough. A hundred pounds is often paid by a wealthy Yorkshireman for bringing his doctor down that distance.'

The same writer, describing a visit to a consultant in Harley Street, reported that there was a card on the mantelpiece in the waiting-room advising that the fee for a first visit was two guineas, with one guinea for every subsequent visit within a period of three months. This two-guinea initial fee had become the custom from the 'seventies onwards.

It is not very clear what first drew doctors to Harley Street, unless it was the proximity of Euston and Paddington stations. Certainly it was not the legend of John St John Long. In 1858, the year the General Register was started, there were 19 doctors in the street, including one baronet. In 1870 there were 37; in 1880, 58. Ten years later there were nearly 100; they included four titled doctors, one woman and two doctors called Harley. By 1900 there were 156 plates, of which three belonged to women.

Steadily Harley Street built up its *mystique*, its sinister reputation as a street where men and women went to learn on the highest authority whether they were to live or die. As likely as not, the door was opened by a butler and in the background footmen could be seen hovering. In the hall and waiting-room were

Nineteenth Century Doctor—still water gazing

busts of Hippocrates or Galen or Harvey on their white marble pediments and portraits of distinguished physicians long since dead. The great mahogany bookshelves were full of Latin works. In the hushed, musty atmosphere the patient had plenty of time to ponder the contents of the letter of introduction in his pocket. Did it contain dire tidings couched in unintelligible jargon? Or did it (as the wags said) contain a message like 'The bearer is a fat Wiltshire clothier. Make the most of him?' The patient also had time to worry about that vexatious problem of how to offer a fee to a baronet. After an hour or two of waiting he might begin to ponder another financial problem: dare he slip a *douceur* into the footman's hand (as he suspected others were doing) in order to accelerate his admission to the consulting-room? If so, what was the minimum sum unlikely to wound the honour of such a superior servant? It was said of Sir Morell Mackenzie, the laryngologist, that he kept the titled waiting only for a few minutes, but allowed actors and singers and those with well-known faces to kick their heels rather longer, so that their presence might adequately impress the other patients. Some consultants were reluctant to give fixed appointments, leaving it to their servants to determine the order of admission. The luckless might have to wait until two o'clock, only to watch the doctor drive away. By that time the patients of Sir Morell Mackenzie, at least, would have been able to help themselves to a plate of sandwiches brought in by a footman. This genial custom seems to have died out.

Many of the more eminent Victorian consultants kept up considerable social state in their Harley Street dwellings. The street was a street for living in, not merely for holding consultations. In near-by Wimpole Street, also a stronghold of doctors, Sir Henry Thompson, founder of the first cremation society, entertained the distinguished in all walks of life to his 'octaves'—eight-course dinners for eight guests at eight o'clock. One of the last octaves of a series of 301 was attended by the Prince of Wales (later George V) in 1904.

A more solemn occasion than a visit to Harley Street was a visit by Harley Street to a bedside. One by one the coaches would arrive at the door of the stricken home, and the grave callers in formal clothes would be ushered into the library. Then, deferentially, the general practitioner would lead them to the bedside. The master of the house would probably be excluded from their deliberations. Nervously, he would hover about hall and stairs until a bell was rung summoning him to his own library, which he would enter with due apprehension. There he would hear the verdict, solemnly announced. He might never know whether it was a unanimous verdict or a majority one. As the consultants left he would distribute neat envelopes among them.

There was (and is) an unwritten law that consultants should advise patients only through their family doctors. Nothing made a family doctor angrier than a suspicion that consultant and patient were going behind his back. Many a general practitioner was cynical about the pretensions of consultants, for not all of them had higher qualifications or hospital appointments. Often, in big towns a leading practitioner became a consultant merely by virtue of his prosperity and social standing. Occasionally there was collusion between practitioner and consultant, the latter secretly returning part of his fee to the man who called him in. Fee-splitting was unethical, easy to suspect but hard to detect. It was known in the profession as 'dichotomy,' and from time to time doctors were sternly warned against it by their governing bodies.

No more violent contrast to the genteel guinea-raking of Harley Street was to be found than the mass processing of patients in the great voluntary hospitals (where, however, many Harley Street men gave their services free). The young physicians and surgeons who filtered the clamant multitudes and sent them away with bottles of iron tonic could reflect, when they had time to do so, that they were paid less than the men who fastened shoes to the wheels of omnibuses. At St Bartholomew's Hospital a future Poet Laureate, Dr Robert Bridges, helped to diagnose the patients who poured through that venerable institution at the rate of 157,947 annually. Of these, Bridges personally 'filtered' more than 30,000 a year, giving them, on an average, 1.28 minutes of his time. He described how it was done in a famous article in *St Bartholomew's Hospital Reports* in 1878. At nine o'clock the doors were opened just sufficiently to let the patients squeeze in one by one, otherwise the hospital would have been engulfed. By ten o'clock they were shut, and the great hall was full of medical and surgical patients. An hour later it was almost empty, having been effectively cleared by a junior assistant physician, three casualty physicians, an assistant surgeon and four house surgeons with dressers. It was not unusual for a casualty physician to see 150 patients in less than two hours. Many of these patients, said Bridges, were seriously ill, 'some mortally, many but slightly, but nearly all in considerable bodily inconvenience or pain.' There was the occasional patient who admitted having nothing wrong with him but who thought that, as he was passing the hospital, he might as well drop in for a bottle of medicine. Of one such, Bridges writes: 'I should have been sorry to have drunk the dose that was prescribed for him.' It was impossible for the diagnosing physician to allow the patients, especially the women, to talk freely. Information had to be extracted from them by questioning, and the questions were repeated, if necessary loudly, until they were answered. Some experience of this soon led Bridges 'to assume a tyrannous air that forbade them to seek sympathy by plaintive recitals.' Any necessary auscultation had to be performed amid the shuffling of feet, crying of babies and hammering of carpenters. Bridges strove to follow up the patients who were admitted to the surgical wards, if only to discover whether they lived or died, but had to give up because he could not remember such an infinite progression of faces and symptoms. The remuneration of a casualty physician worked out at seven-tenths of a penny per patient, presenting 'an amusing discrepancy with the 30,000 odd guineas which the Royal College of Physicians might consider us annually entitled to.' Indeed, as Bridges noted, the 'sixpenny doctors' who plied in the mean streets near the hospital were rich men by comparison.

It is perhaps superfluous to say that the young doctor who accepted a hospital appointment did so for the experience, not for the money. It was a post where he could extend his clinical and operative knowledge while studying for those higher examinations which would give him enhanced prestige in the profession. Besides which, a hospital tour of duty allowed a man to acquire a few wrinkles—in the literal as well as in the slang sense. The average young doctor was painfully aware that his youthful appearance, even in frock coat and top hat (with stethoscope tucked inside), was no recommendation for the role of family doctor.

If the fledgling doctor could find no opening on the staff of a hospital, if the poor law guardians had no crumbs to offer, if no doctor was advertising for an assistant, there was usually a job somewhere for a *locum tenens*. It was an excellent way of learning general practice, in that any mistakes made would be made at the expense of someone else's patients.

To be alone for the first time with a patient was a memorable moment. There were none of the resources of a hospital on which to fall back, no colleagues whose learning could be tapped (to call in the rival practitioner was not done). In the wards, diseases had been recognisable because usually they were far advanced; now the doctor was expected to diagnose them in their early stages, with nobody to correct him if he was wrong. If all this did not serve to breed a proper humility in a young man the reception he faced from surprised patients certainly did; as when a pregnant woman would dissolve into tears on first sight of him, explaining that she had expected 'the proper doctor.' One who had need of many locums was Dr W. G. Grace, who was a parish doctor in Bristol in the 'seventies. His practice was not wholly forgotten on the cricket field. It is said that during a match in which he made two centuries he sat up all night with a poor woman whom he had promised to attend while in her labour.*

Failing a post as *locum* to an orthodox practitioner, a young man could offer his services to a 'sixpenny doctor,' attending patients who rapped on the counter and called 'Shop!' This also helped to breed humility. Or he could become a ship's doctor, humouring rich dyspeptics in a passenger liner or patching up quarrelsome sailors in a whaler; praying, always, that he would not be called upon to extract the captain's appendix or to handle a berserk lascar. Not much medicine was to be learned at sea, but a doctor widened his knowledge of human nature.

Again, there were posts in asylums, both public and private, for those who were willing to take the risk of being clubbed or strangled, and who did not shrink from the peculiar tensions of dance nights and amateur dramatics behind locked doors. Less alluring, perhaps, was the post of medical attendant in a retreat for dipsomaniacs, an appointment hallowed, and indeed demanded, under the Inebriates Act. The advertisement pages of medical journals in the 'eighties were studded with pictures of handsome hotels run for drunkards of the middle and upper classes, of both sexes. One proprietor would stress the size and

* Bernard Darwin: *W. G. Grace.*

airiness of his billiard-rooms and drawing-rooms; another would offer good hunting and stabling; another, fishing and shooting. Among the less attractive retreats, from the patient's point of view, was 'a pleasant island off the West Coast of Scotland where no stimulants can be obtained.' Almost all the advertisers made it clear that they would admit only respectable drunkards, but one of them was ready to make special arrangements for 'second-class patients.' Third-class patients were not mentioned. Some of these advertisements were inserted by medical men who not only attended the patients but owned the establishments.

The prison service usually had vacancies for doctors, to whom fell not only the grim offices attaching to floggings and executions, but such tasks as certifying that prisoners were fit to operate the treadmill, an institution which survived, in several prisons, into the twentieth century. Repeatedly, the *British Medical Journal* advised its readers to think very hard before entering the prison service, since the conditions were so bad as to drive doctors out in disgust after two or three years. An assistant doctor was paid less than the chief warder or the clerk of works and his word carried little weight. The *Journal* pointed out that the prison doctor was responsible for the health of the prisoners, not for maintaining discipline. 'Young men recently appointed,' it said, 'will frequently find a sort of moral pressure put on them to back the executive; let them, however, bear in mind that they must be held responsible for any results.'

Many large factories employed their own surgeons, the forerunners of the industrial health officers of today. Even boarding schools had their own doctors. And there were still opportunities for men who were prepared to live in with wealthy patients. The author of *My Doctors* tells of an old lady who had trouble with her oesophagus and feared that, at any moment, she might choke. For this reason, she felt it necessary to have round-the-clock attendance. Her doctor was handsomely paid for doing nothing, but stipulated that he should be allowed to go out and do something for two hours a day—between noon and 2 p.m. For that period a substitute was found: a young man fresh from university who, during three years, never once saw his patient but had a capital lunch every day and pocketed the guinea wrapped in tissue paper placed beside his plate.

Abroad, there were medical posts in plenty throughout the colonial service. In the more primitive places of the earth, far

from the protection of the British Crown, there was scope for
medical missionaries, men of tough spiritual fibre who did not
flinch from handling a plague single-handed, and whose voca-
tional risks included being imprisoned, tortured and eaten. Dr
David Livingstone won the headlines, but scores of medical
missionaries performed unadvertised prodigies, notably in the
Chinese hinterland and on the North-West Frontier. The regi-
ments of the Queen still needed their surgeons. It may be that,
after 1898, some few young men were induced to put on scarlet
by the prospect of being addressed as captain, major or colonel—
a long withheld privilege for which the British Medical Association had industriously campaigned.

In reminiscence, many a doctor has told of the shifts and sub-
terfuges to which he had to resort when, at long last, he plucked
up courage to start in practice on inadequate capital. On putting
up his plate, he was supposed to pay courtesy calls on the other
practitioners in the area and convince them that there was room
for one more, but dread of snubs dissuaded the sensitive from this
course. Nervously, the newcomer settled to the time-honoured
routine : the hovering at the windows on the look-out for the first
patient, the furtive polishing of the plate in the early morning
before the neighbours were up, the excuses for opening the door
in person or for arriving at a patient's house on foot, the return
home in topper and frock-coat to fry kippers over a gas-ring, the
long-deferred decision to join the local chapel, or the local Free-
masons. The first ring at the bell might turn out, ominously, to be
a debt-collector touting for custom. It was likely that his first
patients would be people who had exhausted the patience of their
own doctors, or who were unable to look them in the face because
of the fees they owed. He would make friends with publicans and
policemen, with vicars and even with editors, who in those days
were willing to mention the name of a doctor who had treated a
traffic casualty. Often, to the hard-up Aesculapius it seemed that
the mere nailing-up of his plate had brought the curse of barrenness to the neighbourhood. As a student in his last year he had
formed an unrealistic idea of the incidence of childbirth (young
Dr Somerset Maugham attended 63 confinements in three weeks
while a student at St Thomas's). But somehow the patients began
to dribble in, and if he was a good doctor word-of-mouth publicity

did the rest. If he made between £100 and £150 in his first year he was fairly lucky. When really hard-pressed, a doctor might take in a paying patient, perhaps someone suffering from a 'breakdown' or a consumptive. Domestic life was not made any easier and obviously a servant or two were necessary, but substantial sums could be charged.

Sir Arthur Conan Doyle started in practice at Southsea with an empty villa, £4 worth of second-hand furniture, a stock of drugs obtained on credit and £2 cash. He found that he could live 'quite easily and well on less than a shilling a day.' Bread, bacon and tea were his staples, with an occasional saveloy. His young brother joined him to perform some of the chores and one day was able to record, 'We have vaxenated a baby and got hold of a man with consumption.' They also got hold of a man with epilepsy, whose fits kept them in butter and tea. 'Poor fellow,' writes Sir Arthur, 'he could never have realised the mixed feelings with which I received the news of a fresh outbreak.'*

A famous picture which pins down the general practitioner of the late Victorian years is Sir Luke Fildes' 'The Doctor,' hung at the Royal Academy in 1891 and now occupying a place of honour in the Tate Gallery. It shows a scene of crisis in a country cottage. Lying on a rough bed composed of chairs is a pallid little girl with her eyes closed. Gravely, the bearded, formally dressed doctor sits watching her. In the background the mother hides her head and the father stands, frightened, trying to comfort her. Symbolic of failure is a half-consumed bottle of medicine.

The doctor is obviously the best type of family doctor. Equally obviously, he is up against it. That discarded medicine bottle tells its own story. The parents are hoping against hope that he has another trick in his bag.

That is how the painting strikes one observer, though the artist may well have intended it as a more flattering tribute to the profession.

In the last decade of the century the General Medical Council began to tackle a notable abuse : the employment by doctors of unqualified assistants. There were some ten thousand of them, ranging from striplings to old men. The striplings, as a rule, intended to go on to medical school; it was a side door to medicine

* *Memories and Adventures.*

through which many doctors and surgeons passed. In theory the youngster, like the old-time apprentice, confined his activities to his master's premises, spending much of his time mixing routine medicines; but every now and then, in his master's absence, he would go out with a black bag and bring a baby into the world, a daunting assignment, as it would now seem, for a youth in his middle 'teens. The best that could be said for such a practice was that it bred self-reliance in the assistant, even if it bred consterna-tion in the patient.

A high proportion of unqualified assistants were dispirited older men, who perhaps had failed to pass their final examina-tions. These were hired to look after (and sleep in) branch surgeries by commercially minded doctors who put up their brass plates all over the district and ran their practices like a chain of dairies. In Manchester, in 1891, was a doctor whose 'business' involved between 100 and 140 visits daily. He made 20 calls himself and left the rest to two assistants, one qualified and the other unqualified. The latter made up between 150 and 180 bottles each evening, his wage being 35s. a week. In the same city a 'sixpenny doctor' had a similar business worth £1,500 a year. He called only on special cases and those considered likely to die, for the signing of death certificates could not legally be left to the unqualified (though occasionally it was). On their daily rounds the unqualified assistants faced many humiliations, not only from protesting patients but from registered practitioners who cut them ostentatiously. Their masters claimed that they were more reliable than fledglings with university degrees and professed reluctance on these grounds, as well as on financial grounds, to turn them into the street.

All through the 'nineties coroners in industrial areas raised their voices against this unethical practice. So did county court judges, who struck out of doctors' bills those charges which repre-sented the work of assistants. The whole system, they said, was a swindle on the poor; if a person paid for a doctor he was entitled to be treated by one. When it could obtain satisfactory evidence, the General Medical Council struck the names of offending doctors from the Register, but for one reason or another many culprits escaped being disciplined. In 1897 the *British Medical Journal* recorded: 'Hardly a week passes without a rider being added to a verdict of natural death to the effect that "We desire the Coroner to communicate the facts in this case to the General

Medical Council." ' The *Journal* complained that the Council had been slow and uncertain in its handling of the problem.

The offence of maintaining an unqualified assistant was known in the profession as 'covering'—a word which was also stretched to include those unlawful occasions when a registered doctor acted as assistant to, or otherwise collaborated with, an unregistered practitioner.

G. K. Chesterton was no doubt thinking about the General Medical Council's campaign against unqualified assistants when he likened that body, not unkindly, to a medieval guild, and said: 'It does not permit one professional man to buy up all the practices, as one grocer can buy up all the grocers' shops.'*

Such was the seamy side of medicine in the 'nineties, the period when the discoveries of Pasteur, Lister and Koch had begun to revolutionise the entire science of healing. While the 'sixpenny doctors' were handing out their iron mixture, the smart physicians of Europe were scrambling for the much-publicised, and much-commercialised, extract of pigs' testicles prepared (more or less) according to the recipe of Charles Edward Brown-Sequard, the Mauritius-born endocrinologist who claimed to have rejuvenated himself with the aid of such injections.

There was much excitement. Had the doctors at last stumbled on the elixir of youth? Old gentlemen dreamed naughty dreams, moralists were shocked, journalists were gratified, comedians were delighted (as they were a generation later in Serge Voronoff's day); but the elixir in the end proved delusive and the 'sixpenny doctors' with their iron mixture had the last laugh.

* *Chaucer*

XXI

A CLUTCH OF CONTROVERSIES

IT will be convenient to group together some of the more animated controversies in which public and doctors found themselves embroiled in Queen Victoria's reign. Notable among them are those which revolved round the admissibility of women into the medical profession, the control of prostitution and the practices of vivisection and vaccination.

There were, of course, many lesser controversies, often with a fascination beyond their intrinsic importance. One of these sprang up when the British Medical Association and other bodies sought to abolish the insanitary custom which required witnesses in court to kiss the Bible. Since doctors had to give evidence more often than most people, they had a personal interest in this reform. For their pains, they were accused of trying to destroy yet another fine, old-established tradition. One of the more peculiar objections to ending the custom, as revealed in a Commons debate on the Oaths Bill in 1887, was that witnesses of easy virtue strove to kiss their thumbs instead of the Bible. If they succeeded in doing this undetected, they felt at liberty to give false evidence without imperilling their souls. Hence, lawyers contended, if a witness was allowed to swear by merely holding the book, perjury would be given a free charter. Some courts had Bibles with washable covers, but these were never washed often enough. Old-fashioned judges made it plain that they preferred all witnesses to kiss the book, even when it had already been touched by diseased lips. Nevertheless, the reformers carried their point; from 1887 onwards a witness was entitled, if he insisted, to swear the oath with right hand upraised in Scots fashion. The practice of kissing the book did not die out completely until well into this century.

Discussion of the medical attitude to birth control may be left to a later chapter. What the General Medical Council thought on the subject in the year of Queen Victoria's Jubilee may be gauged from the fact that a doctor was struck off the Register for publishing a cheap booklet called *The Wife's Handbook*. Had it been a more expensive publication he might have escaped punishment.

On the question of smoking, a fast-spreading habit, doctors were as divided as they are today, but not many who censured the practice went as far as Dr James Copland, a fellow of the Royal College of Physicians, who in 1861 told a meeting called by the Anti-Tobacco Society at St Pancras: 'There is no vice that visits its sins upon the third and fourth generations more completely than smoking . . . It is seldom that smokers have great-grandchildren or grandchildren.'

Another wrangle to be mentioned in passing was that over cremation, a practice vigorously advocated by the surgeons Sir Henry Thompson and Sir Spencer Wells, who carried the campaign initiated by 'Graveyard' Walker to its next logical stage. The objections to cremation were sentimental, religious and legal. A crematorium was ready at Woking in 1879 but its use was banned by the Home Secretary, pending a test case. In 1885 an elderly woman made history by becoming the first person to be legally cremated in Britain, her corpse being satisfactorily reduced to white ash in one hour.

From the start, the proposal that women should be allowed to become doctors attracted the bitterest censure from the opponents of feminism. Of all professions, they pointed out, this was the one in which a woman was most likely to lose her modesty, to blunt those finer sensibilities which were the ornament of her sex. Were women to dissect the human body—and in the company of male students? Were women physicians to attend bachelors in their apartments? Were they to ride 40 miles a day over the moors, or go down pits to cut off miners' legs, or extract small shot from the posteriors of poachers?

Even those advanced thinkers who held that women ought to be doing something to justify their existence, instead of spending their days reading three-volume novels about adultery, flinched at the notion of a woman doctor. How could a gently nurtured woman summon up the hardihood to follow such a career? Surely it could appeal only to the mad or bad?

There were graver considerations than that of modesty. A doctor held human life in his hands. He had to be steeped in science, trained in logic; whereas it was well known that women were ruled by emotion and were incapable of harbouring two related thoughts. Anatomists and physiologists were ready to show that the brain of the female was inferior in size, and therefore in capacity, to that of the male; one of them said that 'it exhibits a smaller amount of departure from the infantile condition than is to be found in a man.' Thus, it would clearly be a crime against humanity to let loose on the sick an inferior race of doctors whose only assets would be gentleness and sympathy, always supposing that these qualities were not destroyed in the dissecting rooms.

One who doubtless followed the earlier stages of the controversy with private amusement was Dr James Barry, who entered the Army as a hospital assistant in 1813, and, by 1858, had become Inspector-General of the Army Medical Department. Not till one morning in 1865, when Dr Barry's negro valet brought up his morning tea and found him dead, was it discovered that Dr Barry was a woman. The tale was that she had loved a young doctor who was ordered to Spain to serve under Wellington, and had taken up a medical career in order to join him. She had always looked suspiciously well-shaven and fresh complexioned, but had gone out of her way to act the gentleman, as by issuing challenges to duel.

The first British woman doctor of medicine to practise undisguised was Elizabeth Blackwell, who was born in Bristol in 1821. She received her basic medical education in America, not at one of the big medical schools but at the enlightened University of Geneva, New York State. The day came when the authorities thought she ought to absent herself from the anatomy class, but she refused to do so unless the rest of the class wished it. They were quite willing for her to attend, and she did. When Miss Blackwell subsequently paid a visit to Britain, she was regarded by the medical profession as more of a freak than a threat and had a civil enough reception. In 1859 her name was entered in the new Medical Register. Her best work was done in America, where she and her sister, not without opposition, opened a hospital for women.

In 1860 Elizabeth Garrett (afterwards Mrs Garrett Anderson) persuaded her father to call on various consultants in Harley Street to see what encouragement they could give her to become a doctor. She received very little, but persevered in her studies and won a diploma from the Society of Apothecaries. Her name went on the Register in 1865. Aghast at what it had done, the Society then took steps to prevent the same thing happening again.

It would be tedious to list the various frustrations which were put in the path of women doctors by licensing bodies, universities and hospitals. In 1862 the refusal of the Royal College of Physicians in Edinburgh to grant medical diplomas to women encouraged *Punch* to say : 'It is very true that it is necessary that a practitioner of medicine should be endowed with reflective faculties; but perhaps reason is not quite exclusively the prerogative of man. One or two women could be named whose works exhibit undeniable evidence of some logical faculty and judgment of causation. A female Harvey or Sydenham or Hunter or Abernethy would possibly turn up if the portals of medicine were not shut in her face.'

By the 'seventies it became clear that the New Woman was making a more determined attack on the medical citadel and the opposition noticeably stiffened. Why could not these tiresome females become nurses, now that nursing, thanks to Miss Nightingale, had become respectable? Or missionaries?

Edinburgh proved to be the cockpit. There the male students based their objections to women on the ground that professors would be unable to lecture freely if females were present. Egged on by their professors, the male students showed themselves to be distinctly less enlightened and gentlemanly than those of Geneva, New York, a generation before. In 1870 the appearance anywhere in the city of Sophia Jex-Blake, the torch-bearer of the day, and her colleagues was the signal for overt incivilities, ranging from catcalling to the throwing of filth. In an all too literal sense, the doors of medicine were slammed in their faces. Everything was done that the minds of schoolboys can devise for the torment of their fellows. When the women were sitting an examination a sheep was pushed into the room. 'Let it alone,' said Professor P. D. Handyside, 'it has more sense than those who sent it here.' This persecution would never have been attempted if it had not enjoyed the approval of many of the university and infirmary office-holders; but the campaign defeated its purpose, for the more decent-minded students began to act as bodyguards to Sophia Jex-Blake and her friends. Moreover the general public, which had always deplored the ways of medical students, began to take the side of the persecuted. The *Glasgow Herald* was alarmed to think that the students of Edinburgh, so conspicuously lacking in delicate and gentlemanly qualities, would some day be let loose on women patients.

In 1875 the Government embarrassed the General Medical Council by asking for its views on the admission of women into the profession. In a three-day session the Council left no argument, however foolish, unexamined. The debate was, in fact, as depressing as the annual performance by the House of Lords on the Deceased Wife's Sister Bill. 'Leave the female sex to be what God made them and what Nature intended them for,' pleaded Dr Andrew Wood. 'Leave them to command our esteem, our deference and our love and do not put them in a position in which you would not like to see them.' In the following year an Act was passed enabling all medical licensing bodies in Britain to open their examinations to women, at their discretion.

This was by no means the end of the fight. In 1878 Sir William Jenner said he had only one dear daughter but he would rather follow her bier to the grave than see her become a medical student; a statement which flattered his daughter as little as it flattered his profession. In 1878 Dr Charles West published a pamphlet *Medical Women* in which he asked: 'Will the beauty of womanhood, distinct and widely different as it is from that of manhood, be increased? Or will it be lessened by those new studies?' There was risk of 'gravely modifying the mental and moral characteristics of women.' Besides which, he felt that women doctors could never pull their weight. The medical corporations, he said, were required 'to grant their commissions to officers who own their inability to share with others the hardship of a campaign, but confess themselves equal only to garrison duty, to taking charge of the depot while the rest of the regiment is on active service.' And yet these stay-at-homes would claim their full share of medals and decorations. Nor did that exhaust Dr West's armoury of objections. It was customary at examinations, he said, for students to simulate conditions for other students to diagnose and treat. How could male medical students possibly submit themselves to such examinations by women?

By the end of the century there were perhaps 200 women qualified as doctors, but few as yet in private practice. Those who did practise gravitated to the bigger cities, since in a small com-

munity there were unlikely to be enough patients willing to put
their lives in the hands of a woman. The anonymous author of
My Doctors claims to have fled in embarrassment from the house
of a woman doctor who proposed to examine his chest with a
stethoscope. 'Chest? Examine my chest? Appear before a member
of the opposite sex in my shirt sleeves? Good Lord! What next?'

The cry 'What next?' was widely echoed by television viewers
in 1958 after they heard a woman doctor explain how she
selected donors for artificial insemination.

In mid-Victorian times the doctors burned their fingers by
lending too-enthusiastic support for a scheme to control prostitution on the Continental plan. Their motives were admirable : to
check the ravages of venereal disease, even if it meant curbing
the 'rights' of prostitutes.

It has been widely forgotten that a registration scheme of this
kind was enforced between 1864 and 1886 in a number of
garrison towns in the British Isles. These included Portsmouth,
Plymouth, Woolwich, Chatham, Sheerness, Aldershot, Colchester,
Shorncliffe, Windsor, Canterbury, Dover, Gravesend, Maidstone,
Winchester, Southampton, Cork, Queenstown and the Curragh.

In these areas special police had power to lay before a Justice
of the Peace a complaint against any woman if they had reason
to suppose that she was a common prostitute and diseased. The
Justice could then direct that the woman be medically inspected.

If the scandal of venereal disease could be abated in the seaport towns by police regulations, doctors now contended, what
could be the moral or physical objections to extending the system
elsewhere? For long enough the profession had been mocked by
the Chadwicks of this world for being unwilling to espouse preventive measures. Here was an admirable scheme for checking
the spread of one of the worst diseases to which mankind was heir.

So, in the late 'sixties, leaders of the medical profession threw
themselves into a campaign to enlarge the application of the
Contagious Diseases Acts to the whole of Britain. Soon, they had
an association with a network of 40 branches, and behind them
were the presidents of the Royal College of Physicians and the
Royal College of Surgeons. So were a number of generals,
admirals, dons and bishops.

The would-be reformers were puzzled at the stubbornness of

The Woman Doctor

Doctor Evangeline: By the Bye, Mr Sawyer, are you engaged tomorrow afternoon? I have rather a ticklish operation to perform—an amputation, you know.

Mr Sawyer: I shall be very happy to do it for you.

Dr Evangeline: O, no, not that! But will you kindly come and administer the chloroform for me? (1872)

H

the opposition. There were critics who said the proposed extension was an infringement of the rights of the individual, and who were not ready to concede that the rights of humanity at large outweighed those of degraded females. Others objected to a system of police rule which might well suit the corrupted nations of the Continent but which was contrary to the letter and spirit of the Great Charter. Shrill in their denunciation of the Acts were the feminists, who (in the words of the *Annual Register*) were 'not ashamed to use arguments in public which men on their side were too modest to answer.' These vociferous females objected that the Acts were degrading to women, even to degraded women, and served to maintain different standards of morality for the two sexes. They also protested, not without cause, that while doctors could express themselves as they liked on this topic, women, in marshalling the contrary arguments, were accused of being prurient and indecent.

In 1871 *The Times* roundly condemned the behaviour of an immodest body of men and women who, 'fresh from the oratorical excitements of a conference,' descended on an embarrassed Home Secretary, who nevertheless rallied sufficiently to rebuke them with great sternness. There had been no scene like it, said *The Times,* since the notorious day when the Reform League took possession of the Home Office.

The opposition to the Acts was ill-organised and often ill-advised. It gathered strength and cohesion when James (later Sir James) Stansfeld gave up his political career to further the fight. He sought to show, not only that a system of registration was contrary to British tradition, but that it actively encouraged vice and did not decrease the incidence of the disease.

Year in, year out, the wrangle went on. Both sides were sincere. Both sides had what seemed incontrovertible moral arguments. Unfortunately neither side had statistics which were conclusive. The special police claimed that they were the means of reclaiming prostitutes from their trade, but social workers told of prostitutes who waved their 'tickets of health' in front of guileless young men as a token that they might be brought to bed with impunity. The Duke of Cambridge, Commander-in-Chief, was convinced that the system as already operated in Britain had been of moral benefit not only to the Services but to the community at large, and his view was endorsed by the Army's regimental surgeons; but Sir John Simon, now Medical Officer to the Privy Council, contended that the registration system on the Continent had proved a failure. It was left to Mrs Josephine Butler to describe vividly and with emotion the humiliations of the less-hardened prostitutes under the police system. Nobody dramatised the lot of the unhappy surgeons in the seaport towns who did their best to discipline long queues of impatient, derisive and intractable women waiting for the ordeal of introspection.

In 1874 a rival association of doctors began to work for repeal of the Acts, and steadily increased its support. Eventually it became clear that, in spite of the regulations, disease was slowly increasing in the seaport towns (it was increasing elsewhere, too). In 1886 the Acts were repealed and a vexed chapter of social history was closed. Cynics noted that doctors had helped to defeat a reform which doctors had struggled to introduce.

In 1875 Queen Victoria, echoing the distress of many of her subjects at reports of animals undergoing vivisection, begged Joseph Lister to lend his powerful voice to censuring the practice.

The Queen was taken aback by Lister's reply. He sent her a long letter in which he made it quite clear that he was in favour of experiments on animals. The only alternative, he said, was to try out new remedies on human beings, as was the practice in the Dark Ages. As tactfully as possible, Lister drew the Queen's attention to one of the less-advertised facts of life, namely that . . .

'. . . all oxen and the great majority of our male domestic animals, such as sheep, pigs, and horses, have been subjected to an operation involving exquisite agony in its execution, and often severe pain from subsequent inflammation in the wound, the object being to make them more easily fattened for slaughter, their flesh more fitted for human food, or in the case of the horse to render them more patient and docile servants. Compared with practices like these, that which has received the odious appellation of vivisection is justified by far nobler and higher objects; not the ministering to the luxury or comfort of a generation, but devising means which will be available throughout all time for procuring the health of mankind, the greatest of earthly blessings, and prolonging of human life.'

Lister went on to argue that the sensibilities of an animal were less acute the lower it stood in the scale of creation. Hence, the pain suffered by frogs, the most common subjects of experiment, was 'really of an insignificant and trifling character.' The lower animals lacked the faculty of reflection and knew nothing of the agonies of anticipation; 'they have not the ability to reflect on and appreciate the horrors of their situation. The story sometimes told of a dog licking the hand of a physiologist in the course of an experiment is, if properly regarded, much more striking as a proof of absence of suffering in the animal than of cruelty in the physiologist.'

Finally, Lister said : 'All the so-called vivisections that take place in a year in Great Britain would, if done without anaesthetics, cause less torture than may result from the winging of pheasants in a single day's sport on the *battue* system.'

The Queen was left with something new to think about when next she rode behind docile horses in the Mall, or watched the guns return from a day's sport at Balmoral.

The controversy over vivisection had grown steadily more acute as the science of physiology had advanced. Albrecht von Haller had laid down, in the previous century, that 'it is not sufficient to make dissections of the dead bodies of animals. It is necessary to incise them in the living state. There is no action in the dead body; all movement must be studied in the living animal and the whole of physiology turns on the motions, external and internal, of the living body . . . A single experiment will sometimes refute the laborious speculations of years.'

Sir Charles Bell, whose work on the nervous system put him in the Harvey class, was one of many British experimenters who accepted Haller's dictum with reserve. In 1822 he informed his brother : 'I shall write a third paper on the nerves but I cannot proceed without making some experiments which are so unpleasant to make that I defer them. You may think me silly but I cannot perfectly convince myself that I am authorised in nature or religion to do these cruelties . . . and yet what are my experiments in comparison with those that are daily done and are done daily for nothing?'

This was from a man who had amputated limbs on the field of Waterloo, from six a.m. to seven p.m., for three consecutive days.

Bell's contemporary, John Abernethy, was another eminent surgeon who did not approve of experiments on living animals. His biographer, George McIlwain, also a surgeon, was of like mind, condemning 'the thousands of dreadful experiments which have been made on living animals and the utter inconclusiveness of them for any useful purpose.'

Those who deemed it necessary to experiment on animals usually took pains to ensure privacy, but news of their activities leaked out by way of window cleaners, charwomen and students. In many a community there was a dog-catcher who was rumoured to kidnap pets for supply to surgeons (Sir Astley Cooper's servant Charles was one of them), and such *entrepreneurs* demonstrably exist today. The more inquisitive layman could always glean a good idea from medical writings of the kind of experiment that was going on. There were journals with advertisements for 'Czermak's rabbit-holder' or 'Brunton's holder for dogs and rabbits.' There was a textbook describing how the nerves of a 'fresh, strong frog' could be delicately destroyed so that 'the left leg will remain motionless, being simply dragged along by the rest of the body.' Other recommended experiments began, 'Give the dog a hearty meal, so as to distend the stomach completely . . .' or 'In a curarised rabbit, in which artificial respiration is maintained in the usual way . . .'

Those who cared about such things could not help wondering how many experiments of this sort were conducted with an eye on the relief of human suffering, how many for routine demonstration, and how many for mere dilettantism. Was it essential for every medical student to see a live heart beating? Anyway, how did the doctors *know* that the lower animals could not feel? Having seen dogs cringe, the public found it hard to believe that an animal could not share man's 'agonies of anticipation.' They could not follow the logic of those who defended the killing of animals by saying that to an animal death was only an eternal sleep, whereas to a man it was the beginning of a new existence. If animals had no after-life—and it was a big if—why send them prematurely to their eternal sleep? It was possible to entertain these doubts without accusing the doctors, as did critics at a later day, of a desire to pursue professional knowledge free from the restraints of law, honour and pity. In fact, it was the doctors who first precipitated the vivisection controversy. A group of them protested against the experiments at Norwich in 1874 by a Frenchman who reduced dogs to unconsciousness with absinthe (this was one experiment, it was felt, in which human volunteers might well have been forthcoming).

The leaders of the profession pooh-poohed the doubts and qualms being voiced by the public. If there was any risk of pain, they said, the creature was anaesthetised. Many of the tales they dismissed as mere window-cleaners' tittle-tattle. Would those who complained loudly about experiments on animals shrink to take advantage of knowledge acquired in that way? Or were they humbugs in the same class as the anti-anatomists?

There was enough unrest, however, to justify the Government setting up a Royal Commission on Vivisection, which heard evidence in 1875. Among its members was Professor T. H. Huxley. Though strenuous attempts were made to show that cruelty to animals, in so far as it existed, was a purely Continental vice, the Commission felt obliged to voice certain qualms, not least on the subject of frogs. Why, they asked Lister, was the frog so popular as the 'physiologist's animal?' The answer was: 'It is selected for its convenience, because it is so tolerant of severe treatment, and also undoubtedly largely from the fact of its being not supposed to suffer materially.' This was not quite what Lister had told Queen Victoria. The Commission, after commenting on the import trade in large frogs from Germany, and on the fact that a good many of the creatures were denied the privilege of anaesthesia, said that the doctrine of 'frogs can't feel' was 'one which ought not to be too readily admitted.'

Among the witnesses was Dr T. L. Brunton, lecturer on *materia medica* at St Bartholomew's, who spoke of the research he had been conducting into cholera. For this he used large numbers of cats—60 in a series.

'How do you procure your cats?—They are supplied to me by a man.

'Who steals them for the purpose, I suppose?—I make no enquiries.'

Similar evidence came from Dr J. Burdon-Sanderson, Professor of Human Physiology in University College, London, who said he depended on his servant for his supply of animals. He complained: 'There is no proper provision in this country by which one can obtain dogs even for the most legitimate purposes and of course I am not informed as to the way in which they are obtained. They are always paid for at a proper price.'

Dr W. Sharpey, Professor of Physiology at University College, said that as a young man he had been 'utterly repelled' by the demonstrations on animals by Majendie in Paris. These had been conducted in pre-anaesthetic days, had involved much pain and had no sufficient object, one of the more superfluous experiments being to show that the skin of a rabbit was sensitive by making cuts in it. He said that no medical students in Britain were required to conduct experiments on animals. As against this, a veterinary surgeon told how, when he was a student at Edinburgh, veterinary and medical students used to go out on dog and cat hunts, a sport which, seemingly, had replaced the 'Vesalian crusade,' catching their victims by poisoned baits and, after administering antidotes, subjecting them to agonies in cupboards in their lodgings; all with 'no other motive than idle curiosity and heedless, reckless love of experimentation.' He exonerated the professors from complicity.

John Colam, secretary of the Royal Society for the Prevention of Cruelty to Animals, said he thought that many experimenters on animals were exceeding 'the legitimate province of science,' but he made no charges of wanton cruelty. It emerged from his evidence that the Royal Humane Society had asked the profession to devise more effective ways of resuscitating the drowned. This had led to a series of experiments in drowning and reviving animals, which was perhaps not the type of research the Royal Humane Society had had in mind.

The possibly brutalising effect of cruelty on the experimenter— a subject on which psychologists and psychiatrists would be only too happy to discourse today—was touched on by the Rev. S. Haughton, M.D., a fellow of Trinity College, Dublin. Already, he said, it was a moral trial for a young man to pass through the hospital death-house and the dissecting room ('it degrades some characters and elevates others'). If, on top of this, young men were to be familiarised with the sight of animals under vivisection, he believed that 'many of them would become cruel and hardened and would go away to repeat these experiments recklessly, without foresight or forethought; science would gain nothing and the world would have let loose upon it a set of young devils.'

Perhaps the most startling glimpse of the spiritual agony to which vivisection, supposedly, could bring its devotees was the fate which was said to have overtaken a fellow of the Royal College of Physicians in Edinburgh. This distinguished anatomist was attacked by cancer of the tongue, which he regarded as a punishment for the tortures he had inflicted on animals. Before his death he spent 'sleepless nights of unquenchable agony,' punctuated by 'demon voices reiterating blasphemies and hoarsely whispering "Curse God and die!"'

Although no real evidence of enormities against animals was laid before the Royal Commission, the members apparently felt themselves unable to overlook such views as those expressed by Sir William Fergusson, Sergeant Surgeon to the Queen, who said there was much needless repetition of experiments.

'You think that if the public really knew what was actually going on in this country at this time they would expect an interference on the part of Crown and Parliament? — I do think so, just as much as with reference to the disinterring of dead bodies years ago.'

The Commission, therefore, recommended the necessary 'interference,' and in 1876 an Act was passed controlling experiments on all but invertebrate animals. To the leaders of the profession this was a slur on their good name. It was no great consolation that the factory owners had also suffered a slur in being prevented by law from exploiting children. A historian of the British Medical Association has complained that the Act was passed 'without any valid evidence of the need for it being produced.' He says: 'It has never been demonstrated that in this country any cruelty has attended physiological investigations.'*

Henceforth, all experiments on animals were to be conducted in registered places, open to Government inspection, by operators who had obtained the requisite licences. Animals were to be anaesthetised, unless anaesthesia would spoil the object of the operation, and, if likely to suffer pain on recovering consciousness, destroyed.

The controversy was not, of course, stilled. Many of the arguments which were bandied about in 1875 are just as applicable to the projection of dogs into space. But there were doctors, as well as laymen, who welcomed the restrictions. In his *Memories and Adventures,* Sir Arthur Conan Doyle tells of his studies in Edinburgh in the 1870s, under Professor William Rutherford (who served, in part, as a model for 'Professor Challenger'):

'He was, I fear, a rather ruthless vivisector, and though I have always recognised that a minimum of painless vivisection is necessary, and far more justifiable than the eating of meat as a food, I am glad that the law was made more stringent so as to restrain such men as he. "Ach, these Jarman frags!" he would exclaim in his curious accent as he tore some poor amphibian to pieces.'

Professor Rutherford, it is relevant to note, had been one of

* E. M. Little: *History of the British Medical Association.*

the witnesses before the Royal Commission. He had assured the members that frogs were 'almost always' anaesthetised or rendered insensible before experiment, and that students would resent the cruelty involved in allowing an anaesthetised animal to recover consciousness after being subjected to severe experiments.

The fact that a frog successfully performed certain functions after death ensured it a place in the medical student's teaching— and the championship, in due course, of Shaw, who has never been more eloquent than when attacking 'the sensual villainies and cut-throat's casuistries of vivisection.' It had not occurred to the anti-vivisectionists of 1875 to accuse doctors of deriving a sensual thrill from cruelty.

The Act of 1876 encouraged the anti-vivisectionists to new efforts. Much of their propaganda was now directed towards try-ing to make experiments on dogs illegal. Periodically the doctors drew their attention to the ten million or so acts of vivisection performed annually without anaesthetics on farm cattle, and enquired how many of their critics were consistent enough to be vegetarians, but the 'shambles of science' remained the favourite target.

As a pendant to the vivisection controversy, there was the long-drawn-out fuss in the 'eighties and 'nineties over the muzzling of dogs. The doctors argued with some force that muzzling and quarantining would cut down rabies. Obtuse sentimentalists, who were ready to argue that rabies could come of its own accord or be contracted from a broken leg, formed themselves into a Dog Owners' Protection Association. The doctors replied with a Society for the Prevention of Hydrophobia and Reform of the Dog Laws, under Sir Victor Horsley, the surgeon. For many years the muzzling orders were enforced haphazardly and ineffectively. Dog owners in muzzling areas regarded it as a point of honour to take their dogs to non-muzzling areas for a free scamper. To all but the besotted it became statistically clear that when muzzling was imposed deaths from rabies dropped, and increased when it was lifted. At last in 1897 a strong man came to the Board of Agriculture in the person of Walter (later Viscount) Long. Despite furious protests he ruthlessly enforced, all over the country, muzzling, quarantining and detention orders, and at the same time exterminated thousands of pariahs. As a result, he wiped out rabies in Britain.

The medical issues in the controversy over vaccination are beyond the scope of these pages. What is worth recalling is the extraordinary virulence with which the profession was assailed by the anti-vaccinationists and the charges of racketeering and bad faith which were hurled at them. When Lady Mary Wortley Montagu had first sought to introduce inoculation against small-pox into Britain, a century and a half earlier, she had doubted whether the doctors had 'virtue enough to destroy such a con-siderable branch of their revenue (from treating smallpox) for the good of mankind.' Now, in the great smallpox pandemic of 1870–73, the doctors were accused of even more cynical wicked-ness, namely of clamouring to make people undergo vaccination purely for the sake of the fees they could derive from the opera-tion, being well aware that it was a gigantic fraud and would do nothing to lessen the incidence of smallpox.

Vaccination had an unhappy history. Since Jenner's day there had been much trial, much error. Many persons who had been vaccinated caught smallpox; nor was the theory of immunisation helped by the fact that some who had already had smallpox caught it again. On top of it all, a thin trickle of deaths had been directly caused by vaccination. But that pandemic of 1870, as it now appears, would have caused an even greater death-roll in Britain had it not been for the fact that compulsory vaccination had been in operation for nearly a generation. It had been enforced with varying degrees of efficiency. A smallpox scare would bring a rush of patients; but in between scares the public and the authorities grew slack.

During the visitation in the early 'seventies—the worst in memory—the public which had rushed to be vaccinated began to entertain serious doubts as to the efficacy of the treatment. They could not see the emergency in the perspective of history; all they knew was that both the vaccinated and the unvaccinated were dying of smallpox. Even doctors began to doubt the worth of vaccination and some refused to practise it. The subject was ready-made for pamphleteering. In 1874, for instance, appeared a booklet with the compendious title: *The Terrible Effects of Vaccination and Re-Vaccination (so-called) one of the great causes of disease, suffering and death, smallpox in particular . . . supported by evidence from the first annual report of the Birmingham Medical Officer of Health that out of 794 smallpox*

*cases for the year 1873, 713 had been vaccinated and out of 122
deaths, 81 had been vaccinated. By Henry Port FSA.*

This pamphleteer seems to have had no difficulty in finding
statements from doctors opposing vaccination. Dr William Hitch-
man of Liverpool, described as president of the British Medical
Reform Association, was quoted as saying that 'vaccination was
only intended to fill the pockets of vaccinating doctors with
hundreds of pounds per week,' and Dr Garth Wilkinson knew
of a colleague who boasted that a smallpox panic was worth
£2,000,000 a year to the profession.

Presumably there were some doctors who got credit for being
sincere when they made such remarks as 'a man has no more right
to allow his child to go unvaccinated than to set fire to his house.'

Towards the end of the century anti-vaccinationists forced the
Government to yield some ground. Parents could defy the vac-
cinator if they were able to convince Justices of the Peace of their
conscientious belief that a child's health would be prejudiced.
Long-suffering benches had to listen to such arguments as 'bulls
go mad every seven years and the cows make them mad; cows
are used to vaccinate children, and the children go mad.' Justices
of the Peace are accustomed to being given impossible tasks to
perform, and they seem to have discharged this one tolerably well.

XXII

RISE OF THE SURGEON

FOR a full generation after anaesthetics were introduced, almost any operation other than a purely surface one was something to be resolutely avoided, but by the end of the century much of the stark terror had gone out of surgery and the day was dawning when an operation would be the smart thing to have.

In theory, the use of anaesthetics had opened up new vistas of opening up; but such was the incidence of infection that the exploration of hitherto forbidden territories had to be severely curtailed. A man could penetrate the Amazon only so far before the poison darts of an unseen enemy stopped his progress.

It is plainly unfair, at this day, to condemn the medical profession for the failure of so many of them to grasp the idea that an invisible lethal taint could be carried about by an apparently clean person. It is harder to forgive them for tolerating in their operating rooms standards of uncleanliness which even the eighteenth century had recognised to be undesirable. Hospital surgeons had grown fatalistic about deaths. All they knew was that they could expect runs of good luck and then runs of bad luck. This applied, in a lesser degree, even to the general practitioner in his role as man-midwife.

The Victorian novelists had a tremendous tragic theme if they had cared to use it : that of the honoured family doctor who, after bringing hundreds of babies into the world, suddenly found himself a pariah. In quick succession, half a dozen of his mothers would die of puerperal fever, along with their infants. As the news got round, mothers-to-be who had once begged his services appealed to him to stay away from their doors, and sent for far-away practitioners. In his agonised mind the doctor would debate his duty : should he continue his daily round, hoping that his luck might change, or should he abandon his career? Or perhaps strike out fresh somewhere else? Occasionally a doctor would decide to go out of practice for a while, if not for good, reflecting bitterly that, over the years, he had slain more than he had saved.

That these tragedies did happen anyone can discover from the bitter essay by Oliver Wendell Holmes on *The Contagiousness of Puerperal Fever*, originally published in 1843. Holmes was not the first to draw attention to the way in which medical men and midwives carried their own contagion. He republished his essay, with additions, in 1855. In the interval Ignaz Semmelweiss had shown, in Vienna, how students from the dissecting rooms carried death into the hospital wards, and how the lives of mothers could be saved by the use of chlorinated lime water. For this, incredibly, he was driven from his appointment by angry rivals, and, not being a natural fighter, he failed to make the stand for which humanity was waiting.

It was not only the doctors of the Old World who were unable to see the light. Eminent contemporaries of Oliver Wendell Holmes bitterly repudiated the notion that a doctor could be a minister of death. The professor of obstetrics at Jefferson Medical College, Professor Charles Meigs, said of deaths from puerperal fever: 'I prefer to attribute them to accident or Providence, of which I can form a conception, rather than to a contagion of which I cannot form any clear idea.'

Often, these puerperal deaths were caused because a doctor had picked up the contagion at a post-mortem and then continued on his rounds with no more than a routine wash, if that. Holmes has a nigh-incredible story of an Edinburgh doctor who, after attending a post-mortem on a woman who had died from puerperal fever, carried the pelvic viscera in his pocket to the classroom, then that same evening attended a woman in labour without changing his clothes. She died. Next day he delivered another woman, who also died. Nor was she the last.

In British hospitals, as in those of Vienna, eager but unscrubbed students carried infection into the lying-in wards. It was as well that a student could never know how many deaths he had unwittingly caused before he set out on the business of saving life.

Holmes, after outlining the precautions to be observed by practitioners who had come into contact with puerperal infection, wrote:

'Whatever indulgence may be granted to those who have heretofore been the ignorant causes of so much misery, the time has come when the existence of a *private pestilence* in the sphere of a single physician should be looked upon not as a misfortune but a crime; and in the knowledge of such occurrences the duties of the practitioner to his profession should give way to the paramount obligations to society.'

This grim period between anaesthetics and antisepsis was, of all periods, the one in which it could be said that 'the operation was successful but the patient died.' According to Sir Rickman Godlee, a nephew of Lord Lister, the pre-Lister surgeons had grown to dread the blind Nemesis that presided over their work. 'Operations of mere expediency—"operations of convenience"— were seldom performed. To undertake them was thought to be tempting Providence.'* Sir John Erichsen in the 'seventies had a mortality rate in his amputation cases of between 24 and 26 per cent. This, he said, 'may be considered a very satisfactory result, although there can be no question that it is one that admits, and that ought to be susceptible of, improvement.'† In Edinburgh Infirmary the rate was 43 per cent, in Paris as high as 60 per cent, in America as low as 24 per cent.

Sir Rickman Godlee is one of many who have written sorrowfully about that homicidal fetish—the blood-caked frock-coat which many eminent surgeons reserved for use in the operating theatre. In earlier days surgeons wore aprons, which they were supposed to change when bloody, if only to avoid frightening the patient; but the wearing of aprons seems to have died out and an old frock coat was considered correct wear for the operation theatre through most of Victoria's reign. Often this garment had already done duty in the dissecting room before being relegated to the theatre, where it would be kept behind the door. Sometimes it would be so caked with blood and filth that it could have stood up by itself. Yet, in the words of one chronicler, it was revered by its owner as a peer reveres his faded ceremonial clothes. Nurses, since the days of Florence Nightingale, had been clean and even fastidious, yet it was left to the operating surgeon to set an example of uncleanliness of which he was perversely proud.

The coats worn by the assistant surgeons were many degrees

* *Lord Lister.*
† *Ibid.*

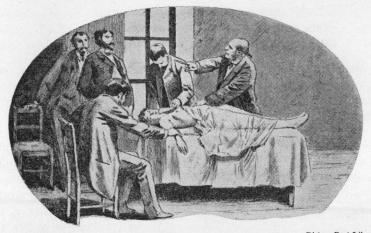

An operation, 1890

less repulsive, but were a long way from being clean. It was customary for the house surgeon to have in his lapel half a dozen needles already threaded with silken strands, dangling over his clothing.

How Lister initiated the reform which changed all this is an oft-told story. First came antisepsis, with carbolic sprays drenching the atmosphere. Then was spread the idea that, instead of having sprays working in a dirty room among dirty people, it would be better to have clean people in a clean room, without sprays. The revolution was not achieved without heavy opposition. The old, dyed-in-blood surgeons in their obscene frock coats mocked the young for the pantomime of white overalls, of boiling and scrubbing and sterilising. Some of these hygienic ideas came from America, which was enough to condemn them. Berkeley (later Lord) Moynihan, after returning from a transatlantic visit about 1903, caused amusement by wearing rubber gloves. When a witty Frenchman saw him putting on white rubber shoes before starting an abdominal operation, he said, 'Does he then stand in the abdomen while he works?'*

The poet W. E. Henley, who was an inmate of the old Edinburgh Infirmary in the 'seventies, has left a sharply etched picture of hospital life from the viewpoint of the patient waiting for an operation.† Physically as well as psychologically, the atmosphere was all wrong:

* Donald Bateman: *Berkeley Moynihan.*   † *A Book of Verses* (1888).

'A tragic meanness seems so to environ
These corridors and stairs of stone and iron,
Cold, naked, clean—half workhouse and half jail.'

No bells rang for strong men to hold the patient down, but the notion of sparing his feelings by anaesthetising him before entry into the operation theatre was yet to come. Henley feelingly describes how :

'You are carried in a basket,
Like a carcase from the shambles,
To the theatre, a cockpit,
Where they stretch you on a table . . .'

There, before succumbing to

'The thick, sweet mystery of chloroform,
The drunken dark, the little death in life,'

the patient might still be privileged to listen to a blood-spattered old man describing him as 'the case.' Only the bravest of altruists, or the Ailies of this world, on seeing a hundred students peering down, could feel pleasure in being of so much help to so many. Afterwards there was the ordeal of the surgeon's rounds :

'Surging along,
Louts, duffers, exquisites, students and prigs—
Whiskers and foreheads, scarf pins and spectacles—
Hustle the Class !'

Who these louts, duffers, exquisites and prigs were, if they were not students or junior surgeons, is difficult to say.

Henley was a patient of Lister, about whom he wrote a far from captious sonnet ending :

'We hold him for another Herakles,
Battling with custom, prejudice, disease,
As once the son of Zeus with Death and Hell.'

It may well have been the first sonnet ever written in honour of a surgeon by a grateful patient, and as historic an event in its way as the peerage which Lister earned in 1897—the first ever granted to a medical man.

As the perils of sepsis receded, the status of the surgeon changed dramatically. Tremendous conquests were now within his grasp.

An operation in the early Listerian period. Note carbolic spray

Well before the century's end the human belly was open to the knife. So was the chest. So was the womb. So was the brain. Surgeons were performing feats for which, as Sir W. Mitchell Banks said, they would have been prosecuted a generation before. Sir Spencer Wells took a dangerous, discredited operation like ovariotomy and, in the face of professional apprehension and antagonism, showed how it could be made safe. Surgeons of his calibre deserve no less credit for their moral bravery than their technical brilliance. In 1887 the first successful operation for appendicitis was performed. Two years later delegates to a meeting of the British Medical Association were shown a new method of operation on the prostate and were led to a waiting-room where they saw 'the astounding spectacle of seven or eight old men sitting on a bench with their prostates in bottles on their knees.'*

Sometimes progress was too fast for the ruling bodies. When Sir William MacEwen was questioned for his F.R.C.S., he described the brain operation and was asked, 'Whose operation is that?' He replied 'Mine,' and was greeted with laughter. He said, 'Well, I have done 300 or 400 cases already,' and was again laughed at. His operation became a recognised one.†

These surgeons who ventured into new caves of the living body still had to work rapidly. Only with the improvements in anaesthetics, in the early years of the twentieth century, could they begin to develop an unhurried, deliberate technique. But the fabulous operators who had taken off legs and arms as if by legerdemain were no longer wanted. It was one skill which humanity could afford to lose, though not without awed gratitude to the hardy individuals who had mastered it.

For some time inventors had been producing ingenious searchlights for illuminating the orifices of the body, but in 1895 came a more valuable aid to diagnosis in the shape of the X-ray. Certain sections of public and press were greatly upset by this invention, supposing that it would enable the lecherous to go round peering at women through their clothing. As it turned out, the physical dangers of X-rays were greater than the moral dangers; but it proved the great diagnostic boon for which surgery had been waiting.

The surgeon entered the new century as something of a popular

---

* Sir Charles Brown: *Sixty-Four Years a Doctor.*
† Dr H. B. W. Morgan, *Hansard*, July 14, 1950.

hero, a man henceforth destined to share the not-always-welcome
limelight turned on him by an inquisitive press. In the popular
mind his prestige had begun to outweigh that of the physician;
the plain 'Mister,' as he obstinately called himself, was outstrip-
ping the 'Doctor.' Here was a man who had as much skill and
subtlety in his fingers as a great violinist, a brain as cool and
calculating as a general's, even though it was steeped in so many
recondite sciences. When lesser men were still yawning at their
office desks in the morning, the surgeon was displaying courage,
subtlety, strength and judgment at an operating table, recovering
not only tin whistles from the stomachs of children but bullets
from the skulls of policemen. Of course he soaked the rich (and
good luck to him!) but he remained faithful to the old tradition
of aiding the poor for nothing. What greater stature could a man
desire? What higher satisfaction than to see, happily going about
their lawful occasions, men and women who but for his interven-
tion would assuredly have been six feet underground? Was it not
a surgeon who, in 1902, saved the life of the new monarch by
relieving him of his appendix? Nobody grudged Sir Frederick
Treves his baronetcy. Surely (reflected the common man) there
was no more awesome assignment than to rip open the paunch
of a king.

Unhappily, the animosities—now nearly a century old—in the
Royal College of Surgeons were not yet stilled. The College was
still immensely conscious of its dignity and privileges, so much so
that one member likened its proud hall to the cave at Boeotia
which so awed those who entered it that they never smiled again.
Two dozen strangely privileged elders could still do virtually anything they pleased, irrespective of the advice or judgment of the
1,200 fellows who elected them and the 14,000 members who
kept the College in funds. These members, with the co-operation
of many of the fellows, formed themselves into an association to
fight for their rights. They demanded a share in electing the
council; they sought permission to hold meetings in the College;
and they called for free access to its facilities at all reasonable
times. When the College, in the 'eighties, began to negotiate for
a new charter its move was opposed by the largest petition ever
signed by medical men and a deputation of protest waited on the
Privy Council. In 1889 the rebels called a meeting in the College
but found themselves locked out, whereupon they retreated
wrathfully to the Holborn Restaurant. It was time, they decided,

to go to law against the president and council of the College, and
they did. Three years later, Mr Justice Romer, without calling
on the defendants, ruled against the dissident members. 'To the
lay mind,' he said, 'there may appear to be something in the
plaintiffs' contention, but it is evident to the legal mind that there
is nothing in their case.'

To some lay minds, it must have seemed that if a grievance
could last for a century there was probably something in it. However, there were welcome signs that, at the eleventh hour, geniality
and brotherliness were beginning to radiate from the Trophonic
cave.

XXIII

SHADOW OF SOCIALISM

By Edwardian times, the general practitioner was beginning to grow apprehensive about his status.

It was becoming dismayingly clear that, with the leaping advances in physic, surgery and their new ancillary sciences, no one man could master the whole field of medicine. Soon the practitioner would face the choice of picking up a smattering of everything or of becoming a specialist. In the previous century the specialists had embraced mainly the eye, ear, nose and throat men, the obstetricians and the 'mind doctors,' who wrestled empirically with a problem other men preferred to dodge. Now, specialisms showed signs of multiplying more rapidly. No longer could a family doctor make any pretence to omniscience. His patients knew it and he knew that they knew it. Often, indeed, they offended him by the eagerness with which they suggested recourse to a specialist. In his heart, the established family doctor knew that he was in danger of being stranded at the rear of the column; while he was tending the wounded the vanguard were marching over the hill and out of sight. As in Fisher's Navy, the newcomers knew more of the science of their profession than those who had spent a lifetime in it, though the old men might well know more about the art. Anyway, how was a busy practitioner to keep abreast? The medical journals, with their digests of esoteric knowledge, their pictures of hobnailed livers, lay in unread stacks in the corner of the surgery.

There was much discontent in the profession, some of it engendered by the revolution through which it was passing. In the first place, there were too many doctors. For every practitioner who charged a guinea, there was one who charged five shillings and another who was ready to take sixpence. The friendly societies were as unfriendly as ever, and the boards of guardians

245

as tyrannous. A new breed of midwives, trained in accordance with the Midwives Act of 1902, were cutting into the doctor's income (how the ghost of Mrs Nihell must have laughed at that one!). Well-to-do patients were contriving to obtain cheap treatment in hospitals. Quacks were still prospering and there were curious instances of adventurers impersonating doctors who had died or emigrated. The Peculiar People, a sect who tried to cure their children's measles and pneumonia by hard praying, often with disastrous results, were being handled much too leniently by the authorities; so were the Christian Scientists. Unscrupulous manufacturers were teaching the nation to dose itself with medicines which ought to be prescribed, if at all, by doctors. In 1906 a newspaper announced that it would give free medical advice to anybody who filled in a coupon, a threat which was fairly speedily overthrown. Ungrateful or opportunist patients had taken to suing surgeons for what they fancied to be malpractice, but the formation of a Medical Defence League was beginning to discourage the litigious. The spread of that newfangled instrument, the telephone, was making it easier for patients to get the doctor up in the middle of the night, and harass his wife by day. On top of it all, Socialists were openly urging that all doctors should be turned into Civil Servants.

The most vexatious of these Socialists was George Bernard Shaw, whose play *The Doctor's Dilemma* was first staged in 1906. It can hardly be said that the dilemma propounded—whether a doctor should seek to save the life of a brilliant but amoral artist at the expense of a dull but decent member of society—bore much relation to real life, but the public enjoyed the piquant and apparently knowledgeable medical exchanges. 'We shall not say that he (Shaw) has used his opportunity unfairly,' wrote the *British Medical Journal,* 'and we could even wish *The Doctor's Dilemma* when played in London this week had been more successful.' The *Journal* thought that the part of the elderly doctor to whom every new discovery was merely a revival of an old one was very well drawn. It did not believe in the Jewish doctor who had prospered by dint of using the slogan 'Cure Guaranteed'—'we must confess that we have never met this person.' Sir Ralph Bloomfield Bonnington was too much of a donkey.

The Preface to the play, published later, showed that Shaw had a great deal more to say about doctors than he could cram into a play. Medical practice, he declared in his opening sentence, was 'a murderous absurdity.' Thanks largely to its attitude on vivisection, the medical profession had an 'infamous character'; it was also a brigand class and like all professions a conspiracy against the laity. There was much in the Preface that was silly, much that was inflammatory, and much that, if taken literally, was scurrilous; as, for instance, the allegation that surgeons were deliberately cutting off limbs and extirpating organs for the sake of the guineas (a charge which could not have been sustained against any individual practitioner). Equally scurrilous were the charges that any doctor would allow a colleague to decimate a whole countryside before violating the bonds of professional etiquette, and that the final test applied to every treatment was, 'Is it lucrative?'

Stripped of its nonsense, the Preface was a potent argument for increasing the doctor's self-respect, and diminishing his temptations, by paying him a fixed salary. Freed of the need to depend on the prevalence of illness, the profession could then become 'a body of men trained and paid by the country to keep the country in health.'

In so far as it may have encouraged the population to attach greater value to their organs, the Shavian blast may have done some good. Equally, it may have done harm. As Shaw concedes, it is rarely that anyone can prove after the event that an operation would have been unnecessary. The layman cannot pretend to know what goes on in a surgeon's mind. He knows that a criminal handful of surgeons will perform illegal operations for gain, but he finds it hard to believe that, in the profession at large, the prospect of gold ever swayed more than a negligible number of surgeons into reaching a decision to operate. It is much easier to see that a surgeon would prefer to play safe rather than risk letting his patient die, or live to sue him for neglect. The fact that one surgeon will refuse to operate while another will consent to do so does not mean that the first is an honourable man and the other is thinking only of his fees. If, at the time of which Shaw is writing, there were unnecessary operations, the blame is to be attributed to the imperfect state of medical knowledge rather than to a crude itch for wealth. That there were, as Shaw says, unbalanced individuals ready to try to bribe surgeons into performing unnecessary extirpations, and others who wished to bask in the notoriety of a sensational operation may be conceded; but their numbers cannot have been many.

The Preface contains a friendly reference to *The New Religion* (1907), a melodramatic novel by Maarten Maartens about medical chicanery in general and sanatorium abuses in particular, the villain being a doctor who sends a wife on an unnecessary visit to Switzerland and then acquires her house to turn into a nursing home. One of Maartens' characters says that operations have been financially successful for the last 25 years but are now being played out; the public has decided that the thyroid gland and the appendix may not be entirely superfluous. The doctors are described as 'an immense international association for drawing on the loss of religious faith by the modern well-to-do.'

'The world has given up caring about its soul; it has got all the more anxious about its body. The old beliefs have gone; your digestion's your conscience today . . . We cannot make half out of our own "homes" what the priests made out of hell ! But the convents of the twentieth century to which the new fanatics come crowding are the Sanatoria.'

For all the epithets he hurled at them, Shaw claims to have been on good terms with doctors, though once in Ireland, according to St John Ervine's biography, Mrs Shaw had some difficulty in persuading a practitioner who had read *The Doctor's Dilemma* to look at her husband's twisted ankle. His secretary, Miss Blanche Patch, maintains that he was not prejudiced against the profession : 'It was never really difficult to persuade him to call in the doctor if he was really ill.'* To the scandal and dismay of his vegetarian friends, he allowed himself to be inoculated with liver extract.

The idea of a doctor becoming a vassal of the State, which was what Shaw appeared to be recommending, was one which heartily shocked the traditionalists in the profession. Yet, in fact, large numbers of doctors were already labouring in varying degrees of bondage to Oddfellows, Druids, Foresters, Rechabites, Gardeners, and, of course, Poor Law Guardians. Often, their vassalage was abject.

At this date, there were many kinds of contract practice. A

* *Thirty Years With George Bernard Shaw.*

doctor might organise his personal club for impecunious families, imposing his own conditions and 'means test.' The charge would be, perhaps, twopence or threepence a week per family. A few hard-pressed doctors employed canvassers to persuade people to join their clubs, the canvasser taking a 25 per cent commission (or, occasionally, the entire proceeds). Alternatively, a doctor might be appointed to serve a friendly society, trade union lodge or benefit club, or a number of such bodies, at an agreed salary, on the understanding that he treated all members who presented themselves. Again, he might be under contract to a colliery, undertaking to perform underground amputations and resuscitations as well as looking after the miners' families, all for threepence or fourpence a week (confinements half a guinea). Quarries, foundries and railway yards similarly had doctors under contract.

In the Highlands of Scotland a doctor might operate an estate medical club in which cottars, ghillies and shepherds contributed a trivial dole and the landowner, if enlightened, added a sum equal to his workers' contributions, perhaps even providing the doctor with a pony.

Another variant of club practice was the 'district provident dispensary,' employing several doctors, where treatment could be obtained at the rate of three-halfpence a week for man and wife and a halfpenny for each child under 14. Those who waited until they were ill before joining paid a fine of five shillings.

Whether a contract practice worked smoothly depended largely on the conscience of the doctor. The more tactful and tolerant seem to have lived on good terms with their 'clubbers,' recognising that without their contributions, meagre though they were, they could not have remained in practice. At least the scheme served to cut bad debts and enabled men and women to look their doctor in the face instead of crossing to the other side of the road when they saw him coming, or bolting out of the back door of the house at his unsolicited approach. It was clear to any doctor of sense and humanity that, failing a State medical service, some such scheme had to be operated if the working classes were to receive any medical attention at all.

There is a good description of a humanely run club practice in Francis Brett Young's novel *My Brother Jonathan,* which describes how a young doctor takes over an industrial practice from an older man. Far from being irritated by imposture and importunity, the newcomer is made humble and conscious of his own deficiencies by the uncomplaining courage of his working class patients. There are few whiners among them. Some of them come for encouragement and reassurance, which they are able to derive from a sympathetic doctor even in the very few moments he can allot them.

A number of practitioners, however, were unable to conceal their disdain for contract practice and were perpetually at odds with their flock, who knew only too well that the doctor regarded them as an inferior class of patient. For their part, many patients, notably the healthier ones, cherished the notion that they were doing the doctor a favour in joining his club and were determined not to be fobbed off when their turn for treatment came. If they had a stomach ache in the night, well, they had a *right* to send for the doctor. They had paid for him already.

The abuses to which contract practice was subject were many. Master tradesmen, publicans and others who often earned more than the doctor had no qualms about joining clubs which entitled them to treatment at a penny a week. Towards these, the doctor's attitude was somewhat like that of the present-day author who sees his wealthier neighbours borrowing his books for nothing from the local library. Sometimes the man who had got on in the world remained a club member from a desire to show that he was no snob and was still 'one of the lads,' but the nobility of this motive was lost on an impecunious doctor. As these master tradesmen were often office-bearers in the clubs they would demand a high standard of service, letting the doctor understand that he could always be disciplined or replaced if he proved un-co-operative. Knowing that he was underpaid, they would be all the more alert to catch him out in the sort of dereliction which, they felt, he could hardly avoid. The thought of being hauled up before a working man's committee and accused of malpractice was enough, perhaps, to keep many a practitioner conscientious. The doctor might even be expected to march behind the banners of these procession-loving bodies and to attend their annual dinners, perhaps in the hope that if he was 'buttered up' he would be less likely to ask for more money.

In a contract practice the doctor was under constant pressure to issue perjured certificates. Older patients who had paid in for years would decide that the time had come to get something back out of the club and would ask, on trivial grounds, to be certified as unfit for work. Similar requests came from younger work-shies, malingerers, hypochondriacs and 'waiting-room lawyers'—a class whom the self-respecting practitioner would ordinarily have kicked from his door. Many a doctor complained that the system made him automatically doubt a patient's motives and honesty. His function was to be a doctor, not a detective. Yet he put up with it for his bread and butter and in the hope that he would be able to work up an orthodox practice among the families of the insured. It was peculiarly galling, therefore, to find that some club members, as an exercise in snobbery, made a point of calling in an outside doctor to attend their families, on the grounds that a club doctor was not good enough.

Early in the present century the British Medical Association conducted a canvass of its members on the subject of contract practice. The results, as published in the *British Medical Journal* of July 22, 1905, showed a wide divergence of views. There were those who thought that contract practice was ungentlemanly or should be banned as infamous conduct, one contributor contending that it was degrading to take money for nothing. Others were more concerned to purge the system of its abuses and to raise the sweated rates imposed by the friendly societies. There were plenty of hard luck stories. In a South Wales village a patient received a bottle of medicine almost every day for two and a half years, and the doctor's remuneration was four shillings a year. Another doctor paid more than 1,500 visits, in five years, to a member of the Foresters who was ill with spinal caries—at 1s. 1d. a year. A London doctor complained of being driven out of his home by tipsy members of his society. His neighbour helped, 'somewhat roughly,' to clear out the invaders, and in consequence the doctor was asked to resign. In a Welsh village a farmer worth £12,000 paid 2s. 6d. a year to a doctor who had to travel four miles to see him. A man who had made £30,000 on the sale of a public-house and who owned 'acres of houses' paid his doctor one penny a week. Another doctor wrote: 'I pay the railway porter one shilling for bringing up a parcel to the house; he pays his doctor a shilling a month for his family and himself.'

It was sadly evident that very often, when attempts were made to raise the rate of 4s. a year to a more reasonable figure, fledgling doctors from outside were willing to take on the job for as little as 2s. 6d. Because many doctors canvassed for club posts, and a few even offered bribes, the societies were fortified in their arrogance as dispensers of patronage.

The doctoring of sick paupers came up for investigation once more when another Royal Commission on the Poor Law began to hear evidence in 1905. Once again, as in the days of the young Queen Victoria, the Poor Law doctors described their tribulations. These were the forgotten doctors—men who certified that tramps were fit to weed cobbled drives, who arranged for the removal of lice-covered lunatics from mountain hovels, who amputated gipsies' fingers at the roadside, who battled over stormy straits to attend patients who had no wish to be attended, who examined school children pretending, on parental orders, to have stomach ache in order that they might be withheld from school to attend to more important duties. There were many classes of patients to whom the Poor Law doctor could bring no help and very little hope. Among these were consumptives in crowded dwellings or sunless valleys, and workmen discarded by the industrial machine with their inner economy wrecked. What they needed was what no doctor could supply: food, fresh air, decent houses. All the practitioner could do was palliate their lot or give them illusory hope with bottles of cheap medicine. Occasionally, however, the news got round that there were better things to be had than medicine. There was a macabre episode when the public heard that sufferers from lupus could be cured by the new Finsen light apparatus installed at the London Hospital. The historian of the Hospital, Sir Ernest Morris, tells how men and women with this hideous disfigurement began to creep from their hiding-places. One day the department was a jostling mass of lupus patients. 'There were cheap excursions from all parts of England for the final Football Cup-tie at the Crystal Palace, and these poor people in hundreds had availed themselves of this cheap trip to come up and be cured.' Already, however, the healing lamps had been booked up for two years.

The Royal Commission found itself being alternately nagged and gingered by Beatrice Webb, who was easily the most conscientious and industrious member of it. Her views are contained in the Commission's Minority Report and also in the book *The State and the Doctor* which she and her husband published in 1910. The Webbs said that they were very much impressed by the vast amount of laborious, unrecognised and very ill-paid service done by district medical officers under the Poor Law and by medical officers of health, as well as by private practitioners. 'Such ungrudging and devoted service to the community merits a less invidious method of remuneration and a more adequate reward,' they said. Only a very few district medical officers gave full-time service. In all, one-sixth of the doctors in practice in Britain held poor law appointments.

One of the tragedies of the system, as the Webbs saw it, was that pride so often kept the poor from applying for medical help under the Poor Law. The policy of many boards was to treat all applicants as potential swindlers, and to hector them as to their drinking habits. By the time the poor had screwed up courage to brave the insolence of the relieving officer, it was often too late. The result was that workhouses were choked with people who would never have had to go there if their illnesses had been attended earlier.

If pride caused pauperism, so did shame. Clubs and dispensaries barred patients suffering from venereal disease and neither poor law nor public health authorities would treat it, until the time came for the sufferer to enter the workhouse as destitute. Many general practitioners charged double fees for treating venereal disease.

The Webbs urged that the poor law and public health services should be combined in one preventive and curative service. They did not propose that the whole population should have free treatment and were at pains to suggest ways in which 'the stingy person of the lower middle class' and the 'prosperous labourer' should be made to pay suitable fees. 'What the private practitioner should insist on,' they said, 'is the maintenance intact of his monopoly of the practice of those who prefer a "free choice of doctors." '

Although there was much public dissatisfaction with the state of the Poor Law, Edwardian England was in no temper for large-scale social reform. Recognising this, Lloyd George as Chancellor of the Exchequer and John Burns as President of the Local Government Board produced plans for a less dangerous experiment, a mere first instalment of revolution. They hoped that this measure, which was partly inspired by the system of social insurance introduced in Germany under Bismarck, would go through without undue opposition.

They reckoned without the doctors.

XXIV

THE DOCTORS' REVOLT (1)

'NEVER was legislation more needed. Never was it less wanted,' said Mr Lloyd George of his National Insurance Bill.

The duchesses who refused to lick stamps were only the froth of the opposition. Primarily, it was a show-down between the State and a powerful profession. In some ways, the doctors' revolt in defence of their traditions and privileges was reminiscent of the uproar which was created when the State took steps to prevent the officers of the Army from trafficking in commissions, though as yet there was no move to put down the traffic in medical practices. Unlike the Army officers, the doctors were in a position to organise opposition; but, like the officers, they were split on the fundamental issue.

When he explained his Bill to Parliament in 1911, Lloyd George contended that 30 per cent of pauperism in Britain was caused by sickness and a good deal more by unemployment. Already between six and seven million people were insured against sickness, and about a million-and-a-half against losing their jobs. He proposed to increase these totals by including in his measure all persons earning less than £3 a week. The individual would pay fourpence, the employer threepence and the State twopence ('Ninepence for Fourpence'). A doctor would receive 6s. a year for each insured person on his books.

The eagerness with which the Bill was initially hailed was deceptive. One of the first reactions was that such a beneficent measure must be jealously protected from unscrupulous foreigners who might be tempted to descend on these shores for free treatment (an objection which has a latter-day ring about it). The Opposition seemed civilly disposed; so did the trade unions. But after only a day or two the nation heard the clank of the doctors girding on their armour.

The newspapers began to give much space to doctors' letters, signed and unsigned. Notably hospitable were the columns of the *Daily Mail,* which had a day-to-day headline 'The Doctors' Revolt.' Up and down the country, practitioners began to call mass meetings of protest. They complained that this ruthless extension of contract practice would ruin their private practices. Because of the high wage limit of £3, the lower middle-classes and artisans who could afford to pay ordinary fees would rush to go on the panel. The next complaint was that patients were not to have free choice of doctors, who were to be allotted at the discretion of friendly societies. Surely the Government knew that it was vital for a patient's recovery that he should be treated by a doctor in whom he had faith? Other objections were that the capitation fee was too low to cover the demands of the more weakly patients; that doctors would be swept off their feet by floods of patients; that only inferior doctors would presume to work such a system; and that doctors would be expected to practise under the surveillance of State watch-dogs.

In the *Daily Mail* a doctor with a working-class practice said he had several societies on his books; now all his club patients would be forced to transfer to a State doctor. 'It means taking away at one stroke all the fruits of my years of labour among the working classes.' Another wrote to say that the week before the Bill was introduced his country practice could have been sold for £2,000, but 'this week it would not sell at any price.'

Addressing some 800 doctors and surgeons in Manchester, James Fergusson used words which chimed inharmoniously with those of the Hippocratic oath : 'The fact is we have a commodity and are practically monopolists of that commodity. As business men are we going to demand a fair price for our services?' The meeting urged a boycott of the scheme if their demands were not met. According to the Lancashire and Cheshire branch secretary of the British Medical Association, the status of the doctor henceforth would be that of the man who called to read the gas meter. In the fervour of these demonstrations it was rashly assumed that there would be no 'blacklegs.' The profession had only to stand firm in order to dish the politicians.

After a good deal of this, the Chancellor was stung to remark that he wished the doctors would spend as much time reading his Bill as censuring it. He claimed that his measure would free the doctors from persecution by the friendly societies and reminded

them that hundreds of them were working for less than 4s. a
year, some for as little as 2s.—'a position of bondage not only
discreditable to the clubs, but stupid.' He complained that if any
doctor had succeeded in negotiating a general rise to 5s. he would
have been hailed as a hero; 'I have arranged 6s. and I am
a villain.' To which a doctor retorted in the *Daily Mail* : 'If any
man had suggested that the bulk of private patients should be
swept into the net of club practice even at 6s. per annum he
would have been a blithering idiot.'

One of the more extravagant broadsides of the period (which
survived to be quoted in the Parliamentary debates on Mr
Bevan's National Health Service Bill) included these statements :

'The State Insurance Bill must be killed . . .
      because we can't afford it;
      because it will ruin the British workers;
      because it will severely tax the British manufacturer
        and subsidise the foreign manufacturer.
'The ill-feeling that is going to be created in every British home
by this Act cannot be overestimated.
'Servants and mistresses will become deadly enemies.'

Despite the sound and the fury, it was evident that the profession were not unanimous against the Chancellor. Some doctors
wrote to the press to say that they welcomed the idea of being
better paid to look after their humbler patients; now they could
give better treatment. There would be no more need to go round
collecting pennies. One doctor said he had six clubs which paid
him altogether £179 5s. a year, an average of 3s. 4d. a member.
He had treated 3,448 club patients at his surgery and had
travelled 3,500 miles in a year to attend them. Allowing £100
for travel, and £62 5s. for drugs (at 1s. 6d. a person) his annual
profit on the entire operation worked out at £17. This doctor
thought he would have little to lose at the hands of Lloyd George.

In June, 1911, the British Medical Association drew up its list
of demands which, it said, must be conceded by the Chancellor,
and 27,400 members of the Association pledged themselves not
to enter the scheme unless this was done. The demands included :
free choice of doctor by the patient; doctors to be answerable, not
to friendly societies, but to insurance committees on which the
profession was represented; medical and maternity benefits to be
administered by insurance committees, not friendly societies; an

THE DAWN OF HOPE.

Mr. LLOYD GEORGE'S National Health Insurance Bill provides for the insurance
of the Worker in case of Sickness.

Support the Liberal Government
in their policy of
SOCIAL REFORM.

The Welfare State on the Horizon

I

income limit of £2 per insured person; and a capitation fee of 8s. 6d., exclusive of drugs.

Before the Bill received its Royal assent in December 1911 most of the concessions had been granted. The Chancellor refused to modify the £3 wage limit but promised further negotiations on capitation fees. These concessions did not satisfy an angry assembly of 2,000 doctors who met in the Queen's Hall, Westminster and shouted down Sir Victor Horsley, the surgeon, who for many years had laboured on their behalf. This meeting prompted the *Westminster Gazette* to comment : 'We all admire people who do not know when they are beaten, but the trouble with the British Medical Association is that apparently it does not know when it has won.' It was a comment which should have been carved on the walls of the Association's council chamber for the benefit of later generations.

The provisions of the Bill were not due to take effect until January 1, 1913, and the doctors had a year in which to try to wring concessions. They were not compelled to enter the National Insurance Scheme, but if they abstained *en masse* it would be tantamount to wrecking an Act of Parliament. The choice they faced was not unlike that offered to the Army officers at the Curragh two years later. In both instances, refusal to give the hoped-for answer was liable to be construed as 'mutiny' against the State.

Early in 1912 Lloyd George complained that some of the attempts to stir up trouble among the doctors were dastardly. He conceded that, so far, the British Medical Association had been reasonable in its dealings, but said that when he invited the Royal Colleges to send representatives to meet the Insurance Commissioners he had received, from each, 'a curt, undignified, discourteous refusal.' There were members of the British Medical Association who thought their leaders had been altogether too reasonable in their dealings with the Chancellor. What did the London men and the Harley Street consultants know about the lot of the general practitioner in the provinces?

By the end of the year the situation had grown tense. The Chancellor eventually agreed to a capitation fee of 9s., of which 7s. was for the doctor, 1s. 6d. for drugs and the odd 6d. for additional drugs as necessary. Thus doctors would receive between 7s. and 7s. 6d. per patient. At least half the 27,400 members of the British Medical Association who had signed the 'no co-operation' pledge were believed to be wavering. The

Chancellor had conducted his own canvass of doctors and was confident he had enough to fill his panels. In a new poll, 11,219 voted against participation, 2,408 in favour; the rest ominously abstained. There were threats by certain doctors to boycott colleagues who went on the panel. Excitement rose high in Fleet Street. Here was a great profession fighting for its ideals, said the Conservatives. Here was a selfish clique seeking to induce others to frustrate the nation's will, said the Liberals.

When the New Year dawned the dispositions in the country were reported almost as if a civil war was in progress. Nearly the whole of Scotland and Wales, and almost all the North of England had rallied to Lloyd George. Against him were the Midlands, the South and the Capital. Many counties had not a single panel doctor, among them Herefordshire, Shropshire, Bedfordshire and Radnorshire. But the statistics were deceiving. Behind the scenes a furious free-for-all was in progress between those who wanted to wreck the scheme, or run it on their own terms, and young ambitious doctors who were eager to break into it. The Chancellor intervened to urge those doctors who were co-operating to take on partners and assistants. He was prepared to send a sufficient number of doctors to complete partly filled panels, and in the more stubborn areas he was ready to appoint salaried doctors at £500 a year, with certain practising rights. This threat to draft in doctors stung a Member of Parliament to enquire whether 'blacklegs' would be given police protection, as in dock disputes.

The fight in Bradford was an example of how the revolt was broken—by the doctors themselves. After the local practitioners had refused to touch the panel scheme the town's insurance committee advertised for candidates, and at once received applications from three times as many doctors as they needed. All, according to Lloyd George, were exceptionally well qualified. It was announced that 50 of these applicants were to be appointed at £500 a year, three as specialists at £1,000 and one as a consulting surgeon at £1,200. Hurriedly, the dissenting doctors decided that, after all, they would work the panel scheme.

Sheffield doctors also defied the Chancellor—until, one night, four of their representatives returned from a visit to London with the news that plans were in hand to install State-salaried men in their place. Next morning one hundred of the town's doctors gathered at the town hall to sign the terms of surrender.

In his book *An Apple A Day* Philip Gosse tells how dissentient doctors in the New Forest were rushed into joining the panel by a report that an omnibus with drawn blinds containing (it was rumoured) imported Scots doctors had arrived quietly in Lymington.

So, amid cries of 'Scab!' 'Blackleg!' and 'Intimidation!' to the accompaniment of headlines like 'STAMPEDE OF THE DOCTORS,' 'DOCTORS' ROUT CONTINUES,' and 'DOCTORS AT BAY,' were laid the foundations of the welfare state. The *Daily Chronicle* said on January 3: 'The individual doctor has merely to consider whether he will mount (the Act's) triumphant and beneficent car or whether he will lie down in the British Medical Association's mud for the wheels to run over him.'

A circular thrust through letter boxes in Upper Tooting was headed 'FREE CHOICE OF DOCTOR.' It read:

Shall free-born Britons have their doctor **thrust upon them,** any more than their Minister, by a petty, tyrannous, bureaucratic method—made in Germany? . . . Why have yourselves foisted on a **panicky panel doctor,** anxious to do his brethren, as well as make an extra sixpence, by cutting down the chemist's trade bill, when your own doctor would give you the **best drugs** in his surgery to make you well and fit for work again **as quickly as possible?**

Insist upon your right, therefore, as free-born Britons, instead of slaves, to really free choice of doctor by **contracting out,** as Sub-Section 3 of Section 15 of the Act allows you distinctly to **make your own arrangements.** And don't allow the packed Insurance Commissioners or Local Authorities to bluff you out of it.

How much longer shall Englishmen be dragooned by a Taffy and his brag and bluff?

A 'Panel' is really a 'Taffy Chapel'—of Doctors!

Not only the public were bombarded with leaflets. Many doctors received a circular which contained the statement: 'You will have to treat the chronic residue whether you like it or not.'

The Lancet, though critical of the Act, commented (January 4):

'A year ago the policy of the British Medical Association was to a large extent shaped by a Council favourably inclined towards the Act and optimistic as to the future of the medical profession under it. Now the machinery of the Association is almost entirely controlled by members who take an absolutely opposite view.'

The acrimony grew still sharper. On January 7, members of the British Medical Association, meeting at Queen's Hall, West-

The B.M.A. : " I want it all. and I want to carve it myself."

From the *Daily News*, December 24, 1912

minster, hurled the bitterest abuse yet at the Chancellor. One of them described him as 'a malign comet, dragging behind him a lengthening tail of threats, inconsistent statements and promises.' Another said, 'We are not going to take orders from moral lepers.' Not all the dissentients were content with oral abuse. On a Sunday morning a member of the newly formed National Insurance Practitioners' Association woke up to find his house covered with posters. These assured the public that 'Your so-called free choice of doctors will be limited mainly to men who have broken their pledge,' 'The men will be so few and far between that you will have to go a long way to consult them,' and 'After visiting the doctor you will have to go to the chemist and wait again for your medicine.'

There had already been accusations of picketing, but a spokesman of the British Medical Association said that the doctors who had gathered outside a hall in which panel men were consulting insurance commissioners were merely curious 'to ascertain the type of men who were going to serve.' The Association had always maintained that only the inferior members of the profession would staff the panels, and evidently they needed reassurance on this point.

Other forms of persuasion seem to have been used. A Willesden doctor told the *Daily Chronicle* how a body of his colleagues called on him with threats of professional boycott and social ostracism. When these tactics were seen to be unsuccessful, one of the visitors said, 'We know you are a poor man, but in order to produce unity in the profession in the district we would not see you go down. We would put our hands into our pockets for, say £20 or £30, and I am sure the others would do the same.' The bribe was rejected, whereupon one of the deputation offered to shake hands for the last time.

When the New Year was less than three weeks old the British Medical Association found itself in the mortifying position of having to release its members from their pledge. Many of them had already released themselves, on various grounds. Before the final vote was taken the Queen's Hall rang to the sound of massed doctors singing 'Rule Britannia,' with special emphasis, according to the *Westminster Gazette,* on the line 'Britons never shall be slaves.' The same newspaper had earlier published a cartoon showing a bull labelled 'British Medical Association' rushing up a tunnel to repel the locomotive of progress. It now published another cartoon showing the bull being swept from the tunnel on the locomotive's cow-catcher.

The Opposition press were in no mood to concede defeat and searched busily, as they had done all along, for material with which to discredit the new scheme. One of the earliest casualties of the fray was a London practitioner whose night out earned him two headlines on a main news page : PANEL DOCTOR FINED : CHARGE OF BEING DRUNK IN THE STREET. A month earlier, his lapse would have gone unnoticed. This was followed by stories of doctors overwhelmed by queues of would-be patients, of sick men and women vainly trudging about in search of a panel doctor and being rebuffed by bureaucrats, and of chemists unable to read the increasingly illegible prescriptions of hard-pressed practitioners.

In that first month it seemed that a malign fate was conspiring to supply the Opposition press with ammunition. On January 21 came a report of an inquest on a London labourer, a panel patient, who had died of a strangulated hernia. The doctor explained that, because he had been pressed by a queue of between 200 and 300 people clamouring to sign on his panel, he had not had time to examine the patient, but had given him a prescription. This dialogue occurred between the coroner and a pathologist witness:

'If this man had gone to a hospital he would have been alive now?—Probably.

'As it was he went to his National Insurance Act doctor and he is now dead?—Yes.'

The jury expressed the view that more care should be bestowed on panel patients, but exonerated the doctor 'owing to the scandalous amount of work imposed upon him under the Act.'

Less than a week later a domestic servant died at Enfield in similar circumstances. The headlines read:

INSURANCE ACT TRAGEDY
Overworked Doctor's Explanation

And only three days later appeared a report headed:

OVERWORKED DOCTOR
Death in Street
VICTIM OF INSURANCE WORRY
Widow's Pathetic Evidence

Such a windfall of tragedy made it hardly necessary to expose the shortcomings of panel practitioners who had taken a drop too much. In any event, a celebrant had only to blame his condition on Lloyd George and he would have been hailed as a hero.

A Member of Parliament who asked, 'How many people have died because they were unable to get the services of a doctor under the National Insurance Act till too late?' was told that no such deaths had occurred.

In the eyes of many, the British Medical Association had been revealed as just another stubborn trade union, with the difference that other trade unions were able to invoke more solidarity in their ranks. Its leaders had been spoiling for a fight and their noses had been bloodied. Their performance in the last round, as *The Lancet* pointed out, was well calculated to give the impres-

sion that the Association was against the whole principle of
national insurance. Somehow, their own proposals for an insurance scheme were buried in the battle. The fact that, for many
generations, the same Association had campaigned for numerous
schemes of social betterment and improvements in public health
(its most recent cause being the school medical service), was
forgotten, if it was ever known. There was bitterness in the
Association when the revolt collapsed, and there were a number
of resignations, but the bulk of the members got down to the job
of making the new scheme work. The more far-sighted of them
campaigned hard in the next two decades to widen the application of the scheme and extend its benefits.

Those 'unsaleable' practices turned out to be saleable after all,
and some of them fetched bigger sums than they would have
done before the 'panel' came in. To doctors in industrial areas,
the Act brought a feeling of security they had never known before.
The *Westminster Gazette* published the 'complaint' of a practitioner who said he was being coerced and intimidated by 'this
wicked Welshman' into accepting 7s. per head in respect of
patients who before the Act had brought him only an average of
2s. each. One who showed how the system could be operated was
Dr Harry Roberts, of Stepney. Even before the Act came in,
relates his biographer Winifred Stamp, he had the biggest and
best-run practice in London, with four doctors, two nurse-mid-
wives, a secretary and dispensers in a self-contained clinic. In
January, 1913, Stepney queued to sign on Dr Roberts's panel and
eventually he had the largest list of patients in England. The *Daily
Chronicle* sent a representative on January 21 to 'sit in' with Dr
Roberts as he interviewed his patients. One of the reflections by
this reporter was:

'Before the Act became operative the doctor frequently hesitated
to recommend another bottle of medicine, lest the patient could not
afford it; the patient on his side was liable to entertain the suspicion
that another bottle of medicine was advised because the doctor
wanted to get the patient's shilling. The Act has for ever removed
such fetters from the doctor and suspicion from the patient.'

Dr Roberts's clinic became a show-place—and a battleground.
In later years his reward for trying to bring the workings of the
Act 'a little nearer to the rhetorical promises of Mr Lloyd George'

was to be harassed for supposed over-prescribing, notably of cod liver oil and malt.*

The millions of patients over whom the battle had been fought welcomed the scheme without bonfires or brass bands. Lloyd George announced with pride that up to two-thirds of the population in some parts of East London could now, for the first time in their lives, call in their own doctor. But in the country at large, and perhaps in the East End of London too, most of the workers would have preferred more food in their bellies and greater certainty of employment. They still had to pay doctors' fees for their wives and children.

Because of the unpleasantness in which the Act was born, many patients were convinced that doctors as a class grudged them panel treatment and were prepared to fob them off with the minimum of attention and the maximum of inconvenience. Thus, they were continually on the look-out for snubs. No doubt, they surmised, the doctor chatted much more affably to the fee-paying patients who arrived by appointment, who did not have to sit in cold and barren waiting-rooms. Some practitioners did not diminish these suspicions by having two entrances to their premises, one for panel patients, one for fee-paying patients. Periodically there were clashes between doctors and the chip-on-shoulder type of patient who knew his rights and was determined to get them, who would have scoffed at the idea that a doctor was intended to be a guide, philosopher and friend, and who called for a bottle of medicine in the same way as he called at the jug-and-bottle department for his beer. This kind of patient was, of course, no new phenomenon; club practice had bred him.

Inevitably, when the panel scheme was talked about, more was heard of grievance than of gratitude, but the history of the scheme, if it could be written, would not be a mournful chronicle of snubs and neglect; it would list innumerable acts of selflessness, solicitude and devotion by panel doctors.

The middle classes and the self-employed were outside Lloyd George's measure. For them, a grave illness or a major operation could be financially crippling; nor was it possible to take out effective insurance against all the calamities which can beset the human constitution. Even when surgeons moderated their fees many a middle-class breadwinner had to start selling up his possessions to meet the bills. But the problems of this class went

* Winifred Stamp: *Doctor Himself.*

unregarded, as the doctors licked their wounds and the duchesses licked their stamps.

Soon, the practitioners who had been quickest to resent the notion of working for the State were rushing to join the most tightly disciplined State medical service of all—the Royal Army Medical Corps.

XXV

SHOULD A DOCTOR TELL?

THE question asked in this heading can be posed in respect of two distinct dilemmas. One is the problem of whether a doctor should tell a patient he is dying, to which the short answer is that the decision depends on the doctor's assessment of his patient's moral courage. The other problem, which is the subject of this chapter, is whether a doctor should divulge, in or out of court, confidences obtained by him in a professional capacity. This issue cropped up repeatedly in the years immediately preceding and following the first world war.

Lawyers had long enjoyed legal privilege which protected them, in carefully defined circumstances, from being required to reveal information obtained from their clients. Roman Catholic priests had no protection in law, but in practice they were never pressed to disclose secrets of the confessional. It was generally assumed that they would go to jail rather than tell. Editors have sometimes chosen imprisonment when ordered to reveal sources of information.

Doctors had no legal privilege and only a limited amount of tolerance was accorded to them. Under Common Law they could be called upon to disclose all communications, however confidential, from a patient. This had been Lord Mansfield's ruling in 1776 when a baggage calling herself the Duchess of Kingston was tried for bigamy, and Sir Caesar Hawkins, her surgeon, was reluctant to testify about the birth of a child to her. Two judges— Mr Justice Buller in 1792 and Lord Brougham in 1833—had been gracious enough to suggest that doctors should share the legal protection enjoyed by lawyers. As a general rule, the courts respected the intimate relationship between doctor and patient and forbore to ask embarrassing questions, but, every now and again, a medical witness would find himself being bullied to give evidence which made nonsense of the Hippocratic oath. It was usual, on such occasions, to give the required information under protest. There were doctors who thought that the aggression of the courts could have been checked if one or two of their harshly treated colleagues had chosen to go to jail.

Occasionally, instead of bullying a medical witness, a judge would censure him for failing to ask for the court's protection. In 1914 a doctor who had treated a workman as a private patient was called to Manchester County Court to give evidence for the employer against whom the workman was claiming damages. The judge refused to hear the evidence of a witness who, he said, was prepared to accept fees from both sides. Next day, having learned that the doctor had been called to court under *subpoena,* the judge apologised, but said that the witness should have made it clear that he was in the box under protest.

Whether he tried rigidly to observe the rule of secrecy or whether he decided to use his discretion, a doctor could find himself in some complex moral predicaments. In 1895 a legal action had shown the financial perils of departing from the rules. An obstetrician conducted a medical examination of his wife's sister-in-law, who was a guest in his house. Recovering from the anaesthetic, the patient thought she heard the doctor say to a colleague that she might have been 'playing hanky-panky.' Subsequently she found that the doctor had told his wife of his suspicions. For this indiscretion, which was committed for the protection of family honour, the obstetrician was ordered to pay £12,000 damages, his plea of privilege failing. The evidence included this passage :

Counsel : Suppose a gentleman did not want to serve on a jury and came to you for a certificate and you found that there was nothing the matter with him. If you were afterwards asked what was the matter with him what would you say?

Defendant : I should say that there was nothing the matter with him.

Counsel : Then you would be betraying his confidence.

In the year that Shaw wrote *The Doctor's Dilemma* a real-life doctor's dilemma in this department of ethics was ventilated in the correspondence columns of the *British Medical Journal.* It was that of a general practitioner who was treating a railway signalman for asthma. The patient's attacks came on suddenly and were sometimes so severe that he fell to the floor and was incapacitated for more than an hour. Often he was alone in his signal box, but so far had not suffered an attack while on duty. The man declined to tell his employers about his condition for fear of being dismissed or being transferred to another job at a lower wage. It would be a breach of confidence between doctor and patient for the doctor to inform the railway company of the man's illness. The reader who communicated this problem to the *Journal* said he had advised the practitioner to send a confidential letter to the general manager of the railway company. What did the *Journal* think? The *Journal* expressed the view that, grave as were the risks to the public, this was not a case for breach of professional confidence, but that the doctor should most strenuously represent to the patient the criminal neglect of which he was guilty. In the next issue horrified readers dissented violently from this advice.

More often the problem 'Should a doctor tell?' was posed in respect of sexual indiscretions committed by patients. In 1914 Mr Justice Avory ruled that a doctor had a legal duty to inform the authorities whenever a case of criminal abortion came to his notice. Medical bodies dissented, on the grounds that if a doctor did so he would be inculpating his own patient and all confidence in the medical profession would be at an end.

Immediately after the war the controversy broke out in acute form. In several court actions doctors were called on to divulge information from the records of the new venereal disease clinics. A typical instance was when a husband suing for divorce caused a *subpoena* to be served on the medical officer of a clinic at Chester, requiring him to testify that his erring wife had received treatment there. The doctor appealed to the judge for protection, pointing out that according to the regulations for the clinics all information obtained within their walls was to be regarded as confidential, and that if it were not so regarded the purpose of the clinics would be frustrated. The judge informed him that the regulations of a Government department could not be considered as over-ruling the laws of evidence, and the doctor then gave the required information. Soon afterwards the Medical Officer of Health for Ilford was summoned to the Divorce Court to give evidence of a still-birth notified to him. His protests were also over-ruled.

One eminent doctor who was much perturbed by these decisions was Lord Dawson of Penn, the first doctor to be sent to the House of Lords as an active representative of his profession. Opening a big debate of the Medico-Legal Society on March 21, 1922, he complained of legal arrogance and described the law as 'the spoilt child of the professions.' He said : 'The privilege we claim is not the privilege of the doctor; it is the privilege of the patient.' Until recently the public had firmly believed that what was told to a doctor was sacred and would be respected by the courts; now, Lord Dawson said, that confidence had been shattered. The intimacies learned by doctors in the course of their consultations were just as intimate as those furnished to priests and were relevant to proper diagnosis and treatment. Was justice more important than life and health?

Lord Dawson knew better than to claim an absolute privilege for doctors. He conceded that if, by respecting a confidence, a doctor knew that a cruel wrong would be inflicted on an innocent party (as by communicating a disease) it would be his duty to speak out, once it was clear that remonstrations with the guilty party were of no avail. Perhaps, he suggested tentatively, there should be privilege in civil cases but not in criminal cases. Certainly, he said, there ought to be no invocation of privilege to cover up malpractice. Again, if a doctor knew that a crime was about to be committed he ought to tell the police; but Lord Dawson was less sure whether it was a doctor's duty to inform the police after knowledge of a crime had reached his ears. On this point he was quickly taken up by Earl Russell, who asked whether a doctor who treated a man for a bullet in the thigh, knowing that a post office had been robbed by a man who had received a bullet in the thigh, would claim the right not to betray his patient. Earl Russell thought that it should be left to the discretion of the judge, who also had his code of honour, to decide when to press a doctor to tell. More frivolously, Lord Riddell suggested that a doctor could always 'forget' embarrassing facts. Lord Justice Atkins was convinced that the law would never grant an absolute privilege to the medical profession, otherwise a doctor could stand mute when in the possession of knowledge which might save an innocent man from execution. Nor was there any good reason why doctors should remain silent and see injustice done in insurance claims and actions for damages.*

'Should a doctor tell?' was (and is) just one of the many questions a doctor must decide on his own responsibility and in the light of his own conscience.

* *The Lancet,* April 1, 1922.

XXVI

THE CHOICE WIDENS

THE story of the Royal Army Medical Corps does not fall within the scope of this book. In the Kaiser's war the Corps, as a whole, performed prodigies, and much was learned of wound treatment, of blood transfusion, of handling 'breakdowns,' of patching up shattered faces (a technique not without value in the age of fast motoring that lay ahead), and of sanitary science. On balance, however, the frustrations of doctoring in uniform were calculated to fortify most of the 13,000 medical officers in their resolve not to be a cog in a State machine in civil life, if they could help it.

The pick of the nation had been killed off. What was left was handed over to a newly created Ministry of Health, to turn into red-blooded and eupeptic citizens. In name at least the Ministry of Health was the realisation of the dream of Edwin Chadwick, though it is likely that Chadwick would have received coolly enough this body of limited powers set up on the remains of the old Local Government Board, with its far from liberal traditions. The Ministry's immediate duties were concerned with housing and town planning.

Between general practitioners and the Ministry there grew up something of that jealousy and distrust which exists between regimental officers and the staff, between the man of action and the planner, between the individual holding a lone position against heavy odds and the Olympian who sees the battle as a whole. From a busy practice, the Ministry seemed an ivory tower inhabited by desk-doctors who never felt a pulse unless their typists fainted, who were hand-in-glove with the politicians, and who sought to bring the rest of the profession into the same state of helotry in which they laboured. Rightly or wrongly, the general practitioner got the impression that these salaried, pensionable

272

'admin. wallahs,' these suburban commuters, looked on him as a less noble form of doctor obsessed with making money.

In 1921 the dentists achieved a new dignity. Their history had been an unhappy one ever since the barbers and surgeons had split in 1745. An Act of 1878 had made it illegal for an un-qualified person to call himself a dentist, and a Dental Register was set up under the control of the General Medical Council. Nevertheless, tooth-pulling was often performed by a doctor's unqualified assistant and there was nothing to stop any un-registered practitioner opening a 'surgery' for the extraction of teeth, or for supplying guinea dentures from a shop with giant signboards. Early in the present century many doctors were will-ing to extract teeth on demand (a reader of the *British Medical Journal* who wrote, in 1905, to complain that the practice he had bought had been built in part on tooth-pulling was told that 'a certain amount of dentistry is frequently done by general practitioners'). Now, however, entrance to the dental profession was closed to all who could not produce medical or dental degrees and a Dental Board was set up in affiliation with the General Medical Council. In a quarter of a century's time the dentists, well organised, would be ready to fight shoulder to shoulder with the doctors against Mr Bevan.

Though specialists were now pullulating on the staffs of hospitals, though the great discoveries of medicine were being made, not at the bedside, but in the research laboratories, the aim of most doctors was still to run a general practice, with a panel if necessary. For a man of slender resources the goal was often elusive. A medical education cost about £1,000. The price of an ordinary practice ranged from £2,000 to £3,000 (it was calculated on the gross average receipts of the preceding three years, the usual charge being the equivalent of one-and-a-half year's income). After graduating, a doctor normally worked for a period in a hospital, where he had no hope of saving. If his parents could not lend the money to buy a practice, or a share of one, he had to borrow it. This meant being saddled with high interest charges for perhaps 15 or 20 years, on top of any other interest charges he might have to pay to a building society. As a rule banks were willing enough to lend money to buy a practice, an ambitious young doctor being regarded as a better risk than almost any woman who wanted to open a hat shop.

Partly because of financial stress, more and more doctors began to set up in partnerships, not only double but multiple ones. If a doctor could not buy a share of a practice, he might become an assistant 'with a view to partnership.' In this way many a young man gradually took over from an older one. The junior member of a 'firm' of four might not be earning big money but at least he was in practice. Not the least advantage was that he could get more time off than he would otherwise have done. From the patient's point of view a multiple partnership had its merits, for a well-balanced firm would have men with special knowledge and aptitudes, and one doctor could consult another when in doubt. Sometimes, because of incompatibility or mistrust, partners were partners in name only, though a united front might be presented to the world. Even if two, three or four ambitious doctors could get along together, it did not follow that their wives could.

Outside general practice, opportunities for doctors were fast multiplying, though the financial rewards were not always attractive. More and more Government departments, in addition to the Ministry of Health, employed full-time and part-time doctors. Since the early years of the century the school medical service, for which the British Medical Association had campaigned, had been gathering momentum. Its salaried doctors were striving to build a new nation out of the rickety, verminous, squinting, ringwormed raw material which was paraded before them (the service owed its inception, in some degree, to the howl which went up over the bad quality of Boer War recruits). A school medical officer might be a full-time servant or he might hold the appointment along with that of medical officer of health. Another opening was that of the industrial health officer, full-time or part-time, whose work included the treatment of casualties, the examination of those subject to occupational hazards and the supervision of canteens. He was pledged not to try to work up private practice among the families of his industrial patients. In the commercial field there were insurance companies, or groups of companies, which employed full-time doctors to examine would-be policy-holders. Most shipping lines, transport undertakings, oil companies, mining corporations, big catering firms and stores had their own medical staffs or advisers, and very odd were the problems that came the way of some of them. Thus, in 1937, the medical adviser to Imperial Airways sought the advice of readers of the *British Medical Journal* on the transport of pregnant women by air. Tentatively he suggested that for European flights, pregnant passengers should be declined if the birth was expected within a month, and that, for longer flights, a two-months' safety margin should be allowed.

Just as a priest had the choice of going out into the world or remaining in cloisters, a doctor who did not wish to tend a flock could now immure himself in a laboratory. Of old a doctor had been a clinician or nothing, though he sometimes amused himself with test-tubes in his spare time; now, on graduating, young men could follow a career in which they had no direct responsibility for the lives of men and women. If their consciences demurred, they could fortify themselves by the thought that a researcher in medicine, though he cured nobody, might be the means of preventing tens of thousands from falling ill. The choice was governed by temperament. A man had the urge for research or he had not—and it was a good thing that some had it. When young Alexander Fleming in 1906 turned bacteriologist under Sir Almroth Wright, at St Mary's Hospital, there was little or no competition for laboratory appointments, which, apart from being underpaid, were regarded as the blindest of alleys. At that time, moreover, research was ill co-ordinated, but the National Insurance Act contained provisions for a Medical Research Council, to be subsidised at the not exorbitant rate of one penny per person per annum. Slowly, after the 1914–18 war, the Council built up prestige and began to attract some of the more questing minds among the new generation of doctor-scientists. Its teams and units and laboratories, ever multiplying, began to turn their attention not only to the obvious challenges like cancer and the common cold but to such problems as gastric troubles in busmen, the extermination of bed bugs, the countering of travel sickness and the colour vision requirements of the Royal Navy. The Council has also provided young doctors with facilities for pure, as distinct from applied, research.

Medical research was, of course, no State monopoly. Since the 'nineties, doctors had been busy in the laboratories founded, not only in Britain but in Egypt, by Sir Henry Wellcome, an American-born, British-naturalised patron of medical research on the princely scale. Without the contributions of such corporations as Burroughs and Wellcome, and May and Baker (who produced the famous M and B 693) there would be many blanks in the history of medicine.

One of the grislier portals beckoning the young graduate was that of forensic medicine, a once-mocked but now much sharpened science for which the public was beginning to entertain a higher respect. The pathologist who specialised in this field had no fear that his patient might die; his patient as a rule was incontestably dead and often scattered. Occasionally the pathologist found himself in the big headlines, as when he helped to fit together human shreds and cutlets found in trunks at left-luggage offices, but much of his work went unrecorded, involving as it did the unmasking of petty abortionists, or the examination of suicides and stifled infants found in women's lavatories. The public's favourite performer in the forensic field was Sir Bernard Spilsbury, who had been a fellow student of Sir Alexander Fleming at St Mary's Hospital. He enjoyed, or at all events received, the peculiar acclaim reserved for those who huddle behind screens in cemeteries at dawn, and whose word is supposed to be able to save or condemn. The first big trial in which Sir Bernard appeared for the Crown was that of Dr H. H. Crippen, an alien and ill-qualified practitioner. The defence medical evidence showed up in a poor light. Each notorious trial that followed heightened Sir Bernard's reputation as an honest, scrupulous and dismayingly knowledgeable witness until, by 1925, Press and Bar were beginning to complain that the courts attached wholly excessive importance to his views. In that year he gave evidence against John Thorne, one of several young men of the period who butchered their mistresses. Thorne's victim, declared Sir Bernard, had been manually strangled. The defence produced a brisk succession of medical witnesses who said that in their view she had been strangled by pressure of a cord, consistent with having hanged herself. Sir Bernard's evidence was accepted. No man did more to bring much-needed dignity to forensic medicine. He showed that clarity, imperturbability and a good presence were vital adjuncts of a medical jurist. Many a witness before him had cut a sorry figure through being fussy, obtuse, careless or nervous.

Between the doctors and the press there were often misunderstandings and even open brawls. The activities of the General Medical Council came in for much attention (Chapter 28) but anything to do with doctors or health was news. Sometimes a doctor who had contributed to a professional journal a paper on an unusual ailment or treatment would see his article lifted and dramatised by a popular newspaper and himself hailed as a great healer—perhaps the day after the same paper had featured an 'amazing health discovery' by an out-and-out quack. There was little or no redress to be had.

The doctors had another grievance against the press. Believing it to be the duty of a doctor not to suggest ill-health, they pointed to the patent medicine and patent food advertising which sought to convince the public that it should take daily remedies for incomplete elimination, night starvation, tell-tale tongue and a variety of other afflictions, real or fanciful. Many a white-jacketed 'doctor' was portrayed beaming approval of the product or directing patients to go out and buy it. The more cynical of the public supposed that attacks on patent medicine advertising were inspired by jealousy on the doctors' part. In 1938 Lord Horder, in the House of Lords, pointed out that in the long run doctors had more patients, not fewer, through the activities of the patent medicine firms 'ultimately the undertaker benefits sooner and oftener than he might.' The Government had been trying to urge the nation to consume more milk, fruit and herrings, but for every £100 spent by the State on making the public health-conscious, he said, the medicine mongers spent £1,000 in making them disease-conscious. Every year these firms disbursed on advertising a sum nearly equal to the total budget of the hospitals. (Not till 1950 did the Advertising Association proscribe the use of words like 'clinic' and 'laboratory' when such institutions did not exist, the use of 'Doctor' in the name of a product and all references disparaging to the medical profession.)

The doctors themselves were not entirely guiltless of popularising new diseases. In his autobiography *Adventures in Two Worlds,* the novelist A. J. Cronin confesses that in his day as a London doctor he 'invented a new disease—asthenia,' the treatment for which was intra-muscular injections, plus diet and exercise. 'Asthenia' was not, of course, a new-coined word. Cronin's autobiography makes a piquant companion volume to his famous novel *The Citadel* (1937), which paints a disillusioning picture of the medical scene between the world wars. His tale begins, like Francis Brett Young's *My Brother Jonathan,* with an idealist young doctor in an industrial practice who finds himself

at war with an unhelpful medical officer of health. Cronin's Dr
Manson moves on to London where he blunts some of his ideals
in the frustrations of Government service. He then works his way
into fashionable practice, a world of cynical guinea-chasing and
fee-splitting. When one of his patients with a stomach cyst is
butchered by a surgeon colleague who is more at home procuring
abortions, Manson recovers his ideals and determines to join two
of his more conscientious colleagues in running a three-man clinic
in a provincial town. Each member will be something of a
specialist, so that the clinic will offer an efficient medical, surgical
and bacteriological service. Group medicine, Manson decides,
must replace the general practitioner system. Another character in
the book mocks the general practitioner as 'the dear old quack of
all trades,' hopelessly behind in medical knowledge, keeping up
his surgery by clumsy minor operations in a cottage hospital. In
passing, *The Citadel* also attacks the dangers and inadequacies of
nursing homes, and the system whereby a doctor without influence would find himself pleading with one hospital after
another for the admission of a seriously ill but impoverished
patient, knowing that his more entrenched colleagues had no such
difficulties.

The Citadel was either a fearless and timely exposure of
medical racketeering or a maliciously biassed attack on an
honourable profession, according to individual viewpoint. Many
of its suggestions and criticisms had been voiced by others in the
profession. The idea of group medicine had many powerful
adherents. As for the dabblings of family doctors in cottage
hospitals, Sir W. H. Ogilvie, the surgeon, had already complained
of general practitioners who 'like to do a spot of surgery occasionally' as other men like to play 'a spot of golf.' Operating as a
sport, he said, was a purely British conception; it was time to
abolish the potterers.*

Since *The Citadel* appeared, not a few doctors have been at
pains to repair some of the damage by publishing—of necessity,
pseudonymously—first-hand accounts of modern medical and
surgical triumphs with just the right blend of human interest,
compassion, medical jargon and 'grue.' Their tales are well told,
and occasionally, one feels, too well told. One of the problems in
reading books of this kind, and still more so in reading memoirs
like Axel Munthe's *The Story of San Michele,* is to know just

* *Surgery, Orthodox and Heterodox.*

how much of the book is legitimate disguise, how much is legitimate flourish, and how much is hard fact. But in the main these
latter-day medical case-books are immensely readable and have
done far more to educate the public in the potentialities of
medicine and surgery than a whole library of the formal medical
biographies of the past.

XXVII

MORE CONTROVERSIES

BETWEEN the world wars the doctors were continually under fire for their shyness to embrace exotic cults—everything from psycho-analysis and Abrams' Box to osteopathy and faith-healing.

Also, they found themselves being urged repeatedly to show a more indulgent attitude towards practices at which, as often as not, their social and professional consciences rebelled; notably, practices which aimed at the prevention of unwanted birth and the easing of desired death.

The school of Freud had drawn on themselves the full fury of orthodox medicine in Europe during the Edwardian years. Much of this abuse, says Freud's biographer, Ernest Jones, was completely unprintable. The distrust of a system which traced back so much to the sexual instinct persisted among doctors of the older school long after the 1914–18 war. In 1925 delegates to a British Medical Association conference urged an inquiry into 'certain practices alleged to be prevalent among some medical men practising psycho-analysis.' The leading speaker said it was not his intention to attack the basic conception of psycho-analysis, but to censure those who taught that 'there was only one thing in our lives and that was sex.' He told of the distress of a mother whose young unmarried daughter had spent numerous twice-weekly sessions with a psycho-analyst, learning from him in detail 'every possible thing that sex could teach her.' The mother had objected strongly but her daughter was now too deeply involved to break herself away. There was also a psycho-analytical school, supported by a well-known London consultant, in which boys and girls had to strip naked for gymnastics and all bathing was mixed. The doctors who heard these revelations seemed undecided whether the best course was 'to purge their house before some-

body purged it for them,' or to leave doubtful practices to the
police and the General Medical Council.

That same year *The Times* based a leading article on the fate
of a young man who had committed suicide because of the 'sense
of degradation' said to have been imposed on him by psycho-
analytical treatment. The 'mind doctor' of the old school, said
The Times, conceived it his duty to strengthen the patient's will
by all means in his power, and looked askance at the notion that
there were elements of the mind lying outside the scope of conscious thought. Because psycho-analysis was capable of inflicting
terrible injuries, a high degree of caution was necessary in exploring the minds of the sensitive.*

Nevertheless, the risks of psycho-analysis seem to have been
cheerfully accepted by society neurotics and semi-hypochondriacs
anxious to be in the fashion. There was a limerick which told of
an old-fashioned doctor, a 'red flannelist' :

> Who groaned at the state of his panel-list,
>   But he grouses no more
>   Now the plate on his door
> Bears the lucrative lure 'Psycho-analyst.'

For the next generation at least the jargon of the psycho-analyst
and the psychiatrist would be pattered by the impressionable
or mocked by the sceptical. The new-style 'mind doctor' would
become a standing butt of humorous artists; he would incur
judges' impatience, commanding officers' scorn and Papal suspicion. His critics would accuse him of shielding cowardice,
moral as well as physical, of whittling away a man's sense of
responsibility. The only thing he could be sure of was that while
his successes would pass largely unnoticed his failures would be
well advertised.

For some time the doctors had been focusing the hostility
which once they had reserved for homoeopaths on to the osteopaths, who were clamouring for the privilege of State recognition
in their own right. Broadly, the attitude of the profession had
come to be this : that so long as a man qualified himself for
admission to the General Register, the methods of therapy he
adopted thereafter—whether homoeopathy or osteopathy or any
other system—were his own responsibility. The osteopaths practised a manipulative technique taught by the American, Dr

* December 31, 1925.

Andrew Still, who as a young man had learned his anatomy on resurrected Red Indians and to whom the truth of osteopathy had come 'like a burst of sunshine' (moonshine, said his critics). His creed was that bodily ills could be traced back to an 'osteopathic lesion' or structural derangement in some part of the body, notably the spine. When this lesion was removed, by manipulation, the body would cure itself. After many years of recrimination between orthodoxy and osteopathy, the House of Lords in 1934 gave a second reading to a Bill, introduced by Lord Elibank, which would have set up a separate register for osteopaths and regulated their practice. Lord Dawson and Lord Moynihan opposed it on the grounds that osteopaths had no systematic medical training. A Select Committee was appointed by the Lords to investigate the cult and in the following year reported that 'it would not be safe or proper for Parliament to recognise osteopathic practitioners as qualified to diagnose and treat all human complaints.' The Committee used blistering terms to describe a school which professed to teach osteopathy in Britain. The Bill was dropped, and the more responsible osteopaths set about putting their house in order. That osteopaths effected some remarkable cures for certain conditions was generally conceded; what was not approved was their attempt to 'erect a new theory of health and disease on an imaginary pathology and unproved hypotheses'—to quote a book published in 1937 by two leading officials of the British Medical Association.*

The public, or a large section of it, had a weak spot for manipulators and bone-setters. During the 1914–18 war the press had attacked the doctors for cold-shouldering Herbert Barker, who successfully treated large numbers of wounded soldiers. There was even a demand that the Archbishop of Canterbury should revive his special powers and grant Barker a 'Lambeth degree' of Doctor of Medicine, though this would not have admitted him to the Register. The knighthood conferred on Barker in 1922, after a petition to the Prime Minister on his behalf by four eminent surgeons, was widely considered to be a deserved cuff on the ear for the General Medical Council.

Another cult which rattled the orthodox was that propagated by Dr Albert Abrams of San Francisco, who had already attracted attention in 1910 by publicising a healing system called spondylotherapy. His method of 'electronic diagnosis' with the

* Charles Hill and H. A. Clegg: *What Is Osteopathy?*

aid of a mysterious not-to-be-opened box—'Abrams' Box'—was a pleasing blend of science and mumbo-jumbo. A drop of the patient's blood, or a smear of his saliva was affixed to the box, which was dignified by the name of 'dynamiser.' This was connected via three rheostats to the forehead of a healthy person, often a boy. Changes in the 'stomach dullness' of the patient were then supposedly measured in the healthy individual; from the vibrations, or emanations, could be deduced the nature of the disease, its locality and much else. By 1923 some 3,500 electronic practitioners were abroad in the world, many of them laymen. It was a matter for regret among the orthodox that Abrams and his disciples, some of whom made enormous incomes, were too busy healing the sick to spare the time to subject their apparatus to controlled experiment. Abrams died in 1924 but the cult had by then taken a grip in Britain, and the last believer in E.R.A. (the 'Electronic Reactions of Abrams') is probably not yet extinct.

It has been noted that, in Queen Victoria's reign, any doctor who set out to popularise knowledge of birth control risked summary removal from the Register. Now, in the jazz age, a Court physician and peer of the realm, Lord Dawson, was to be heard telling Churchmen that sexual intercourse in marriage might be enjoyed for its own sake, not merely as a means of procreation. (This was a far remove, not only from the attitude of the previous generation, but from the views of Sir Thomas Browne, of *Religio Medici* fame, who said he 'could be content that we might procreate like trees, without conjunction.') For Lord Dawson's candour, Fleet Street at all events was not ungrateful. Another medical peer, Lord Horder, became president of the National Birth Control Association, later the Family Planning Association. By 1930 the Ministry of Health had begun to issue circulars on the subject; and, suitably stimulated, local authorities screwed up courage to establish ante-natal clinics in which medical advice on birth control could be given to married women in whom further pregnancies might be 'detrimental to health'—a phrase which could be interpreted liberally or strictly according to the inclination of the doctor. The law said that information on contraception was not to be made available to all comers; but the knowledge was so readily available from other sources (the more out-of-touch parents, it is said, were taught by their children) that the medical profession could hardly hold themselves out as the repositories of arcane knowledge.

Doctors themselves were at sixes and sevens on the subject, involving as it did religious, ethical and social considerations. A 'broad-minded' gynaecologist might accept a fee from a well-to-do married woman for enabling her to pursue her social life unhampered by children; the decision was a matter between him and his conscience. Another consultant might refuse the request and inform the woman that what she needed was half a dozen babies. Again, an old-fashioned general practitioner, invited to advise a bride on 'the best method,' might astonish her by delivering a lecture on the individual's duty to society and even point to the need for populating the Empire. Yet, faced with a similar request from an over-fertile working woman whose children would inevitably be brought up in squalor, he might well accede to it. Medical societies and journals conducted frequent debates on birth control and it was clear that there was no more unison among doctors than there could be in any other profession. The medical officer of one overcrowded city might be in favour of spreading birth control knowledge, the medical officer of another might be against it. A Protestant doctor would point out that the Roman Catholic Church seemed to be accepting the impossibility of abstention by talking of so-called safe periods and the function of marriage in 'allaying concupiscence.' Somebody else would point out that, ethically, there was no difference between frustrating Nature by practical means and frustrating her by the exercise of will-power; both practices were unnatural.

Eventually the profession, in the main, came round to the view that the ideal state of marriage was one in which (to quote a medical investigating committee) there was 'a wisely restrained natural exercise of sexual function with the probable result of a medium-size family.'

One argument in favour of extending birth control knowledge was that it might diminish the incidence of abortion. Just as there were medical men on the National Birth Control Association, so there were medical men on the Abortion Law Reform Association; but the subject of abortion was also one on which the individual practitioner had his own religious, ethical and social views. Although the law said that anyone who procured abortion was liable to penal servitude for life, it was customary to perform the operation when the life of a mother was in danger. Many laymen as well as doctors thought that the law bore harshly on young victims of rape and incest, whose lives were liable to be shattered by bearing an unwanted or tainted child. Others thought that abortion should be permissible in defence of family honour; and a few irresponsibles wanted every woman to be free to empty her womb if she felt like it. (Revolutionary Russia adopted a 'liberal' attitude to abortion, but soon imposed stringent laws against it.)

Medical societies held vexed debates on this subject too. What constituted 'danger to life?' One doctor, it was clear, would by no means wait until the patient was at death's door before performing an operation. Another would postpone his decision, at peril to the patient's life, basing his reluctance to take action on the conventional grounds that the child might be a future Prime Minister. Occasionally a doctor, risking his career, might perform an abortion if a child was likely to be born with a bad trait. The law was unsatisfactory. In a doubtful case the honest doctor was not solaced by assurances that 'no one would prosecute.' He did not want to be in the position of committing a crime.

Dramatically, the law was challenged in 1938 by a leading Wimpole Street surgeon. He operated in a London hospital on a girl of 14 who had been raped by Guardsmen in Whitehall and invited the Director of Public Prosecutions to put him in the dock. The invitation was promptly accepted. From the surgeon's point of view, it was 'an absolutely perfect case.' His counsel at the Old Bailey described his action as 'a work of the purest charity.' In the witness-box the defendant recalled that three years earlier, when he had decided to end the pregnancy of a girl of 15, the house surgeon, a recently qualified man, had objected on religious grounds and had walked out of the theatre. This refusal had led him to think very hard and to resolve to challenge the law on the next suitable occasion, in order to obtain a clarification. In the case in question he contended that it would have imperilled the girl's health and invited the risk of a mental breakdown to allow her to bear a full-term child. He was unable to draw a line between danger to health and danger to life. The jury brought in a verdict of Not Guilty—a popular decision.

This prosecution was, in the view of the *British Medical Journal*, 'less a criminal trial than a co-operative effort by judge, jury, counsel and witnesses to create law out of strong but ill-defined feeling.' Mr Justice Macnaghten, it said, had implied that 'to preserve a woman's life is not merely to save her from death; it is also to save her from illness which would destroy so

much of her life that it would not be worth living.' Yet the
acquittal was not quite the victory it seemed. Another judge and
jury could easily have interpreted the law differently and doctors
were uncomfortably aware of the fact.

At this time an Inter-Departmental Committee on Abortion,
under Mr Norman (later Lord) Birkett was sitting. In 1939 it
reported and recommended a clarification of the law. 'In our
view there should be no question that a medical practitioner who
terminates a pregnancy with the object of averting serious injury
to health is acting lawfully,' said the Report, but it urged that
there should be safeguards in the shape of consultations. The
Committee was not prepared to recommend abortion for eugenic
reasons or for social convenience. It noted with regret that there
appeared to be a few qualified doctors who procured abortions,
with no questions asked, for fees of one hundred guineas; at the
other extreme were the amateurs who were willing to save the
family name for two or three guineas, or even half-a-crown. The
Committee thought that closer co-operation between doctors and
police would help to put professional abortionists out of business.
'Information might well be given without in fact any real breach
of confidence,' said the report. Certain members of the Committee agreed with Mr Justice Avory that it was the doctor's
bounden duty to inform the authorities whenever he knew that
a criminal operation had been attempted.

Sporadically, there was agitation to empower doctors to
sterilise the unfit and the insane, but this, too, was a step for
which both lay and medical opinion were unprepared. Hitler's
Reich had no qualms on the subject. From 1933 onwards,
German doctors were required to notify the authorities of all
instances of hereditary and mental disease. If the Court of
Hereditary Health ordered a person to be sterilised, there was
no appeal. Incidentally, the doctors of the S.S. were charged with
another task which has never fallen to the lot of the general
practitioner in Britain : that of determining by physical examination whether young women, the brides of the racial *élite,* were
likely to be able to produce a succession of high-grade children
without physical difficulty.*

So much for birth. The advocates of voluntary euthanasia,
who included many medical men and churchmen, wished doctors
to have legal power to accelerate the death of a doomed and pain-

* Willi Frischauer: *Himmler.*

racked patient. Many doctors agreed with George Bernard Shaw
that there were circumstances in which it was unreasonable to
persist in living, but how were these circumstances to be legally
defined? It might well be indecent and inhuman to protract a
life by continual injections, merely in order to preserve a professional fetish, when no one would have hesitated, in similar
circumstances, to kill an animal; but the law was the law. Some
who shrank from the idea of accelerating a patient's death by
positive action thought it reasonable to accelerate it by negative
action, that is, by abstaining from ingenious efforts to pump life
into a body which was finished. This attitude could be summed
up in two lines from A. H. Clough's *The Latest Decalogue*.
Though penned in acid, they were yet capable, in this context,
of an honest interpretation :

> Thou shalt not kill, but need'st not strive
> Officiously to keep alive.

Occasionally doctors admitted, even proclaimed, that they had
helped unnamed patients over the last hurdle, or had closed an
eye to the possibility that the patient might, by a subterfuge,
obtain a lethal dose; but other doctors, on hearing such avowals,
expressed surprise and disgust that their colleagues should have
descended to secret extermination. The function of the physician
in such circumstances, they maintained, was to deaden pain and
give courage, not to kill the patient.

Among the questions raised on this issue were : Who can judge
when pain is intolerable? Who can be sure that a patient will
never recover? How would the doctor-patient relationship survive
the knowledge that the doctor stood at the bedside in the double
role of healer and slayer? Or would the executioner be a gentleman from Whitehall, a Ministry doctor who had long forgotten
his clinical practice?

The president of the Voluntary Euthanasia Legislation Society
was the surgeon Lord Moynihan, who did not live to support the
Voluntary Euthanasia Bill in the Lords in 1936. This measure
provided for the 'administration of euthanasia' by a medical man
in the presence of an official witness, provided that the patient
was over 21 and of sound mind, and provided also that, in the
presence of two witnesses, he had made written application to be
put away. The application was to be forwarded to a euthanasia
referee appointed by the Minister of Health, along with two

medical certificates, one from the patient's own doctor and the other from a doctor with special qualifications. To ensure that all was in order, the referee was to visit the patient himself.

The Bill was not intended, as its sponsors pointed out, to enable imbeciles or aged parents to be disposed of, but few Parliamentary measures can have had less chance of success than this. Viscount Fitzalan asked why the Bill had been given a classical title; in his view, it should have been styled a Bill to legalise murder and suicide. Lord Dawson, though sympathetic with the motives of the sponsors, said that doctors would fight shy of the procedure it envisaged. It would be like certifying an insane patient and the atmosphere of bureaucracy would be brought to the deathbed. Lord Horder did not think it was a subject on which doctors should be asked to give a lead; he regretted that doctors had been associated with the propaganda for it. The Archbishop of Canterbury could not dismiss from his mind the possibility of pressure being brought by relatives for reasons other than compassion. He thought that difficult cases could be left to the discretion of the doctors. According to the Earl of Crawford the measure would introduce strife and dissensions into family life. Fourteen peers voted for the Bill; 35 against.

Doctors were thus left to use their discretion, as they had always done; in other words, to break the Sixth Commandment surreptitiously when their sense of compassion became too much for them. It is fortunate, perhaps, that the range of pain-killing drugs is such as to make the problem less acute today than it used to be. No doctor is likely to challenge the law by announcing beforehand his intention of performing a mercy killing.

It may be that one of the factors which made doctors wary of a Euthanasia Act was the way in which certain sections of the press perennially campaigned against 'carelessness' in certifying the insane. A bemused public was left with the impression that the asylums were full of sane men and women and that all the lunatics were sitting at desks in Whitehall. If doctors could be belaboured on these grounds, would they not be belaboured even less mercifully for certifying that the sane merited, not incarceration, but oblivion?

Another ticklish problem of the period was: has a doctor a duty to beauty? There were persons who affected to be shocked at the way in which surgeons had begun pandering to vain middle-aged women by lifting their faces and otherwise seeking to improve their appearance (breast-lifting and breast-reducing operations are among the latest in this line). Were such restorative feats in accordance with medical ethics? Some medical men had their doubts. It was one thing, they felt, to patch up the face of a wounded soldier, but another to try to provide a woman with a better face than God had given her. The answer from the more advanced thinkers was that if such operations increased a woman's confidence and improved her adjustment to life, they were justifiable. Sir Harold Gillies, a famous name in plastic surgery, has written: 'A beautiful woman is worth preserving and should be kept youthful while she is still young enough to enjoy it. Often while lifting a face I have had a feeling of guilt that I am merely making money. Yet is it not justified if it brings even a little extra happiness to a soul who needs it?'*

He could have cited as authority Dr Thomas Dover who, two centuries before, wrote (*à propos* inoculation for smallpox): 'Is Beauty, that arrives at such a perfection in an English climate, of so little importance that it is beneath our care?'†

For that matter, he could have quoted Dr Alexander Bendo, alias the Earl of Rochester, who excused his specialisation in beauty culture with the words:

'Now should Galen himself look out of his grave and tell me these were baubles below the profession of a physician, I would boldly answer him that I take more glory in preserving God's image in its unblemished beauty upon one good face than I could do in patching up all the decayed carcasses in the world.'

---

* *The Principles and Art of Plastic Surgery.*
† *The Ancient Physician's Legacy.*

XXVIII

STRUCK OFF

A FAVOURITE cockshy of the press in the 'twenties and 'thirties was the General Medical Council.

It was attacked, not merely for refusing to give shelter to unorthodox healers, thus turning them into loud-mouthed martyrs, but for the rigidity with which it disciplined the doctors for offences which, in the eyes of many observers, were not offences at all. Advertising, for example.

The Council attracted especial interest, moreover, because it was a tribunal with the privilege of punishing such moral lapses as fornication and adultery. Powers of this kind had not been enjoyed by the ordinary courts since the days of Cromwell and it was the stern exercise of them by an autocratic body of elders which fascinated the man in the street.

The biggest storm which beat about the Council's head was probably that which was inspired by the case of Dr F. W. Axham, who had been struck off in 1911 for acting as anaesthetist to 'one Herbert Atkinson Barker, an unregistered practitioner practising in a department of surgery.' Dr Axham's activities had been revealed in the course of a law suit against Barker by one of his patients. He declined to withdraw his services from Barker, whose manipulative skill he greatly admired, holding that his duty was to humanity rather than to the General Medical Council. In 1922, when Barker received his knighthood, the question arose: if an unregistered practitioner can bask in royal approval, why should his faithful anaesthetist be left in professional disgrace?

The agitation on Dr Axham's behalf did not take serious shape until late in 1925, by which time he was a frail old man of 86. He had given up practice and it was clear that no harm would result to the public if his name was restored to the Register; there was no lack of precedents for such a course. Many influential persons, including ex-patients of Sir Herbert Barker, pleaded on his behalf in *The Times*. It was not to be expected that George Bernard Shaw would remain silent on such an issue. In his first letter to *The Times* he described himself as 'the mouthpiece of a gagged profession' and taunted the General Medical Council with having been afraid to proceed against the four surgeons who had recommended a knighthood for Sir Herbert Barker, since in their infamous conduct they had been 'abetted by the King.' The Council, he said, was 'a trade union of the worst kind,' now 'at the crude stage of preoccupation with professional earnings and sullen defiance of public opinion.'

Reluctant though it was to take notice of a press agitation, the General Medical Council appeared to be having twinges of conscience. Its hands were, however, tied by the fact that Dr Axham now had no qualifications which would admit of his being restored to the Register, for when he was struck off he was automatically deprived of his licences by the Royal College of Physicians in Edinburgh and the Royal College of Surgeons of England. One at least of these bodies would have to restore Dr Axham's qualification before the General Medical Council could act, and it had no control over either of them. Magnanimously, the Edinburgh College agreed to restore the Doctor's licence, but the Surgeons decided that his disqualification must stand. In a defensive letter to *The Times* recapitulating the facts of the case, the Registrar of the General Medical Council referred to Dr Axham as Mr Axham (even in *The Lancet* and the *British Medical Journal* he was Dr Axham).

In December of 1925 it became known that Dr Axham was gravely ill. The press resolved that he must not be allowed to die in disgrace, however technical. Lord Dawson was called in to attend the patient and did not conceal that he favoured an act of clemency. As with Lord Dawson's more distinguished patients, day-to-day bulletins were issued on Dr Axham's progress. Though pressed to call a special meeting, the General Medical Council decided that the matter must stand over until its next meeting in June, 1926. *The Lancet* excused this delay on the grounds that Dr Axham had waited 15 years before appealing for restitution, which 'surely relieves the Council from the responsibility of taking immediate and unusual action.' The journal admitted that the medical profession had much sympathy with Dr Axham; and the

British Medical Journal thought that 'clemency would not come amiss.'

On April 8, Dr Axham died, after saying, 'Let God forgive. I speak generally. For myself I forgive as I hope to be forgiven.' *The Times* said that the public had been led to expect that at its forthcoming sitting the General Medical Council would restore Dr Axham's name to the Register; now the opportunity of performing 'a singularly attractive act of grace' had gone. No one doubted, said *The Times*, that the decision taken by Dr Axham in 1911 had had a valuable effect in bringing to the notice of the profession the value of manipulative surgery.

Anyone who hoped to hear the General Medical Council express contrition at its meeting in June was disappointed. The Council considered it had done all that was incumbent on it, and complained of press misrepresentation. Whether Dr Axham's name would, in fact, have been restored cannot be known, for it was open to the College of Surgeons to make representations against this course and their objections would have had to be weighed by the Council.

One result of the agitation was seen in the appointment to the General Medical Council later in the year of its first lay member in the person of Mr Edward Hilton Young, a lawyer and Member of Parliament. This concession did not satisfy the press, which continued to abuse the Council as a bigoted and tyrannous body from whose decisions there was no appeal. Why, they asked, did not the Privy Council and the universities do something to discipline this body which was so eager to discipline others? The *British Medical Journal* opposed granting the right of appeal on the curious grounds that a certain type of individual would be given a double opportunity of drawing upon himself the publicity he desired.

Many practitioners fell foul of the General Medical Council on the issue of advertising, almost all forms of which, in the Council's view, constituted infamous conduct. A doctor was limited in the amount of information he might impart on his brass plate, or on his writing paper, or on the labels of his medicine bottles. He might even hesitate before installing attractive window-boxes, if his was the only house in a terrace to be ornamented in this fashion. In some areas an old-fashioned red lamp over the door was permissible, but a neon sign flashing the word 'Doctor' would assuredly have led to trouble. There was, of course, no objection to parking a Rolls-Royce outside the door and a doctor shared every Englishman's inalienable right to buy his wife a mink coat.

No matter how famous he became, a doctor was unlikely to see his biography in the bookshops; the convention was that such works must be posthumously published. In compiling his entry for *Who's Who* he would be cautious to list only his qualifications, appointments and professional publications. Sir Herbert Barker's entry in that volume was not calculated to placate the General Medical Council; he described himself as 'specialist in manipulative surgery, rendering unnecessary many cutting operations and orthopaedic appliances,' then listed his 'principal operations,' which ranged from tennis elbow to sacro-iliac displacements. In the view of some not wholly unprejudiced practitioners, the eminent physicians who appended their names in such profusion to bulletins on Royal patients were guilty of self-advertisement.

A doctor could find himself in trouble if he gave his services to any institution which advertised, whether a muscle-building firm, a health-cure establishment or an institute of endocrinology. It was no defence that the doctor's name was not published in the advertisements; if he was associated in any way with an advertising institution he was liable to be arraigned for infamous conduct.

Public speaking was another snare, for the General Medical Council (in the words of *The Times*) seemed 'unduly anxious lest any physician . . . by the exercise of a gift for exposition obtain what is called "an indirect advertisement." '* Thus, a practitioner would think hard and seriously, and perhaps take advice, before consenting to read a paper on miners' nystagmus to an audience of colliery officials and trade unionists, for fear of being accused of touting for patients. Sir William Arbuthnot Lane, founder of the New Health Society, had his name removed from the Register in order that he might more readily urge the public to eat more fruit and keep their bowels free; a laudable enough form of activity, it might seem, for a medical man. Similarly, Dr C. W. Saleeby withdrew his name so that he might not be censured for stressing the benefits of fresh air and sunshine. It was a peculiar irony that these eminent men should have struck themselves off in order to do the work of the Minister of Health when others were qualifying themselves for the Register in order to be able to practise unorthodox treatments under a respectable cover.

* October 26, 1925.

In the eyes of the General Medical Council, self-advertisement was the more heinous if the doctor who indulged in it disparaged the efforts of his colleagues. The indictments of offenders make odd reading. In 1937 (to pick a case at random) a doctor was said to have made 'claims of an extravagant nature as to the benefits likely to result if the method of therapeutic immunisation practised by him at an establishment known as the —— Laboratory were generally practised and had accentuated the inability of other members of his profession to obtain comparable results . . . (thus) commending or directing attention to his professional skill, knowledge, services or qualifications and/or depreciating those of others.' It was a charge on which many a famous figure in the annals of medicine, from Paracelsus onwards, could have been convicted.

Although there may well have been occasions when the rules of the General Medical Council served to inhibit the spread of useful knowledge, it is probable that the ban on self-advertisement has done much to curb the boasting of doubtful cures and to limit that public bickering for which the profession used to be notorious. No doubt, also, it has served to keep a few unseemly bats within their belfries.

Many of the offenders summoned before the General Medical Council had already been convicted by the courts for civil offences or had drawn unwelcome publicity on themselves at inquests. The Council, in effect, tried them over again and imposed additional penalties if it saw fit. Among those disciplined in this fashion were doctors who had been prosecuted for driving cars while under the influence of drink or drugs. As a rule the Council put them on probation for a year, after which they were required to produce certificates of good behaviour from responsible citizens. The gathering of these—from fellow doctors, from ministers of religion, even from patients—was probably the stiffest part of the punishment. It has been argued that the Council has shown undue leniency towards doctors guilty of driving 'under the influence,' but those who work in unexacting routines are not best qualified to condemn the man who works on 24 hours call, under heavy mental and physical stress. In the good old days, of course, the doctor's horse saw him safely home.

Towards practitioners who conducted liaisons with female patients or wives of patients the Council very rarely showed leniency, nor was there any real public desire that leniency should

be extended, however much the plight of a skilful and popular
doctor might be dramatised in the headlines. It was obvious that
by the nature of his calling the doctor must be answerable to a
higher moral code than the stockbroker or the commercial
traveller. The fact that a woman might have set out deliberately
to seduce him was little extenuation; he was supposed to be
impervious to the appeal of 'sweet doctor, be my bedfellow.'
Usually, struck-off doctors made their way quietly to less fastidious lands, where very often they made good. A few offenders
sailed without waiting for the formality of being struck off.

Anyone who goes to the trouble of examining the disciplinary
record of the General Medical Council will find that, though
harsh decisions may be unearthed, there are very many instances
in which leniency has been extended. More is heard about doctors
being struck off than about doctors being restored to the Register,
as very many are.

In the 1930s an accused doctor who was acquitted of the
charges against him said to the Council: 'I have never seen
justice administered as it has been administered today. My case
has been treated with the utmost fairness and dignity and I thank
you all very much.' This brought a brusque retort from the
president: 'We don't want any bouquets, thank you.'

The right of appeal from a decision of the General Medical
Council was not secured until 1950. Under the Medical Act of
that year a convicted doctor may take his case to the Privy
Council. At the same time the Council was given authority to
subpoena witnesses and take evidence on oath. Lack of such
powers in the past had meant that justice was sometimes ill-
served.

XXIX

THE DOCTORS' REVOLT (2)

THE battle over Aneurin Bevan's National Health Service Bill contained many faithful echoes of the earlier struggle over Lloyd George's scheme. A number of doctors served in the front line in both campaigns and must have been both impressed and disconcerted by the way in which history repeated itself.

Once again the doctors found themselves growing angrier and angrier as they tried to counter the machinations of a highly articulate Welsh politician. Once again their leaders heard themselves accused of conspiring to frustrate the will of Parliament and people. Once again they took plebiscites which showed sudden and incalculable shifts of opinion. Once again they allowed themselves to be split.

Between the world wars, the profession had suggested many improvements on Lloyd George's scheme, but always these had been waved aside by the politicians—a 'stiff-necked generation, obstinate and without vision,' to quote Lord Dawson, who had put forward a plan for health centres as early as 1920. The British Medical Association had urged that the State should provide a complete medical service, including hospital and specialist treatment, for all wage-earners. It wanted to see wives and dependents covered (on their own initiative a number of doctors treated families on a club basis). It had also urged the creation of model health centres and the extension of group practice on lines to be determined by the doctors themselves. But the Association was strenuously against any scheme for making doctors full-time State servants.

As often happens, serious talk of reform was deferred until a major war was in progress. In 1942 the Beveridge Report presented a plan under which the whole population, irrespective of income, would be entitled to every kind of medical service, both general and specialist, in home or in hospital, from womb to tomb. There was to be greater emphasis on prevention of disease. Doctors, while welcoming the general concept, resented the statement that 'the possible scope of private general practice will be so restricted that it may not appear worth while to preserve it.'

In the House of Lords in 1943 Lord Dawson protested vigorously against any proposal 'to enclose all doctors within a bureaucratic ring fence,' and to make the profession a nine-to-six branch of the Civil Service. He did not think a State doctor could be expected to show the same individual responsibility to a patient as 'a doctor whose good work brings reputation and later, maybe, material reward.' In his view 'a healthy thought of self is a spur that consorts well with a desire and an endeavour to help others.' But, as his biographer tells, Lord Dawson was anxious that the profession should not be accused of resisting for selfish ends a policy of social betterment which commended itself to the public.* Unhappily, it was for their preoccupation with that 'healthy thought of self' that the doctors came to be widely criticised.

In the same debate Lord Moran (who flew about the war-time world as personal physician to Sir Winston Churchill) outlined his idea of group practice. He said that in their early days in the wards doctors were very much on their toes, the presence of colleagues serving as a spur to professional pride and emulation. 'If doctors instead of practising at their own houses were to be banded eight or nine together and were to see patients at some house built for the purpose, with facilities for diagnosis and with consultative services at their elbow, they would breathe again that atmosphere of their student days in the wards and it would be a great gain to the community.' He thought, however, that most doctors were opposed to the idea of health centres, even though their wives might relish the idea of escaping from the tyranny of the telephone. The public looked on health centres with suspicion, he said, because they feared they would have to accept the services of the doctor who answered the telephone.

Lord Moran took the opportunity to puncture the pretensions of Harley Street. A doctor, he pointed out, 'may have the most modest degrees, he may have no special experience, but he can go to a house agent and rent a room in Harley Street, and, writing to his patients from that address, he will be accepted by many as

* Francis Watson: *Dawson of Penn*

a consultant.' The truth was that there were not enough consultants in the country and they were ill distributed. 'You may be surprised to hear that there are great areas in England, towns with a population of 100,000, where the major surgery and everything else is done by general practitioners, and where no consultant ever comes. One of the largest counties in England a few months ago had not a single gynaecologist. All this must end; it is one of the greatest evils of our times in the medical world.'

A century or two before, no one would have looked for a speech of this tenor and candour from the President of the Royal College of Physicians.

Mr Ernest Brown's proposals for a health service based on the Beveridge Report found no favour with the doctors at large, however much support he may have had from doctors in the Ministry of Health. In 1944 the Government issued a White Paper outlining an ambitious national health service, complete with health centres. Mr Henry Willink, the new Minister of Health, did his best to interest the doctors in it, but without success. In Parliament both Lord Dawson and Lord Horder complained that the scheme had too powerful a whiff of bureaucracy, and Lord Geddes thought the proposed Central Medical Board had the makings of a 'medical Gestapo.'

Such was the background to the National Health Bill which Mr Aneurin Bevan introduced just after the war, a war which had brought, not only social revolution, but a revolution in medical science. The doctors had already poured cold water on health schemes propounded by a National Liberal and a Conservative, and no one expected that they would look any more favourably on a reform brought forward by a Socialist.

Briefly, Mr Bevan's Bill, the terms of which were announced in March 1946, proposed to make medical and dental attention free for all, without age or wage limit. Doctors, dentists and chemists willing to operate the scheme would be invited to register with executive councils on which they would have nearly fifty per cent representation. They would be paid a basic salary plus capitation fees and would be allowed to treat private patients. They would receive pensions. Sales of practices wholly or partly in the public service would be prohibited and their owners compensated as necessary. Almost all voluntary and public hospitals were to be transferred to the Ministry of Health for reorganisation.

The British Medical Association disagreed strongly with various

'How About the Patient?' From the *Daily Mail*, February 9, 1948

of these measures and lost no time in raising a fighting fund to arm the profession for any conflict it might have with the Government, 'should Parliament prove obdurate and refuse to modify proposals in the Bill which the profession might consider to strike at the essential freedoms of medicine.' The phrase 'should Parliament prove obdurate' did not pass unnoticed. Among the objections to the Bill, in the Association's view, were that it called for the direction of doctors, made them part-salaried State servants, banned the sale of practices and thus paved the way for making doctors whole-time State servants. Professional advancement, it argued, would depend on the smile of official approval, as in the Civil Service. Again, the State acquisition of hospitals would discourage local interest and support of these institutions.

The proposed abolition of the traffic in practices ('Should a Doctor Sell?') was one issue on which Mr Bevan refused to give ground. He pointed out that a medical planning commission with which the British Medical Association was intimately connected had already urged this step. 'We regard it as being inconsistent with a civilised community and with a reasonable health service for patients to be bought and sold over their heads,' he said. One doctor succeeded another, not by virtue of his personal qualifications, but by the power of his purse; in these circumstances how could there be 'free choice of doctor'? In any event, it would be improper for doctors to traffic in practices almost wholly built up out of public money. Since it would be 'inhuman and most unjust' not to compensate doctors for the loss of their practices, a sum of £60,000,000 would be provided for their relief.

Bitterly, the doctors denied that they bought and sold patients; all they bought and sold was goodwill. To this Mr Bevan retorted that if the patients did not pass with the practice there would be no virtue in the transaction. The doctors advanced the argument that a practitioner who owned the goodwill of a practice had an incentive to develop it, his investment being a pledge that he would do his best. These arguments were used 70 years before to justify the buying and selling of commissions in the Army.

It was the older doctors who felt most keenly about the proposed ban on the sale of practices, including those who hoped to pass on their practices to their sons. Many of the younger doctors were as keen as Mr Bevan to end the system. It seemed impossible to convince the elders of the profession that there could be any objection to private individuals trading in what would be, in effect, public posts. The Parliamentary Secretary to the Ministry of Health (Mr C. W. Key) pointed out that 'the guarantee of this nation is not something which individuals should barter between themselves.' *The Times* put it this way : 'When almost all practitioners receive almost all their income from public funds the right of the doctor to sell his place in the public service to the highest bidder will certainly not be one of the "essential freedoms of medicine." It would merely retain for him or for his widow, heirs and assigns the right to appoint his successors.'*

Besides banning the traffic in practices, Mr Bevan proposed to prevent new doctors from moving into areas which were already over-doctored, when many parts of the country were in sore need of practitioners. His proposal was that a doctor wishing to open a practice should be referred to a Medical Practices Committee (a

* April 11, 1946.

mainly professional body) which would refuse its permission if the area proposed already had enough doctors. No attempt would be made to unseat doctors from existing practices. This was the policy which the British Medical Association attacked as direction, but which Mr Bevan called negative direction. The doctors argued that the reports of over-doctored areas were much exaggerated, and that it was one of the medical freedoms to be able to choose where to practise. Not the most tactful retort, perhaps, was that by Mr Key: 'If a dustman cannot find a job with a particular local authority because no authority exists he does not start to howl about being subject to bureaucratic direction because he has to go and seek work elsewhere.'

A great deal of nonsense was talked on all sides on the theme of 'free choice of doctor.' It was a topic on which the man in the street, if he thought about it at all, was liable to have cynical views. If his doctor sold out overnight to a new man, where did 'free choice of doctor' come in? Generally patients stayed with the take-over doctor unless they had powerful reasons for disliking him. Even when a person arrived in a new district and was faced with 'free choice of doctor' he made his selection, as a rule, purely for reasons of convenience or on haphazard recommendation, or perhaps because the doctor went to the same church. In Parliament Dr L. Comyns, representing Silvertown, said that 'the public were very prone to assess the medical skill of a doctor by the year and make of his car or, on occasion, by the number of new hats which his wife was seen to be wearing.' Doctors have been chosen on even more frivolous and quixotic grounds than these. Probably the average person spends more care in choosing a car or a television set than in choosing a doctor. In any event, he has neither the means nor the ability to check on a doctor's professional skill and knowledge. These considerations either went unventilated or were lost in the fog of controversy. 'Free choice of doctor' is an excellent ideal, but if the profession imagined that it was a popular rallying cry they were deluded. As well might Fleet Street hope to rally the uncaring masses with a cry of 'freedom of the press.'

Again, the need to safeguard the 'doctor-patient relationship' was apt to be too subtle a concept for the ordinary man. If he had been a patient in a busy club practice or panel he would have difficulty in knowing what the doctors or their spokesmen were talking about when they referred to the 'fugitive and impersonal relationship' that would exist in a State medical service. They were well used to it. What was the practical difference between being treated by a helot of the State and a free man serving the interests of the State? *The Lancet* struck a more realistic note when it wrote : 'The truth is that the doctor-patient relationship in modern form needs improvement rather than preservation; it can never be wholly satisfactory while the doctor (as someone has put it) is not only a friend in need but also a friend in need of his patient's money; nor while there is competition rather than co-operation between him and his colleagues.'*

Much eloquence was expended in sketching the probable horrors of a full-time salaried service. It would bring in collectivism, as against individualism. It would encourage mediocrity, rigidity, laziness, a diminishing of personal responsibility, a truckling to administrators. Such a system, said Dr Charles Hill in a letter to *The Times,* 'would destroy a proper incentive, the relationship between remuneration and the amount and value of work done or responsibility accepted. It would tend to replace competition for patients by competition to avoid them.'† In that last sentence, critics considered, Dr Hill hardly flattered his own profession.

Many of the public decided there was too much emphasis on the idea that a doctor needed a cash incentive to do his best. Surely the 'profit motive' was a tenet of capitalism, not of medicine? As Surgeon Vice-Admiral Sir Sheldon Dudley has written, there *are* other incentives to hard and honest endeavour in a doctor, among them the regard of professional colleagues and his own self-respect.‡

· Another of the supposed disadvantages of a State medical service was set out in a circular which, lacking as it did any publisher's or printer's imprint, became the subject of enquiries by the Attorney-General. It was produced in Parliament by the Lord Privy Seal, Mr Arthur Greenwood, who quoted these statements :

'The National Health Service Bill will turn your doctor into the State doctor. He will become a salaried doctor.

'You want your doctor's certificates to be given on his own judgment of your case.

* March 6, 1948.
† April 17, 1948. ‡ *Our National Ill-Health Service.*

'Under the National Health Service Bill he will be the State doctor
and the State may want to control the doctor's certificates in order
to save the 'social security' funds.

'Will it make you healthier?

'Will Mr Bevan's Bill improve your health by giving you a better
house or better food?

'It will not.'

Mr Bevan's motive for taking over voluntary hospitals was that
these were ill distributed and ill designed for the nation's needs.
Many of the small ones did not contain the elementary facilities
which were necessary. Even at the cost of negativing the endow-
ments of the dead, he said, they would have to be reorganised.
'I would rather be kept alive in the efficient if cold altruism of a
large hospital than expire in a gush of warm sympathy in a small
one,' he declared. To the dismay of many of his Parliamentary
supporters he revealed that specialists would be allowed to have
fee-paying patients in hospitals ('Shame!') and that in certain
beds there would be no limit on the fees that could be charged
('Why?'). He had been driven to make this concession because
otherwise there would have been a rash of nursing homes all over
the country. 'I believe that nursing homes ought to be discouraged
as they cannot provide general hospital facilities and we want to
keep our specialists attached to our hospitals and not concentrate
them into nursing homes.' He argued that if patients wanted to
pay for additional amenities they should be allowed to do so. 'If
the State owned a theatre it would not charge the same prices for
different seats.'

In the view of not a few general practitioners, it was by making
these concessions to the specialists (and the Royal Colleges) that
Mr Bevan was enabled to get them on his side and split the profession.

Although the fact is now largely forgotten, the Bill provided
for the establishment of health centres, to which Mr Bevan
attached 'very great importance.' General practitioners, he
explained, were unable to provide all the apparatus of diagnosis
in their own surgeries; in a health centre they would have these
facilities. A centre might be run in conjunction with a maternity
and child welfare clinic, and the bigger ones would have dental
clinics. Even the small centres would have rooms in which general
practitioners could consult their patients.

The idea of health centres had often been debated by the profession. Back in the 'thirties many had watched with interest the development of Peckham's Pioneer Health Centre, which was a community club with swimming bath, cafeteria, dance floor, theatre, work-room and libraries. Its members had to agree to a double medical examination, one in a laboratory, one in a clinic. The community sense was strong; an interim report on this experiment in 1943 said the Centre was becoming 'a mating and courting centre of salutary significance.' In Mr Bevan's Bill, the style of health centre envisaged was less socially adventurous; but many doctors were keen on the idea of sharing secretarial, diagnostic and laboratory facilities. It meant that a doctor need not necessarily run a surgery or do his paper work at his home and he would have the benefit of a rota system. Because of restrictions on building, plans for erecting health centres were shelved a few months before the Health Service came into effect.

The Act was passed in November, 1946, after 32 days' travail in the Commons and 10 in the Lords. That left the doctors 18 months in which to decide whether to enter or stay outside the scheme. As in the 1912–13 battle, they knew that a general boycott would be construed as defiance of Parliament and people. Early in 1947 the British Medical Association announced the results of a plebiscite of members on whether to negotiate with the Minister. Fifty-four per cent were against doing so, the general practitioners being 10,024 against and 5,479 in favour. Nevertheless, the Association did decide to negotiate, although convinced that the Minister was 'impervious to argument.'

All that year medical discontent smouldered. Sir Ernest Graham-Little, a veteran of the earlier campaign, said in Parliament, 'If I were a young professional man in good health and training I would most certainly leave this country whilst the going is good.' By early 1948 the British Medical Association had decided that the Bevan scheme was 'so grossly at variance with the essential principles of the profession that it should be rejected absolutely by all practitioners.' Another plebiscite was organised. At Pontypridd Mr Bevan appealed to the doctors at large not to let themselves be misled by 'slogans addressed to their emotions and not to their intelligence.' He said: 'Parliament has spoken and the country awaits the co-operation of the medical world.' Dr Guy Dain, Chairman of the Council of the British Medical Association, thought it was a 'damaging and malicious imputation' to say that the profession was defying Parliament; the

Minister ought to 'conduct himself in such a manner that he secured the co-operation and goodwill of those concerned.' Then, on February 9, Mr Bevan vigorously attacked the doctors' leaders in the House of Commons. Claiming credit for having personally refrained over a long period from making provocative statements, he described the leaders of the British Medical Association as a small body of 'raucous-voiced' and 'politically poisoned' people who were exceeding their just constitutional limitations and 'organising wholesale resistance to the implementation of an Act of Parliament.' The nation had not yet appointed British Medical Association House as another revising chamber. He listed the concessions he had made and said that from the first he had never suggested that doctors should join a whole-time salaried service. The glory of the profession, he said, should not be private practice but 'the ability of a doctor to meet his patients with no financial anxiety.' A Liberal spokesman, Mr Frank Byers, agreed with Mr Bevan that much of the propaganda issued by the British Medical Association was a direct challenge to the Act, and said he thought the mass of doctors had been grossly misled by a small clique. At this stage *The Lancet* was urging doctors to enter the scheme and the *British Medical Journal* was urging them to do the opposite.

The new plebiscite, announced on February 18, showed a sensational shift of opinion. There were now 40,814 doctors against participation, 4,735 in favour. Eighty-two per cent of members voted. Somewhat surprisingly, the salaried doctors of the public health service were six to one in opposition to the Act. It looked as though the coming showdown might be even more bitter than that between the profession and Lloyd George.

On April 7, Mr Bevan made a conciliatory speech. He promised at the request of the Royal Colleges to make it statutorily clear that a whole-time salaried service could not be introduced except by Act of Parliament. In later negotiations he agreed that general practitioners could draw all their money in capitation fees if they objected to receiving part of it as a basic salary.

The next plebiscite, announced two months before the scheme was due to start, showed that the pendulum had swung back again. This time 14,620 approved of entering the scheme and 25,842 disapproved. The stipulated majority of 13,000, which was regarded as necessary if there was to be a general boycott, was not achieved. There were a great many abstentions.

It was all over, bar the recriminations. The leaders of the British Medical Association did not conceal their disappointment at the poll, but they decided they must now advise their members to participate. After all, some concessions had been wrung. It must have been obvious that large sections of the press were out of sympathy if not actively hostile, that the Conservative opposition was unable or unwilling to lend any more support, and that masses of the public felt, rightly or wrongly, that progress was being impeded for reasons which, if not selfish, were unimportant and even unintelligible. The doctors' campaign had many lessons, not least in the field of public relations.

After the service had operated for a year 95 per cent of the population were insured. Between 18,000 and 19,000 doctors out of some 21,000 were participating. So were 90 per cent of dentists. Two thousand doctors had elected to draw a basic salary of £300. As for the patients over whose bodies the battle had been fought, 5,250,000 had been supplied with spectacles, with 3,000,000 more pairs on order; 8,500,000 had been taken over for dental treatment; 29,000 had been given deaf aids; 8,359 had been fitted with artificial limbs, 7,266 with glass eyes, and 5,071 with wigs. Immigration officers were charged with the delicate task of turning back foreigners who were descending on this country to take advantage of the health service.

In that first year 382 doctors appeared before disciplinary committees. Thirteen were removed from the service, 110 fined, 69 warned; against 190 no action was taken. Whatever they thought about the workings of the disciplinary committees, doctors could not complain that their lapses were blazoned to the world. It has been a matter for comment that doctors guilty of the most startling indiscretions and derelictions have had their identities concealed as 'Dr A' and 'Dr X.'

XXX

PLAINTS AND PLACEBOS

ONLY a few months after the National Health Service came in, some 700 dissatisfied doctors answered a rallying call from Lord Horder and formed themselves into a 'ginger group' called the Fellowship for Freedom in Medicine.

The health service, Lord Horder told them, had been born in dishonour. 'Our own weakness was partly responsible . . . for we allowed ourselves to be a party to the mad precipitancy of the Government, whereby the public was made to contract for health benefits that did not exist.

'The living power of medicine, resident as it has always been, and must be, in the personnel of the profession, has passed out of its hands to be lost in the dead machinery of the bureau. Medicine has become what we pledged ourselves it never should become—a branch of the Civil Service. We are no longer experts. We sit and sign forms.'

Variations on this theme are sounded whenever the Fellowship meets. In 1957 Sir Francis Walshe complained that Whitehall was grading doctors like fatstock, and continued: 'Lay Civil Servants now control our comings and goings, speaking through the amorphous masks of their Ministers—those ephemeral, fumbling Parliamentary figures taking their first titubant steps in office at the Ministry of Health.'

The Fellowship has urged a new system of health payments based on private insurance contributions. It is not, of course, the only group with ideas on how to improve the health service. There is a Socialist Medical Association, of which it is perhaps sufficient to say that its views do not necessarily coincide with those of the Fellowship for Freedom. The waving of political banners by the hosts of medicine is not the prettiest sight.

That the health service has many imperfections will be dis-

307

puted by few. It is vulnerable on the grounds that only a trivial proportion of the vast sums spent on it is devoted to the prevention of disease, as distinct from the curing or palliating of it. Surgeon Vice-Admiral Sir Sheldon Dudley, a trenchant critic, complains of the unwarranted dominance of the general practitioners over the progressive research workers, pathologists and hygienists who are the real spearhead of medical science.*

There have been allegations that some doctors tried to wreck the scheme by deliberate over-prescription, notably of expensive proprietary medicines. There have been counter-allegations that patients have done much more to weaken it by their greedy importunities. A howl went up among the taxpayers when it became apparent that they were paying gigantic sums to defray the cost of prescribing placebos. A placebo, as many newspaper readers now learned for the first time, was a medicine which had no other purpose than to fortify the patient's confidence. It was thought that more than a third of medicines prescribed under the National Health Service came into this category. Some doctors had sufficient strength of mind, and sufficient time, to try to educate their patients out of the bottle habit. Others, confronted by patients who *knew* they could never get well without a bottle, or thought the doctor was trying to cheat them out of their rights, took the line of least resistance, if only to keep the queue of patients moving. More sophisticated patients who did not want to hurt the doctor's feelings would collect their medicine at leisure and pour it down the sink.

Advocates of salaried medical service have drawn a moral from the wrangle over placebos. A State doctor, they say, need not be deflected from his honest judgment by demands for unnecessary medicines, including tranquillisers, in the fear that, if refused, his patients would exercise their free choice and move on to a more accommodating rival. This is, perhaps, an optimistic view. When doctor and patient can afford to dispense with placebos, civilisation will have passed a major turning-point.

Since 1948 many general practitioners claim to have worked harder for less money, though the majority seem reasonably content. Doctors who, before the scheme came in, had middle-class practices have perhaps suffered more than others, since their fee-paying patients have mostly joined the ranks of the insured. It has been widely asserted that there has been a deterioration in

Our National Ill-Health Service.

the attitude of the patient, as evidenced by the wholly deplorable tendency to bring punitive or frivolous actions against doctors and hospitals. General practitioners complain that they have too little contact with doctors in other branches of the service and that they are being progressively excluded from the hospitals; if they want to watch operations, they must watch them, along with the general public, on television. The fact that merit awards ranging from £500 to £2,500 are given each year, in strict secrecy, to a third of the country's specialists, mostly in the hospital service, has inspired a certain amount of envy in the ranks of family doctors; they would like a similar scheme to be operated for their own benefit—but how? As these lines are written fewer than a dozen health centres have been built under the terms of the National Health Service Act. Various centres have been set up under other auspices, however. Harlow, the new town in Essex, has four group practice centres.

A measure which did not please some of the younger doctors was the Medical Act of 1950, which lays down that when a student has completed his six-years curriculum and obtained a certificate of qualification he must spend one year in resident hospital appointments before he can be accepted as fully qualified. In other words, the State now makes compulsory what most doctors did voluntarily for their own good and for that of their future patients. The exaction of 'forced labour' to the tune of perhaps 100 hours a week, at a salary of £467 rising to £522, is a theme on which Dr Louis Goldman waxes eloquent in his *Angry Young Doctor* (1957).

Dr Goldman also voices the grievances of those doctors who, anxious to make a career in the hospital service, find themselves barred from consultants' posts by the promotion block at the level of registrar. If they decide to become general practitioners, much of their specialised knowledge is likely to go unused.

The National Health Service does not seem to have imported ruin and desolation into Harley Street. According to the *Medical Directory's* last count of plates there were 960 consultants operating there, as against some 800 in 1948. To talk of plates is perhaps misleading; the plates are mere strips of metal hardly any bigger than those aluminium strips on which boys punch out their names at railway stations. The strips are laid neatly one above the other and one door may carry as many as a score. If all doctors with a name-strip in Harley Street resided there with their families, the local medical officer of health would be faced with a frightening problem of overcrowding, but Harley Street nowadays has little social life. The street consists, in effect, of so many offices. Doors are opened, not by butlers, but by matrons in white coats. Some of the newer waiting-rooms may be more like those of advertising agencies, but there are enough musty old ones, complete with busts of Harvey and Hippocrates, to preserve a sense of tradition.

In these days, of course, a plain physician or a simple surgeon is a rare bird in Harley Street. Instead, there are allergists, dermatologists, endocrinologists, paediatricians, orthodontologists, ophthalmologists, otolaryngologists and even otorhinolaryngologists, though others in the same line prefer, understandably, to call themselves ear, nose and throat specialists. There is a whole coven of psychiatrists. Here, too, one may find a medical hypnotist, a naturopath or an old-fashioned homoeopathist. There are also osteopaths, who survived an ingenious attempt a generation ago to exclude them on the grounds that they were tradesmen. Here, again, are such torch-bearers of medicine as artificial inseminationists, who have yet to provide themselves with a Greek-derived designation.

The medical profession has not yet contrived to extrude from Harley Street such outsiders as Actors Equity and a group of television producers; though in view of the increasing number of medical men who now appear on television both these bodies are surely deserving of hospitality.

Are doctors drawn from the same material as of old? In 1958 a Royal Commission on doctors' pay was informed that 74 per cent of medical students were now 'financed by somebody or other' as against 27 per cent in 1938. The Council of the Royal College of Surgeons reminded the Commission that medicine had always attracted a nucleus of students from cultured, though not necessarily wealthy, homes—notably the homes of doctors and clergy. These young men had been brought up to look on medicine as a vocation. 'Medicine would lose immeasurably if the proportion of such students in the future were to be reduced in favour of precocious children who qualify for subsidies from local authorities and the State purely on examination results.'

Most laymen will take a calm view of this peril, not caring greatly whether a doctor is financed by the State or by his father. Too little has been said in this book about the doctor's wife.

Some day an out-of-work sociologist might care to investigate what proportion of doctors marry nurses. The rate is high, though not so high as in women's popular fiction, where the nurse-in-love-with-the-doctor is rapidly ousting the typist-in-love-with-the-boss. It may be that the doctor-nurse relationship is the ideal preparation for the husband-wife relationship, or it may not; let the sociologist find out. Romances between doctors and nurses would have been unthinkable before Florence Nightingale's day; possibly the Royal Colleges have reservations about the desirability of such alliances even today. Perhaps they are happier to see doctors marrying doctors; this also seems to be a popular trend. Large coal-black headlines await the woman doctor who is wooed and won by a male nurse.

It would be rash to prophesy what the doctor's status will be in 50 or even in five years' time. He is in the hands of the politicians. All parties and almost all newspapers tend to take his grievances with a pinch of salt, chiefly because the British Medical Association has a reputation for overplaying its hand; yet it is evident that there is a vociferous section of doctors for whom the Association is not militant enough, quite apart from those doctors who believe it is militant in the wrong direction. The patient, who is not without his irritations at this stage, is apt to grow impatient with the behaviour of doctors in the mass, especially when they group themselves under political labels. Yet, as a rule, he has no quarrel with, and indeed every admiration for, his own doctor. He likes to think *his* doctor will not strike, even if all the others do.

Axel Munthe said, in *The Story of San Michele*, that medical men who dislike the idea of a State salary should leave the profession and go on the Stock Exchange or open a shop. 'The doctors,' he wrote, 'should walk about like sages, honoured and protected by all men.'

No doubt many doctors—and patients—will regret that Dr Munthe never had the privilege of testing out his opinions as a practitioner in Britain's health service.

INDEX